Basic Circuits
and Electronics Experiments

Basic Circuits
and Electronics Experiments

A UNIFIED LABORATORY MANUAL AND TEXT

Louis R. Nardizzi

Institute of Technology
Information and Control Sciences Center
Southern Methodist University
Dallas, Texas

D. Van Nostrand Company
New York / Cincinnati / Toronto / London / Melbourne

To Rossana and my family, to whom I owe more than can
ever be expressed in words.

D. Van Nostrand Company Regional Offices:
New York   Cincinnati   Millbrae

D. Van Nostrand Company International Offices:
London   Toronto   Melbourne

Copyright © 1973 by Litton Educational Publishing, Inc.

Library of Congress Catalog Card Number: 72-6879
ISBN 0-442-25906-9

Published by D. Van Nostrand Company
450 West 33rd Street, New York, N. Y. 10001

Published simultaneously in Canada by Van Nostrand Reinhold Ltd.

10 9 8 7 6 5 4 3 2 1

Preface

The past decade has seen the introduction of a large number of new electronic devices, circuits, and analytical methods. These devices, circuits, and methods have been readily introduced into lecture courses but have not been properly integrated into laboratory courses. Consequently, many educators and students have bemoaned this fact and have suggested numerous ways of improving present-day laboratories. The suggestions from professors, laboratory instructors, and students have ranged from completely structured, to partially structured, to the complete elimination of laboratory courses. All these suggestions have made one thing very clear to me: students can better master the basic concepts of circuits and electronics when they become directly involved—that is, they learn by doing. This implies that the laboratory should function as a learning experience. If this experience arouses enthusiasm and leads students to enjoy learning, they may gain lasting insight into circuits and electronics. Thus, this text is offered as an attempt to improve the present situation. The author invites the reader to offer suggestions and to point out errors either of fact or of presentation. I also hope that some other educators will put words into action and join me in attempting to make laboratories a true learning experience.

It is the aim of this laboratory text to present a number of interesting and challenging experiments which verify the application of reasonably straightforward analytical methods to electronic devices and circuits. The experimental results and analytical methods should complement each other in helping the student understand basic physical principles and mathematical models. On the other hand, these experiments were designed to simulate real applications which cannot be explained or demonstrated satisfactorily in a perfunctory manner. Thus, each experiment in this text has been divided into two coordinated parts. Part One contains an introductory section and a section entitled "Theory," containing a discussion of the physical principles and mathematical models associated with some particular electronic circuits. Part Two contains sections entitled "Laboratory Preparation" and "Laboratory Procedure" which outline the steps to help the student verify some of the material discussed in the "Theory" section of Part One. "Optional" parts are included in Part Two in order to allow the student to experiment on his own after he has mastered the fundamental principles.

The basic equipment required are a cathode-ray oscilloscope, ac and dc voltmeters, ohmmeters, power supplies, sine- and square-wave generators, and such components as resistors, capacitors, inductors, and solid state devices. Today this equipment is available in most electronic laboratories. Apart from the test equipment, the major cost is associated with the solid state devices. However, the experiments have been carefully designed to minimize this cost whenever possible.

These experiments were designed for laboratory sessions lasting from two to three hours, with many experiments requiring more than one laboratory session. The experiments can be used for two or three semesters of laboratory course work. I have found that the most satisfactory results are achieved in the laboratory if the student is required to perform the following steps prior to the laboratory session. Carefully read the experiment and at least one of the references relating to a specific experiment. References other than those given in the experiment can be used. Maintain a laboratory notebook which contains the information requested in the laboratory preparation section of the experiment.

The laboratory sessions should be devoted to performing the necessary measurements and to confirming or refuting the results obtained in the laboratory preparations. Quite often the error between the experimental and theoretically predicted results leads to a deeper understanding of the physical principles and, perhaps, to the need of improving the mathematical models and methods associated with an experiment.

This text is an outgrowth of sophomore, junior, and senior level laboratory courses taught over a five-year period in the Electrical Engineering Departments at Southern Methodist University and the University of Southern California. Many ideas were conceived and inspired by my teachers and colleagues, beginning with my first exposure at Columbia University and New York University. I am indebted to many people, and wish to express my heartfelt thanks to my teachers P. Mauzey, J. Millman, and M. Ghausi. In addition, a special word of thanks to Gordon Cumming and Sidney Wielin, at the University of Southern California, without whose efforts many of these experiments could not have been possible. Lastly and most of all, I want to express gratitude to those laboratory instructors and students whose comments and suggestions have aided and encouraged me in the endeavor which appears on the following pages.

Suggestions for Laboratory Policy and Report Writing

The following suggestions concerning laboratory policy and report writing were found to yield optimum student performance subject to the constraint of minimum laboratory cost per student. Of course, the following *can be modified according to the particular needs of the instructor and students.*

Classes are divided into one- or two-man squads who will work together for an entire semester. Every laboratory student should read those portions of an experiment (Parts One and Two) suggested by his instructor. In addition, each squad should maintain a bound laboratory notebook which contains a record of all laboratory work. For each experiment, the notebook should include the following.

1. A *written preparation* of the experiment to be performed. This preparation should be done by one person in each squad for each experiment. (A scheme suggested for two-man squads is that preparations alternate between each member of the squad so that no person writes a preparation for two experiments in succession. However, each member of the squad should understand the contents of each preparation. The written preparation may be graded by the instructor at the beginning of each laboratory session. Students who are not prepared may not be allowed to perform the experiment. In addition, the instructor can give quizzes at his discretion to determine how well each student has prepared. Some instructors do not require preparations by students when it is certain that the student is capable of adequately performing a laboratory experiment without some sort of preparation. Nevertheless, whatever method is used, a *laboratory notebook is strongly suggested.*

2. *Data* taken in the laboratory during the experiment. The data recorded from an experiment are to be entered directly into the notebook. Mistakes are to be crossed out, marked void, and left in the notebook.

3. *Data processing* indicated in the experimental requirements and additional interpretation necessary for an intelligent discussion of the experiment. Errors associated with the data and analysis should be taken into account. Data processing should be done as a squad effort, and discussion with the instructor is encouraged.

4. *Discussion of results*, which briefly ties together the experimental objectives and the processed laboratory results. This section is to be done by one person in each squad for each experiment, preferably by the person who does not do the preparation in two-man squads. A blank page may be left in the notebook following the discussion to allow the member of a two-man squad who did not write it to agree or disagree with the conclusions. When a laboratory session is divided into two-man squads, it is recommended that each squad member sign his name following his work to aid the instructor in assigning grades.

The notebook is an important part of the laboratory work, and should be kept up to date.

Students may be required to submit formal laboratory reports on assigned experiments performed in the laboratory. A formal report may follow the format presented below and could include the following.

1. *Abstract*, a concise description of the report including the purpose and most important results in the order in which they occur in the report paper (200-word maximum).

2. *Introduction*, a complete statement of the experimental problem, an outline of the theory involved in the solution, and a brief statement concerning the expected results (750-word maximum).

3. *Body* of the report, which should include:

Procedure, a brief outline of the actual experimental methods, including necessary circuit diagrams (500-word maximum).

Presentation of results, an appropriate presentation of the original and processed data for the experiment—lists, tables, graphs. Sample calculations must be shown.

Conclusions, an interpretation of the actual experimental results as they apply to the objectives of the experiment set out in the introduction. Any deviations from the expected or theoretical results are to be accounted for (500-word maximum).

The following information appears in the *IEEE Spectrum*, August 1965, entitled "Information for IEEE Authors," and is included here as an aid in writing laboratory reports.

Organization

IEEE papers usually consist of five parts: title, abstract, introduction, body, and conclusions. Two additional divisions, a glossary of symbols and an appendix, are sometimes desirable. SPECTRUM and the STUDENT JOURNAL papers may be less formally organized than those for the PROCEEDINGS and the TRANSACTIONS.

The *title* should clearly indicate the subject of the paper as briefly as possible. Since a paper is indexed by significant words in the title, and many readers select papers to read on the basis of the title, it should be chosen with considerable care.

An informative *abstract* of less than 200 words is needed for all PROCEEDINGS and TRANSACTIONS papers. It should state concisely, but not telegraphically:

1. What the author has done.
2. How it was done (if that is important).
3. The principal results (numerically, when possible).
4. The significance of the results.

The abstract should be informative, *not* merely a list of general topics that the paper covers, because it will probably appear later in an abstract journal.

The text of a paper can sometimes be simplified by following the abstract with a *glossary of symbols* if the paper contains equations in which many symbols are used.

The *introduction* orients the reader with respect to the problem and should include the following:

1. The nature of the problem.
2. The background of previous work.
3. The purpose and significance of the paper.

Where applicable, the following points may also be included:

4. The method by which the problem will be attacked.
5. The organization of the material in the paper.

The *body* contains the primary message of the paper in detail. The writer should bear in mind that his object is to communicate information efficiently and effectively to the reader. Even workers in the same field appreciate clear indications of the line of thought being followed, and frequent guideposts are essential for nonspecialists who want to understand the general nature and significance of the work. The use of trade names, company names, and proprietary terms should be avoided.

The *conclusions* should be clearly stated, and should cover the following:

1. What is shown by this work and its significance.
2. Limitations and advantages.

Where applicable, the following points should also be included:

3. Applications of the results.
4. Recommendations for further work.

Mathematical details which are ancillary to the main discussion of the paper, such as many derivations and proofs, may be included in one or more *appendixes*.

References

References should usually be footnotes at the bottom of the pages on which they are cited, but extended bibliographies may be placed at the end of the paper. References should be complete and in the form below.

For a periodical: J. A. Rich and G. A. Farrall, "Vacuum arc recovery phenomena," *Proc. IEEE*, vol. 52, pp. 1293–1301, November 1964.

For a book: J. D. Kraus, *Antennas*. New York: McGraw-Hill, 1950, pp. 100–108.

References should be to commonly available publications and books; references to reports of limited circulation should be avoided.

Contents

Basic Circuits
and Electronics Experiments

Experiment 1/Laboratory Equipment and Simple Circuit Elements

Part One

INTRODUCTION

This experiment is intended to introduce the student to modern electronic laboratory instruments. The cathode-ray oscilloscope and other conventional laboratory instruments will be discussed. These instruments will be used to generate and measure such quantities as voltage, current, time, frequency, and phase shift commonly associated with electrical signals. In addition, such discrete components as resistors, capacitors, and inductors will be studied.

THEORY

Cathode-Ray Oscilloscope (CRO)

A CRO is a very useful measuring instrument which displays electrical signals in a visual form. It is an extremely fast X-Y plotter which displays one input signal versus another signal or versus time. Certain electrical effects cause the X-Y pattern to appear on the face (screen) of the cathode-ray tube as on a television screen; in fact, a television set is nothing more than an oscilloscope with a few specialized circuits added. A CRO consists of a cathode-ray tube (CRT) mounted in a case containing the electronic circuitry to generate the operating and control voltages for the CRT, amplifiers, and attenuators to change the deflection sensitivity of the CRT and an oscillator to generate a sawtooth-voltage waveform. The sawtooth-voltage oscillator is used to sweep a spot horizontally across the face (screen) of the CRT.

In order to understand the controls of a CRO and to use them intelligently, it is necessary to have a basic understanding of the major elements of an oscilloscope. However, the following discussion is not intended to describe the complete operation of any particular CRO or to describe the use of every control knob on any CRO. It is suggested that a manufacturer's operation manual and a laboratory instructor be consulted for explanations regarding the idiosyncracies of any particular CRO.

Cathode-Ray Tube (CRT)

The heart of the oscilloscope is the cathode-ray tube shown in Fig. 1–1. The major parts of the CRT are the electron gun, deflection plates, and fluorescent screen. The gun consists of a heated cathode, which emits a beam of electrons accelerated toward the fluorescent screen and thereupon registering a small spot. The brightness and dimensions of the spot can be adjusted by means of the *intensity* and *focus* controls on the front panel of the scope. These controls determine the number and energy of the impinging electrons and how well the various electrons will conform to a single straight beam.

Horizontal and Vertical Deflection System

The electron beam passes through two sets of deflection plates placed at right angles to each other. If an alternating signal voltage is applied to the vertical deflection plates, the resulting electrostatic forces will cause the spot on the screen of the CRT to take successive vertical positions and thus produce a visible vertical trace. Similarly, if an alternating signal voltage is applied to the horizontal deflection plates, a visable horizontal trace appears on the screen of the CRT. A two-dimensional Cartesian display can be achieved on the screen because the deflection plates are placed at right angles to each other. The rest position of the spot on the screen is determined by a dc potential supplied by the oscilloscope to the horizontal and vertical deflection plates. This dc potential is controlled from the front panel by knobs, usually marked *vertical* and *horizontal position*. In many applications, the voltages to be observed are either too small or too large to produce a measurable deflection of the spot on the screen of the CRT. Consequently, amplifiers are inserted between the input signals and the deflection plates to control deflection sensitivity. Most often the vertical amplifier is calibrated to yield a specified deflection for a given input voltage. The specified deflection (sensitivity) is usually given in *volts* and

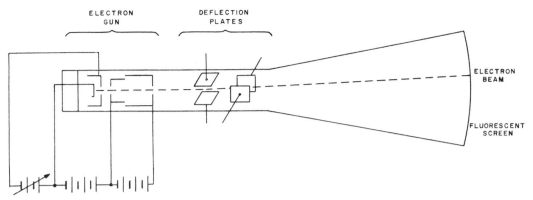

Fig. 1.1 Cathode ray tube.

millivolts per centimeter. A switch attenuator on the front panel allows one to change sensitivity scales. In some oscilloscopes, the horizontal amplifier is also calibrated; in others, it is not. The spot on the screen can now be made to trace any kind of pattern by applying suitable values of voltage to the deflection plates through the vertical and horizontal amplifiers. If a given pattern is retraced rapidly enough (usually an alternating input voltage about 20 Hz), the movement of the spot is not apparent and a continuous pattern is observed on the screen because of our persistence of vision.

Horizontal Sweep System

Frequently it is desirable to have a horizontal deflection proportional to the parameter time. An internally generated sawtooth-voltage can be applied through the horizontal amplifiers to the horizontal plates of the CRT. This causes the spot to sweep horizontally across the screen at a uniform rate, jump back, and then start again. Thus the horizontal position of the dot is in direct proportion to time. Generally, a selector switch is provided on the front panel of the CRO for selection of the adjustable time axis generated by the internal sawtooth generator; this switch is labeled internal. Fig. 1–2 is a schematic describing the connection of the sawtooth-voltage generator and input amplifiers to the deflection plates of the CRT.

The slope of the sawtooth-voltage waveform determines the rate at which the spot moves horizontally across the screen. The slope is adjusted by means of the sweep time/cm control knob, usually calibrated in microseconds, milliseconds, and seconds/cm.

In order to select an appropriate starting point in time relative to the input signal under observation, a "trigger" or synchronizing circuit is employed. The trigger circuit can sample either the vertical input signal, an externally applied signal, or the ac line voltage and lock the internally generated sawtooth-voltage in step with the sample. This provides a stable display for ease of interpretation. In most applications, the sweep can be triggered by the vertical input

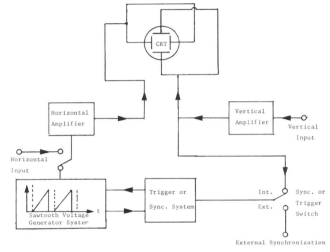

Fig. 1.2 Deflection and sweep systems.

signal, as illustrated in Fig. 1–3. For this mode of operation, the *source switch* is placed at the *internal position.* Sometimes external triggering is useful when signals are to be sampled from different places within a circuit or when the input signal is of small magnitude. For this mode of operation, the *source switch* is placed in the *external position* and the input signal is connected to the external trigger input. If an input signal is being observed which has a fixed time relationship to the line frequency (60 Hz), it is usually convenient but not necessary to use the line as the source of the trigger signal. In this case, the *source switch* is placed in the *line position.*

Finally, the slope, level, and mode of triggering must be selected for a desired sweep operation. The sweep can be triggered on the *positive-* or *negative*-going slope of the triggering signal, as indicated in Fig. 1–3. Usually the selection of the triggering slope (+ or −) is not critical, since either slope will provide a suitable display. The *trigger level control* determines the instantaneous voltage level of the triggering signal. A fixed level control setting may have a small frequency dependence such that the actual level of

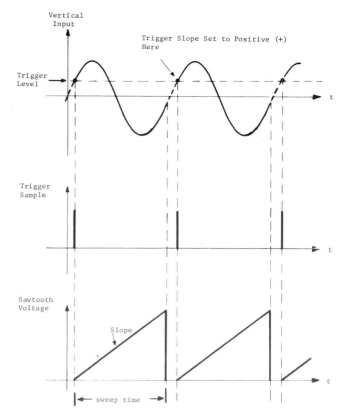

Fig. 1.3 Illustration of trigger and sawtooth-voltage generator system.

triggering may change with the frequency of the input signal. This means that, in order to maintain a display on the screen, the level control setting may have to be adjusted when the frequency of the input signal changes. In order to overcome this difficulty, an *automatic mode* is available on the *level control* knob which sets the triggering level automatically so that any external triggering signal of 1 volt or more will trigger the sweep. The sweep will continue to be triggered at a rate of about 50 Hz without a triggering signal indicating that the CRO is ready to display any signal which might be connected to the vertical input. Most scopes also have a *free-running mode* of operation for triggering on the *level control knob.* At this setting, the sweep is independent of any synchronizing signal and depends upon the setting of the sweep time/cm control. This mode is useful for synchronizing high-frequency signals by adjustment of the variable sweep control.

Measurements with a CRO

Voltage—The amplifier *sensitivity control* adjusts the amount of attenuation or amplification of the input signal before it reaches the deflection plates. By calibrating the sensitivity control in volt/cm and millivolt/cm, the deflection factor is known for each setting of the sensitivity control. In order to make measurements of the spot deflec-

tion, a rectangular grid (called a graticule) is scribed on the face of the CRT. The signal that is viewed on the graticule should be a distortionless reproduction of the input signal that has passed through the input amplifiers. The amount of distortion depends to a great extent upon the bandwidth of the amplifiers. Modern CROs have amplifier bandwidths of about 200 kHz (3db down) and higher.

The ac component of an input signal should be displayed over as large a portion of the screen as possible. Count the number of centimeters between desired points of the displayed signal, and multiply this number by the setting on the sensitivity control knob. Make certain that the *variable control* is in the *calibrated position,* to assure that the setting of the sensitivity control is the true voltage being read.

Often an ac voltage is applied to the input terminals of the CRO by means of a probe. The characteristics of the probe should be such that it does not disturb in any way the circuit that is being tested or the performance of the oscilloscope. Some probes attenuate the voltage by a factor of ten, and consequently the sensitivity control setting must be multiplied by ten in order to obtain a true voltage reading. The probe contains a resistor and a capacitor connected in parallel, which, when connected to the input capacitance and resistance of the CRO, provides a circuit that will accurately transfer (with some amplitude attenuation) the input signal to the input amplifier and deflection plates of the CRT. The circuit of Fig. 1–4 is called a com-

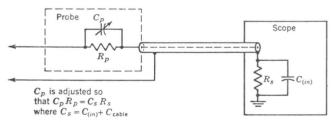

C_p is adjusted so
that $C_p R_p = C_s R_s$
where $C_s = C_{(in)} + C_{cable}$

Fig. 1.4 A probe for a CRO.

pensating attenuator, and is described in the next experiment.

The dc component of an input signal can also be measured by using the oscilloscope. This measurement can be made with or without the horizontal sweep in operation. If the horizontal sweep is being used, set the *level control* to *free-running* and the *variable control* to the *calibrate position.* Set the *input switch* to the *ground position.* Position the horizontal trace to any desired reference line of the graticule; this will be the ground reference line. Set the *input switch* to the *dc position;* the dc level of any input signal can now be measured with respect to the ground reference line.

Current—An oscilloscope can be used to measure the alternating or direct current in a circuit. The technique is to measure the ac or dc voltage difference across a resistor

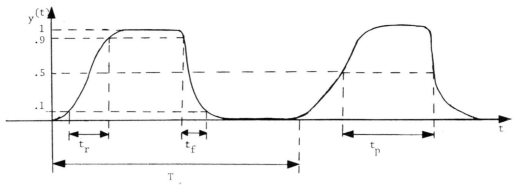

Fig. 1.5 Typical pulse waveform.

whose value is known, and then to divide the voltage difference by the known resistor value to obtain the value of current flowing through the resistor (Ohm's law). The voltage difference across a resistor can easily be obtained by first connecting the ground side of the CRO input terminals to any known ground of the circuit under observation. Next, connect the ungrounded side of the CRO input to each side of the known resistor and record the different voltages appearing on the screen according to the methods described in (a). The difference in the voltage from one side of the resistor to the other represents the voltage difference required to calculate the current through the resistor.

Time—The time interval between two points on an input signal is measured by multiplying the distance in centimeters on the graticule by the setting of the sweep time/cm control. Make certain that the variable control is in the *calibrate position* and that the internal sweep is set to the times one ($\times$ 1) position. Otherwise, if the horizontal control is at times two ($\times$ 2) or more, the time interval measured by the above procedure must be divided by the setting of the horizontal control.

Very often an oscilloscope is used to measure the periodic pulse waveform shown in Fig. 1-5. The rise time t_r is defined as the time it takes the pulse to rise from .1 to .9 of its final value; the fall time t_f is defined as the time it takes the pulse to fall from .9 to .1; and the average value of the pulse width t_p is measured from .5 to .5, as illustrated in Fig. 1-5.

Frequency—There are two common ways of measuring the frequency of a periodic input signal. Let us denote the input signal by $v(t)$. The period of $v(t)$ is defined as the value of T, for which the following is true:

$$v(t) = v(t + T) \text{ for all } t$$

The reciprocal of the time interval T between corresponding points of consecutive cycles is the frequency f—that is,

$$f = \frac{1}{T}.$$

Another method is to use Lissajous figures to determine frequency. This method compares a signal with an un-

known frequency to a signal with a known frequency. The signal with the unknown frequency (f_y) can be applied to the vertical input of the CRO, and the signal of known frequency (f_x) to the horizontal input. A moderately accurate low frequency signal maintained to a tolerance of $\pm$ .1 Hz in 60 Hz is the electrical signal supplied by American power companies, and can be used as the signal of known frequency. Closed-loop Lissajous figures result in the unknown signal frequencies which are rational-fraction multiples of the known signal frequency. After appropriate adjustments of the CRO are made, a Lissajous figure will appear on the screen, so that if the pattern is symmetrical and nearly stationary,

$$\frac{f_y}{f_x} = \frac{\text{number of vertical peaks}}{\text{number of horizontal peaks}}$$

A typical closed-loop Lissajous figure which appears on the screen of a CRO when the known and unknown signal frequencies are in the ratio of 2 to 1 is shown in Fig. 1-6.

Phase Shift—There are two common methods for measuring the phase shift between two input signals using an oscilloscope. The first method uses the operation of external triggering. Set the CRO to external trigger, and apply either of the input signals to the external triggering input. Now apply the first input signal to the vertical input, and display this signal so that an identifiable point of a cycle is placed at a convenient vertical graticule line. Without making any adjustments, connect the second input to the vertical input of the CRO, and measure in centimeters the shift of the identifiable point. Also measure the distance of one period of this signal in centimeters. The result of the shift in centimeters divided by the period in centimeters is multiplied by 360° to obtain the phase shift between the two input signals in degrees.

The second method uses the fact that if both signals applied to the vertical and horizontal input terminals of the oscilloscope are sinusoidal, the resulting pattern on the screen will be an ellipse. In order to demonstrate this fact, suppose that the voltage applied to the vertical input of the

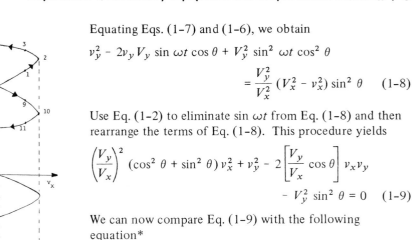

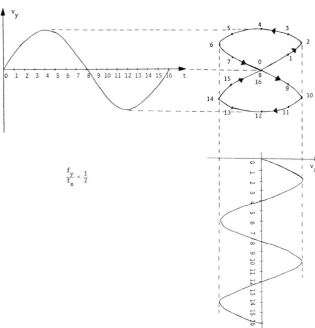

Fig. 1.6 Lissajous figure.

oscilloscope is called $v_y(t)$ and is given by the formula

$$v_y(t) = V_y \sin (\omega t + \theta) \qquad (1\text{-}1)$$

Assume that the voltage applied to the horizontal input of the CRO is called $v_x(t)$ and is given by

$$v_x(t) = V_x \sin \omega t \qquad (1\text{-}2)$$

Observe that v_x and v_y differ in amplitude and by a phase angle θ. If Eq. (1-2) is squared and the fact that

$$\sin^2 \omega t + \cos^2 \omega t = 1 \qquad (1\text{-}3)$$

is used, the following equation is obtained

$$V_x^2 \cos^2 \omega t = V_x^2 - v_x^2(t) \qquad (1\text{-}4)$$

Eq. (1-1) can be rewritten in the following trigonometric form

$$v_y(t) = V_y \sin (\omega t + \theta) = V_y \sin \omega t \cos \theta + V_y \cos \omega t \sin \theta \qquad (1\text{-}5)$$

The terms in Eq. (1-5) can be rearranged, and we can solve for $\cos^2 \omega t$

$$\cos^2 \omega t = \left[\frac{v_y - V_y \sin \omega t \cos \theta}{V_y \sin \theta} \right]^2 \qquad (1\text{-}6)$$

However, $\cos^2 \omega t$ is also equal to the following expression according to Eq. (1-4)

$$\cos^2 \omega t = \frac{V_x^2 - v_x^2(t)}{V_x^2} = 1 - \frac{v_x^2}{V_x^2} \qquad (1\text{-}7)$$

Equating Eqs. (1-7) and (1-6), we obtain

$$v_y^2 - 2v_y V_y \sin \omega t \cos \theta + V_y^2 \sin^2 \omega t \cos^2 \theta$$
$$= \frac{V_y^2}{V_x^2} (V_x^2 - v_x^2) \sin^2 \theta \qquad (1\text{-}8)$$

Use Eq. (1-2) to eliminate $\sin \omega t$ from Eq. (1-8) and then rearrange the terms of Eq. (1-8). This procedure yields

$$\left(\frac{V_y}{V_x} \right)^2 (\cos^2 \theta + \sin^2 \theta) v_x^2 + v_y^2 - 2 \left[\frac{V_y}{V_x} \cos \theta \right] v_x v_y$$
$$- V_y^2 \sin^2 \theta = 0 \qquad (1\text{-}9)$$

We can now compare Eq. (1-9) with the following equation*

$$Av_x^2 + Bv_y^2 + Cv_x v_y + Dv_x + Ev_y + F = 0 \qquad (1\text{-}10)$$

Eq. (1-10) is the equation of an ellipse provided

$$4AB - C^2 > 0 \qquad (1\text{-}11)$$

Applying condition (1-11) to Eq. (1-9) yields

$$4 \left(\frac{V_y}{V_x} \right)^2 - 4 \left(\frac{V_y}{V_x} \right)^2 \cos^2 \theta = 4 \left(\frac{V_y}{V_x} \right)^2 [\sin^2 \theta] > 0$$

Therefore, the oscilloscope pattern will be an ellipse. Now consider Eq. (1-5) as divided into two parts, as follows

$$v_y(t) = v_{yx}(t) + v_{yy}(t) \qquad (1\text{-}12)$$

where

$$v_{yx}(t) = V_y \sin \omega t \cos \theta \qquad (1\text{-}13)$$
$$v_{yy}(t) = V_y \cos \omega t \sin \theta \qquad (1\text{-}14)$$

Observe that $v_{yx}(t)$ is in phase with $v_x(t)$ of Eq. (1-2), and, by eliminating $\sin \omega t$ from Eqs. (1-2) and (1-13), we obtain

$$v_{yx}(t) = \left(\frac{V_y}{V_x} \cos \theta \right) v_x(t) \qquad (1\text{-}15)$$

This is the equation of a straight line with a slope of $\frac{V_y}{V_x} \cos \theta$. Also observe that $v_{yy}(t)$ of Eq. (1-14) is out of phase with $v_x(t)$ of Eq. (1-2) and that combining these two equations and eliminating the ωt terms yields

$$\frac{v_x^2}{V_x^2} + \frac{v_{yy}^2}{V_y^2 \sin^2 \theta} = 1 \qquad (1\text{-}16)$$

Eq. (1-16) is an ellipse whose major axis equals $2V_x$ and whose minor axis is $2V_y \sin \theta$ oriented in the x and y directions, respectively. The combined plot of v_y versus v_x is an ellipse whose major axis is tilted with a slope of $\frac{V_y}{V_x} \cos \theta$.

---

*See Thomas, G. B., Jr., *Calculus and Analytic Geometry*, (Reading, Mass.: Addison-Wesley, 1969), p. 351.

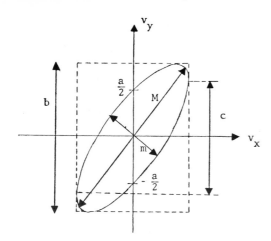

Fig. 1.7 Ellipse on a CRT.

The phase shift θ can be measured if M, m, V_x, and V_y are known. M and m are the lengths of the major and minor axes of the ellipse, and V_x and V_y are the maximum voltage amplitudes of the x and y deflections. For an ellipse

$$M = 2V_x \quad \text{and} \quad m = 2V_y \sin \theta \quad (1\text{-}17)$$

Therefore

$$\sin \theta = \frac{mV_x}{MV_y} \quad (1\text{-}18)$$

It can also be shown that

$$\sin \theta = \frac{a}{b} \quad (1\text{-}19)$$

$$\cos \theta = \frac{c}{b} \quad (1\text{-}20)$$

where a, b, and c are given in Fig. 1-7.

The sign of θ can be measured by observing the direction of motion of the spot on the screen of the CRO. The direction of motion about the origin will be clockwise if $\theta > 0$ and counterclockwise if $\theta < 0$. In addition, if $90° < |\theta| < 180°$, the ellipse will be tilted so that its major axis will lie in the second and fourth quadrants.

In conclusion, there is much more to an oscilloscope than has been discussed. In fact, there are a large number of different types of CROs, such as sampling oscilloscopes, storage and variable persistence, large screen displays—all of which are designed for special tasks. But their basic mode of operation is essentially the same as the elementary scope covered in the previous general discussion.

General-Purpose Voltmeters

Voltage, current, and resistance measurements can be simply accomplished with electronic instruments using meter movements. Most electronic voltmeters use specialized circuits to generate a current proportional to the quantity being measured, which then activates the meter movement. A general-purpose voltmeter is a combination of different meters which can measure ac voltages, dc voltages, and resistance.

Meters indicating ac voltages use one of three common techniques for measurement. Probably the most widely used ac voltmeters combining acceptable accuracy and reasonable cost is the average-responding (absolute value) voltmeter. This meter first amplifies or attenuates the ac input signal and then converts it into a full-wave rectified current which activates the meter. The meter is calibrated to the rms value of the input sine wave. Most average responding ac voltmeters are limited in sensitivity (100 μV full scale) by inherent noise and spurious signals. The second type is the peak-responding voltmeter. These voltmeters generally perform over a large bandwidth (frequency range of voltmeter) and convert the sinusoidal input into a rectified signal having an average or dc value which then activates the meter. The meter is calibrated to the rms value of the input signal. Both of these ac voltmeters will be in error if the measured signal is not a pure sinusoid.

The true-rms responding voltmeter will not be in error if the sinusoidal input signal is distorted. This type of voltmeter assures a high degree of accuracy, and uses a thermocouple to detect the rms value of the input signal. The thermocouple generates a dc voltage at its output proportional to the rms heating value of the sinusoidal input voltage. The dc voltage is then amplified before it activates the meter. The meter is calibrated to the rms value of the input signal.

Very often these ac voltmeters contain a scale for measuring directly in decibels. This type of meter scale can be used to compare electrical powers logarithmically rather than linearly. The unit of the logarithmic scale is called decibel (db), and the ratio by which electrical power P_2 exceeds power P_1 is defined by

$$\text{decibels} = 10 \log_{10} \frac{P_2}{P_1} \quad (1\text{-}21)$$

Readings in db can be obtained from the decibels scale of the voltmeter. The reference level is one milliwatt in 600Ω—that is, zero db corresponds to V = (power $\times$ resistance)$^{1/2}$ = $(.001 \times 600)^{1/2}$ = .7746 volts. Observe that if—and only if—the voltage being measured appears across a resistance of 600Ω, the db reading will be a power reading with respect to one milliwatt. In general, the db reading is a db reading with respect to .7746 volts—that is

$$(\text{reading in db}) = 20 \log_{10} \frac{\text{reading in volts}}{.7746} \quad (1\text{-}22)$$

The decibels scale is drawn relative to the voltage scales by use of this relationship. The reading in db is obtained by algebraically adding the db setting of the range switch to the db indication on the meter scale. Usually only a db reading is wanted, and a reference can be chosen arbitrarily. It is important to remember that this instrument is a voltmeter, not a power meter. For example, if the decibels reading at one point in a circuit, say node 1, is greater than at another point (node 2) by 6 db, one can only conclude that the voltage at node 1 is twice the voltage at node 2.

Dc voltmeters fall into two categories: direct-coupled, and chopper-stabilized. The direct-coupled voltmeter simply amplifies the dc signal before it activates the meter. The chopper-stabilized voltmeter converts the dc input signal into an ac signal, amplifies the ac signal, and then reconverts the ac into a dc signal. In this way, very sensitive dc voltmeter ranges of a few microvolts full scale can be achieved.

Resistance is usually measured by having the ohmmeter apply a known dc voltage V to the unknown resistor. The dc current I passing through the resistor is measured by the meter so that its movement is calibrated to be the value of V divided by the current I ($R = V/I$).

The accuracy, ranges, bandwidth, and loading effects of general purpose voltmeters vary considerably. However, the following experiments have been designed to operate with any one of a number of commercially available general purpose voltmeters. It should be noted that any voltmeter used in the following experiments should be chosen so as not to significantly change the operation of any circuit which it is observing (no loading). In addition, it is suggested that each voltmeter be calibrated at the beginning of an experiment. *Calibration procedures recommended by the manufacturer should be followed.*

Electronic Counters

Electronic counters can measure the frequency of electrical signals. In addition, some counters can measure time intervals and periods, count periodic and random pulses, and perform other specialized counting operations. An electronic counter compares an unknown frequency or time interval to a known frequency or time interval. The accuracy of this measurement depends primarily upon the stability of the known frequency, which is normally derived from the counter's interval oscillator or from the ac power line frequency. Manufacturer's specifications, which include minimum and maximum counting rates and operation procedures, should be consulted for any particular counter.

Signal Sources

Signal sources will be divided into two categories: those providing time-varying signals, such as an ac oscillator; and those providing a time-invariant signal, such as a dc battery. The function generator is a time-varying signal source that delivers a choice of different periodic signals with frequen-

cies adjustable over a wide range. Function generators are available which produce sine waves, triangle waves, square waves, sawtooth waves, and other waveforms. The following experiments can be performed with a simple function generator producing sine and square waveforms from 20 Hz to 500 kHz having maximum amplitudes of about 10 volts peak. The output frequency is usually adjusted in steps with a range switch, with continuous adjustments between steps accomplished with a calibrated dial or vernier. *Dial accuracy* indicates the degree of correspondence between the actual output frequency of the signal source and that indicated on its dial. The *output impedance* associated with a signal source is an important quantity to know, and can usually be obtained from the manufacturer's specifications. A technique for measuring the output impedance of a signal source will be discussed below.

Time-varying signal sources can be divided into three general categories:

1. Oscillators, which provide a sine-wave output with variable amplitude and frequency.

2. Pulse generators, which produce repetitive square waves with variable amplitude, frequency, and pulse width.

3. Function generators, which provide outputs such as sine waves, square waves, sawtooth waves, triangular waves, and others.

Another time-varying signal source is the line voltage provided by your local power company. This line voltage can be fed into a variac, which is simply a variable output transformer. The variac output provides a 60 Hz sinusoidal waveform. Voltage amplitudes up to approximately 100 or 200 volts rms and currents of a few amperes can be delivered by most variacs.

A variac is used in many of the following experiments because the 60 Hz signal produces a flicker-free display on the oscilloscope and is also slow enough so that high frequency effects of the circuit under test do not enter any desired measurements.

Sources providing time-invariant signals are generally called dc power supplies. Electronic dc power supplies are available as either constant voltage sources, constant current sources, or sources which crossover from constant voltage to constant current. Their usefulness and cost depend upon the degree to which they can perform the following functions.

1. Rectify or convert ac line voltage to dc voltage.

2. Provide continuously variable output voltage levels.

3. Provide a relatively constant output voltage independent of load conditions, line voltage, and environmental conditions.

Frequently dc power supplies have a three-terminal output arrangement. Two terminals (+ and -) provide an output isolated from ground, while the third terminal ($\equiv$, ground) is connected to the chassis and the ground of the power cord. These terminals can be connected in three

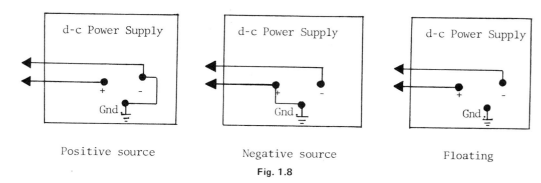

Positive source   Negative source   Floating

Fig. 1.8

configurations, as shown in Fig. 1-8. The power supply is connected as either a positive or negative source in most of the following experiments.

Circuit Board Equipment

There are numerous ways of interconnecting electronic components and instruments; consequently, a large number of circuit boards (breadboards) are commercially available. A few simple laboratory rules have been found helpful in conjunction with their use.

1. *Neatly lay out all circuits* and electronic testing equipment. Circuits should be built to look like the schematics they represent whenever possible.

2. *All connections* (soldered or solderless) *should be secure.*

3. Secure mechanical mounting of all components is desirable to keep components in fixed positions.

4. *Keep all connecting leads as short as possible.* Connect shielded cables to testing equipment whenever possible.

5. *Connect the grounds of all laboratory equipment to a common grounding point.*

6. Be extremely careful in the use of all laboratory equipment and tools. When in doubt, consult a laboratory instructor for advice.

Simple Circuit Elements

Three types of discrete circuit elements which will be used extensively in the following experiments are resistors, capacitors, and inductors.

Resistors—A resistor is the electrical element which dissipates energy in the form of heat. The ideal current voltage relationship in a resistor is known as Ohm's law

$$v_R(t) = R(t) i_R(t) \qquad (1\text{-}23)$$

The current and voltage directions in a resistor are specified in Fig. 1-9. The resistor $R(t)$ in the following experiments will not be time-varying, but will simply be a constant value R whose mks unit is the ohm (Ω). Note that the current direction specifies the direction of the voltage drop.

Many types of physical resistance elements closely approximate ideal resistors. Carbon composition, wire-wound,

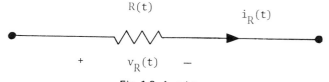

Fig. 1.9 A resistor.

metal film, and carbon film resistors—to name a few—are widely used as discrete circuit elements. Silicon chip resistors are very popular in integrated circuits. Usually the diffusion of boron onto the *n*-type silicon substrate produces a resistive element whose value is controlled by varying the device geometry. The resistance value and tolerance are generally indicated on the resistance body through a color code or numerical code for discrete resistor elements. The resistance color code is given in Fig. 1-10 and Table 1-1.

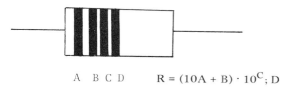

A   B C D $R = (10A + B) \cdot 10^C; D$

Fig. 1.10 Resistor color code.

TABLE 1-1.

A, B, C Bands (resistance)		D Band (tolerance)
0 – Black	5 – Green	5% – Gold
1 – Brown	6 – Blue	10% – Silver
2 – Red	7 – Violet	20% – No band
3 – Orange	8 – Gray	
4 – Yellow	9 – White	

Another important resistor parameter is the power rating, which indicates the amount of power the element can dissipate without being destroyed. Carbon composition resistors are normally supplied in ¼, ½, 1, and 2 watt sizes, which are identified by the size of their physical body.

Capacitors—A capacitor is a device which stores electrical charges on its plates; we say that electrical energy is stored in the electrical field of the capacitor.

The ideal charge-voltage relationship across a capacitor is

$$q(t) = C(t)v_C(t) \qquad (1\text{-}24)$$

with $C(t)$ the capacitance of the capacitor in farads, and $q(t)$ the charge in coulombs. The capacitors in the following experiments will be assumed not to be time-varying unless otherwise specified. That is, $C(t)$ will be constant for all time. The current through the capacitor is the time rate of change of the charge.

$$i_C(t) = \frac{dq(t)}{dt} = \frac{d}{dt}\, C(t)v_C(t) \qquad (1\text{-}25)$$

The current-voltage relationship when $C(t)$ is a constant is

$$i_C(t) = C\frac{dv_C(t)}{dt} \qquad (1\text{-}26)$$

with the directions shown in Fig. 1-11.

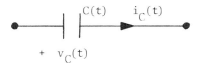

Fig. 1.11 A capacitor.

Alternatively, the charge-current and voltage-current relationships for a capacitor can be given in integral form

$$q(t) = \int_{-\infty}^{t} i_C(t')\, dt' \qquad (1\text{-}27)$$

and

$$v_C(t) = \frac{1}{C(t)} \int_{-\infty}^{t} i_C(t')\, dt' \qquad (1\text{-}28)$$

It is important to note that the limits of integration range from $-\infty$ to the instant t and that t' is a dummy variable of integration.

Suppose we know that the voltage on the capacitor for $-\infty \leqslant t \leqslant 0$ is a constant value, V_C. In this case, Eq. (1-28) becomes

$$v_C(t) = V_C + \frac{1}{C(t)} \int_{0}^{t} i_C(t')\, dt' \qquad (1\text{-}29)$$

V_C can be thought of as an initial voltage appearing on the capacitor before the current $i_C(t')$ begins to flow. Eq. (1-29) also expresses the fact that the complete time history of the voltage across the capacitor prior to time t must be known in order to specify the voltage $v_C(t)$ on a capacitor at time t.

Capacitors come in a wide variety of shapes and materials. Often the capacitance value is given on the body. There are

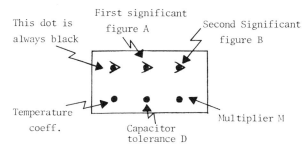

Fig. 1.12 Capacitor color code.

a number of color coding schemes used for capacitors. A color code (Jan 6–Dot) for rectangular mica-dielectric capacitors is given in Fig. 1-12 and Table 1-2. The voltage rating and polarity are very critical with electrolytic type capacitors. These ratings are printed on the body, and must be observed or heating will destroy the capacitor.

A very popular integrated circuit capacitor is the metal-oxide-semiconductor (MOS) capacitor. The capacitors are built by depositing an oxide layer on low resistivity n-type silicon and then evaporating aluminum over the silicon dioxide. The aluminum acts as one plate of the capacitor, and the silicon substrate serves as the other. The thickness of the oxide is varied to obtain the desired capacitance value in the range from 1–500 pf.

Inductors—An inductor is a device which stores electrical energy in its magnetic field. The energy is a result of the current flowing through the inductor. The ideal flux-current relationship in an inductor is

$$\phi(t) = L(t)\, i_L(t) \qquad (1\text{-}30)$$

with $L(t)$ the inductance of the inductor in henries, and ϕ the flux in webers. The voltage across an inductor is given by Faraday's law

$$v_L(t) = \frac{d\phi(t)}{dt} \qquad (1\text{-}31)$$

The voltage-current relationship in an inductor is obtained by substituting Eq. (1-30) into Eq. (1-31):

$$v_L(t) = \frac{d}{dt} L(t)\, i_L(t) \qquad (1\text{-}32)$$

and the directions are shown in Fig. 1-13.
Once again, inductors will have constant values independent of time in the following experiments unless otherwise speci-

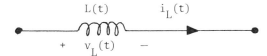

Fig. 1.13 An inductor.

TABLE 1-2.

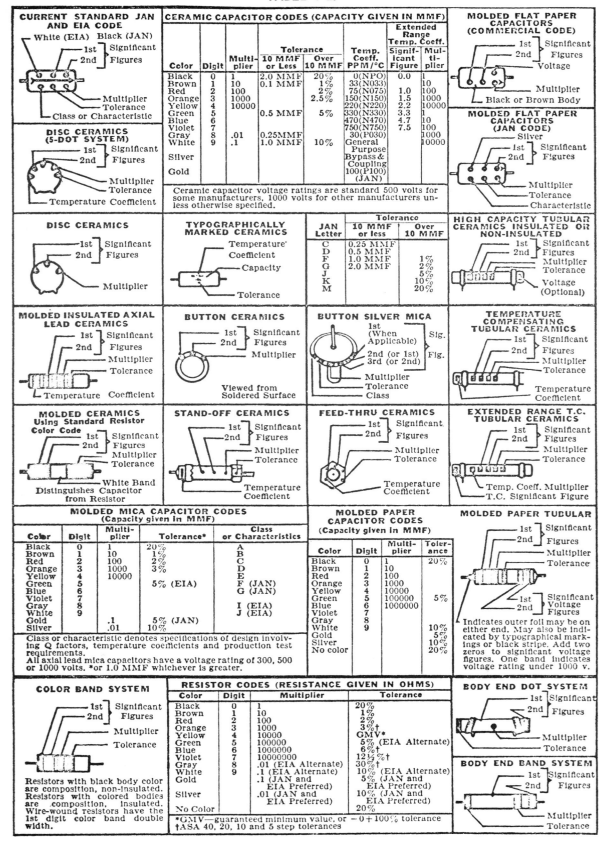

CURRENT STANDARD JAN AND EIA CODE
White (EIA) Black (JAN)
1st / 2nd Significant Figures
Multiplier
Tolerance
Class or Characteristic

DISC CERAMICS (5-DOT SYSTEM)
1st / 2nd Significant Figures
Multiplier
Tolerance
Temperature Coefficient

CERAMIC CAPACITOR CODES (CAPACITY GIVEN IN MMF)

Color	Digit	Multiplier	Tolerance 10 MMF or Less	Tolerance Over 10 MMF	Temp. Coeff. PPM/°C	Extended Range Temp. Coeff. Significant Figure	Extended Range Temp. Coeff. Multiplier
Black	0	1	2.0 MMF	20%	0(NPO)	0.0	1
Brown	1	10	0.1 MMF	1%	33(N033)		10
Red	2	100		2%	75(N075)	1.0	100
Orange	3	1000		2.5%	150(N150)	1.5	1000
Yellow	4	10000			220(N220)	2.2	10000
Green	5		0.5 MMF	5%	330(N330)	3.3	1
Blue	6				470(N470)	4.7	10
Violet	7				750(N750)	7.5	100
Gray	8	.01	0.25MMF		30(P030)		1000
White	9	.1	1.0 MMF	10%	General Purpose Bypass & Coupling 100(P100) (JAN)		10000
Silver							
Gold							

Ceramic capacitor voltage ratings are standard 500 volts for some manufacturers, 1000 volts for other manufacturers unless otherwise specified.

MOLDED FLAT PAPER CAPACITORS (COMMERCIAL CODE)
1st / 2nd Significant Figures
Voltage
Multiplier
Black or Brown Body

MOLDED FLAT PAPER CAPACITORS (JAN CODE)
Silver
1st / 2nd Significant Figures
Multiplier
Tolerance
Characteristic

DISC CERAMICS
1st / 2nd Significant Figures
Multiplier

TYPOGRAPHICALLY MARKED CERAMICS
Temperature Coefficient
Capacity
Tolerance

JAN Letter	Tolerance 10 MMF or less	Tolerance Over 10 MMF
C	0.25 MMF	
D	0.5 MMF	
F	1.0 MMF	1%
G	2.0 MMF	2%
J		5%
K		10%
M		20%

HIGH CAPACITY TUBULAR CERAMICS INSULATED OR NON-INSULATED
1st / 2nd Significant Figures
Multiplier
Tolerance
Voltage (Optional)

MOLDED INSULATED AXIAL LEAD CERAMICS
1st / 2nd Significant Figures
Multiplier
Tolerance
Temperature Coefficient

BUTTON CERAMICS
1st / 2nd Significant Figures
Multiplier
Viewed from Soldered Surface

BUTTON SILVER MICA
1st (When Applicable) Sig. / 2nd (or 1st) 3rd (or 2nd) Fig.
Multiplier
Tolerance
Class

TEMPERATURE COMPENSATING TUBULAR CERAMICS
1st / 2nd Significant Figures
Multiplier
Tolerance
Temperature Coefficient

MOLDED CERAMICS Using Standard Resistor Color Code
1st / 2nd Significant Figures
Multiplier
Tolerance
White Band Distinguishes Capacitor from Resistor

STAND-OFF CERAMICS
1st / 2nd Significant Figures
Multiplier
Tolerance
Temperature Coefficient

FEED-THRU CERAMICS
1st / 2nd Significant Figures
Multiplier
Tolerance
Temperature Coefficient

EXTENDED RANGE T.C. TUBULAR CERAMICS
1st / 2nd Significant Figures
Multiplier
Tolerance
Temp. Coeff. Multiplier
T.C. Significant Figure

MOLDED MICA CAPACITOR CODES (Capacity given in MMF)

Color	Digit	Multiplier	Tolerance*	Class or Characteristics
Black	0	1	20%	A
Brown	1	10	1%	B
Red	2	100	2%	C
Orange	3	1000	3%	D
Yellow	4	10000		E
Green	5		5% (EIA)	F (JAN)
Blue	6			G (JAN)
Violet	7			
Gray	8			I (EIA)
White	9			J (EIA)
Gold		.1	5% (JAN)	
Silver		.01	10%	

Class or characteristic denotes specifications of design involving Q factors, temperature coefficients and production test requirements.
All axial lead mica capacitors have a voltage rating of 300, 500 or 1000 volts. *or 1.0 MMF whichever is greater.

MOLDED PAPER CAPACITOR CODES (Capacity given in MMF)

Color	Digit	Multiplier	Tolerance
Black	0	1	20%
Brown	1	10	
Red	2	100	
Orange	3	1000	
Yellow	4	10000	
Green	5	100000	5%
Blue	6	1000000	
Violet	7		
Gray	8		
White	9		10%
Gold			5%
Silver			10%
No color			20%

MOLDED PAPER TUBULAR
1st / 2nd Significant Figures
Multiplier
Tolerance
1st / 2nd Significant Voltage Figures

Indicates outer foil may be on either end. May also be indicated by typographical markings or black stripe. Add two zeros to significant voltage figures. One band indicates voltage rating under 1000 v.

COLOR BAND SYSTEM
1st / 2nd Significant Figures
Multiplier
Tolerance

Resistors with black body color are composition, non-insulated. Resistors with colored bodies are composition, insulated. Wire-wound resistors have the 1st digit color band double width.

RESISTOR CODES (RESISTANCE GIVEN IN OHMS)

Color	Digit	Multiplier	Tolerance
Black	0	1	20%
Brown	1	10	1%
Red	2	100	2%
Orange	3	1000	3%†
Yellow	4	10000	GMV*
Green	5	100000	5% (EIA Alternate)
Blue	6	1000000	6%†
Violet	7	10000000	12½%†
Gray	8	.01 (EIA Alternate)	30%†
White	9	.1 (EIA Alternate)	10% (EIA Alternate)
Gold		.1 (JAN and EIA Preferred)	5% (JAN and EIA Preferred)
Silver		.01 (JAN and EIA Preferred)	10% (JAN and EIA Preferred)
No Color			20%

*GMV—guaranteed minimum value, or −0+100% tolerance
†ASA 40, 20, 10 and 5 step tolerances

BODY END DOT SYSTEM
1st / 2nd Significant Figures
Multiplier
Tolerance

BODY END BAND SYSTEM
1st / 2nd Significant Figures
Multiplier
Tolerance

fied. The voltage-current relationship will become

$$v_L(t) = L \frac{di_L(t)}{dt} \qquad (1\text{-}33)$$

Alternatively, the flux-voltage and current-voltage relationships in an inductor are

$$\phi(t) = \int_{-\infty}^{t} v(t')\,dt' \qquad (1\text{-}34)$$

and

$$i_L(t) = \frac{1}{L(t)} \int_{-\infty}^{t} v_L(t')\,dt' \qquad (1\text{-}35)$$

Suppose we know that the current in an inductor for $-\infty \leqslant t \leqslant 0$ is a constant value, I_L. In this case, Eq. (1-35) becomes

$$i_L(t) = I_L + \frac{1}{L(t)} \int_{0}^{t} v_L(t')\,dt' \qquad (1\text{-}36)$$

I_L is called the initial current. Eq. (1-36) implies that, in order to calculate the current in an inductor at a given time t, the complete past-time history of the current in the inductor must be known.

Inductors will be the least used element. They are either color coded similar to a resistor or have inductance values printed on their bodies. Their large size in proportion to reasonable values limits their application in many electronic circuits. Table 1-2 is a summary of some of the more common codes used to specify resistor, capacitor, and inductor values.

Impedance Bridge

A useful device available in many laboratories for measuring resistance, capacitance, and inductance is an impedance bridge. The impedance bridge uses the "balanced bridge" condition to measure the unknown element values. The operation manual provided by the manufacturer describes the required procedures for using the impedance bridge.

Part Two

OBJECTIVE

The operation of a number of important laboratory instruments will be studied by using them to observe sine and square waves, to check the frequency calibration of an audio oscillator, to measure the phase shift in a series RC circuit, and to measure the values of some discrete circuit elements.

REFERENCES

Chirlian, P. M., *Basic Network Theory*. New York: McGraw-Hill, 1969, Chapter 1.

Cruz, J. B., and Van Valkenburg, M. E., *Introductory Signals and Circuits*. Waltham, Mass.: Blaisdell, 1967, Chapters 1, 2, 3, and 4.

D'Azzo, J. J., and Houpis, C. H., *Principles of Electrical Engineering*. Columbus, Ohio: Merrill, 1968, Chapter 2.

Desoer, C. A., and Kuh, E. S., *Basic Circuit Theory*. New York: McGraw-Hill, 1969, Chapters 1 and 2.

Ghausi, M. S., *Electronic Circuits: Devices, Models, Functions, Analysis, and Design*. New York: Van Nostrand, Reinhold, 1971, Chapter 1.

Hayt, W. H., and Kemmerly, J. E., *Engineering Circuit Analysis*. New York: McGraw-Hill, 1971, Chapters 1 and 2.

Romanowitz, H. A., *Electrical Fundamentals and Circuit Analysis*. New York: Wiley, 1966, Chapters 1, 2, and 10.

Skilling, H. H., *Electrical Engineering Circuits*. New York: Wiley, 1968.

Smith, R. J., *Circuits, Devices, and Systems*. New York: Wiley, 1968. Chapters 1, 2, and 21.

LABORATORY PREPARATION

1. Read all portions of this experiment in order to become thoroughly familiar with the functions of the CRO and other laboratory instruments. If possible, obtain manufacturer's specification for the instruments in your laboratory.

2. The periods of some sinusoidal signals were measured as 10 sec, 20 millisec, and 50 microsec. What are the frequencies of these signals?

3. What is the difference between the peak and the peak-to-peak voltage of a sinusoidal signal? The average (dc) value $\overline{v}(t)$ of a periodic signal $v(t)$ is defined as

$$\overline{v}(t) = \frac{1}{T} \int_{0}^{T} v(t')\,dt'$$

and the rms value of $v(t)$ as

$$v_{\text{rms}}(t) = \left[\frac{1}{T} \int_{0}^{T} v^2(t')\,dt' \right]^{1/2}$$

with T the period and t' a dummy variable of integration. Calculate the average and rms values of $v(t) = 1 \sin 2t$, $v(t) = 5 \cos 3t$, and $v(t) = 3 + 7 \sin(t + 45°)$.

4. A Lissajous figure results when two sinusoidal signals of different frequencies are applied to the vertical and hori-

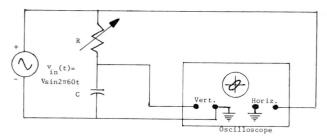

Fig. 1.14 Circuit for measuring phase shift.

zontal inputs of an oscilloscope. Draw the Lissajous figures for two sinusoidal signals whose frequencies are in the ratio of 3 to 2 and 2 to 3. Can an unknown frequency be measured when two periodic but nonsinusoidal signals are supplied to an oscilloscope? Give an example and draw the figure appearing on the screen of the oscilloscope.

5. The phase angle between the voltages applied to the vertical and horizontal inputs of the scope in terms of R and C of Fig. 1–14 is given by

$$\theta = -\tan^{-1} 2\pi 60 \cdot R \cdot C$$

Plot the figure appearing on the screen of the oscilloscope if

$$C = .1 \; \mu f \quad \text{and} \quad R = 25 \; k\Omega.$$

6. Derive Eqs. (1-19 and 1-20).

7. Two voltages read across a 600Ω resistor are 6 db and 20 db. What are these readings in volts?

8. A carbon resistor is color coded brown (A), black (B), red (C), and gold (D). What are its resistance and tolerance? A mica capacitor is color coded (Jan–6 dot)— black (JAN), black (A), red (B), brown (M), and gold (D). What are its capacitance and tolerance?

LABORATORY PROCEDURE

1. The first step in using a CRO is to turn the power on and to obtain a well-focused spot on the center of the screen. This is accomplished by adjusting the beam focus and intensity controls. A *bright dot* or *halo* surrounding the dot means that the intensity is too high and *should not be left in one position* on the screen for more than a few seconds. The second step is to determine the type of horizontal sweep desired. Often it is desirable to observe an input signal as a function of time. In such a case, the internal sawtooth sweep generator should produce a horizontal line on the screen when there is no externally applied signal at the vertical input. Set the trigger source switch to internal, the horizontal mode to internal or normal, and the triggering level control to automatic. Vary the vertical sensitivity switch over its entire range and observe the trace on the screen with the sweep time/cm switch set to 10 millisec/cm. Now obtain a dot moving horizontally at a rate of 1 cm/sec.

2. Connect a sinusoidal signal from an oscillator (function generator) to the vertical input of the oscilloscope and with a 500 Hz signal from the sinusoidal oscillator obtain a three-cycle screen pattern about 4 cm from peak to peak and about 8 cm wide. Repeat this procedure for several settings of the oscillator frequency dial. Determine the maximum amplitude output of the oscillator at 1000 Hz.

3. Apply a 1000 Hz square-wave signal directly to the vertical input of the scope and measure the peak-to-peak voltage of the signal. Do not change the settings on the square-wave oscillator. If a probe is available, connect it to the vertical input of the scope and to the output of the square-wave oscillator. Measure the peak value of the waveform. Discuss the differences in the waveforms with and without the probe. Adjust the probe to produce a signal on the screen which approximates a square-wave as closely as possible. Set the trigger source to external trigger and the level control to free-running. Apply the square-wave signal to the vertical input (with or without a probe) and to the trigger (external) input terminals. Adjust the CRO controls to produce a trace which starts at different horizontal positions on the screen.

4. The horizontal mode switch should be changed from internal sweep to the 2 volt/cm setting if a horizontal amplifier control is available on the scope. If not, set the mode control to external. Apply a sinusoidal signal (60 Hz and approximately 5 to 10 volts peak) from a source to the scope's horizontal input terminals provided the scope has a horizontal amplifier control. If not, connect this signal to the external input terminal. Set the sinusoidal oscillator frequency dial to approximately 120 Hz and observe a Lissajous pattern on the screen. Adjust the frequency dial just slightly until a completed, symmetrical, and stationary Lissajous pattern appears on the screen. Record the dial setting. The dial accuracy should be checked over as wide a range of frequency as possible. Plot the frequency obtained from the oscillator dial versus the frequency calculated from the Lissajous figure. If available, use a counter to measure the output frequency of the oscillator.

5. Construct the circuit of Fig. 1–14. The phase angle between two voltages of this circuit should be measured for several values of R. Cover as wide a range of phase angle as can be measured with reasonable accuracy ($C = .1 \mu f$ and $R = 0$ to 100 kΩ.) Disconnect the leads to the horizontal input and connect them to the external input (for scopes with horizontal inputs). Now use a different method to measure the phase shift between two voltages.

Now change $v_{in}(t)$ to be a periodic and square waveform of frequency 100Hz. Disconnect the horizontal input to the oscilloscope. Adjust the oscilloscope sweep, as in Part 1, to view on the CRT a few cycles of the voltage appearing across the capacitor. Measure the rise time t_r, the fall time t_f, and the pulse width t_p as R and the period T of $v_{in}(t)$ are varied. Describe the effect of T and R on t_r, t_f, and t_p.

6. Adjust your general-purpose (ac or dc) voltmeter according to the instructions obtained from the manufac-

turer or from your laboratory instructor. Use an rms reading voltmeter to measure a sinusoidal signal from the oscillator. Note that the rms value is $1/\sqrt{2} = .707$ times the peak value of the sinusoidal signal. Apply the same signal to the vertical input of the scope and measure the peak value of the signal. Also measure a positive and negative dc signal from a battery or dc source with a *dc* voltmeter. Finally, measure the resistance of a number of different resistors using an ohmmeter.

7. (Optional) Learn to use an impedance bridge to measure resistance, capacitance, and inductance if a bridge is available in your laboratory.

LIST OF EQUIPMENT

1. Cathode-ray oscilloscope
2. General-purpose voltmeter or ac voltmeter, dc voltmeter, and an ohmmeter
3. Signal sources: function generator or sine- and square-wave oscillators, dc power supply, or battery and 60 Hz signal source
4. Circuit board
5. Discrete circuit elements: resistors, capacitors, and inductors
6. Impedance bridge (optional)
7. Frequency counter (optional)

Experiment 2/Kirchhoff's Laws and Low-Order Circuits

Part One

INTRODUCTION

Two of the most fundamental and useful laws in basic circuit theory and electronics are called Kirchhoff's current and voltage laws. Kirchhoff's current law (KCL) is equivalent to the law of conservation of charge for a region surrounded by a closed surface. Kirchhoff's current law states that in any electrical system the net current entering a closed region which contains no sources or sinks of charge is zero—that is, the current entering equals the current leaving. Kirchhoff's voltage law (KVL) is equivalent to Faraday's law for conservative fields, which states that no work is done in carrying a unit charge around any closed path. Analogously, Kirchhoff's voltage law states that the net potential around any closed loop is always zero. The application of Kirchhoff's laws to circuits containing ideal resistors, capacitors, and inductors produces either algebraic or differential type equations. The solution of some of these equations will be discussed in this experiment.

THEORY

Kirchhoff's Laws

Kirchhoff's current law can be stated mathematically as

$$\sum_{k=1}^{n} i_k(t) = 0 \qquad (2\text{-}1)$$

Eq. (2-1) expresses the fact that the sum of the currents entering and leaving any portion of a network containing no sources is zero at any time t (see Fig. 2-1). For example, applying Eq. (2-1) to Fig. 2-1 yields

$$i_1(t) + i_2(t) - i_3(t) + i_4(t) - i_5(t) = 0 \qquad (2\text{-}2)$$

Eq. (2-2) assumes currents entering as positive quantities and remains valid if it is multiplied by minus one. This means that all directions of currents could be reversed and that Kirchhoff's current law is still valid. However, currents now entering are expressed as negative quantities.

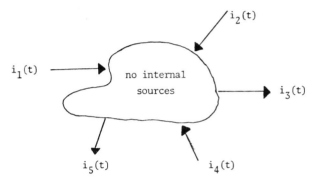

Fig. 2.1 Currents entering and leaving a network.

These statements imply arbitrariness about current directions, which will be discussed later.

Kirchhoff's voltage law can be expressed mathematically as

$$\sum_{k=1}^{m} v_k(t) = 0 \qquad (2\text{-}3)$$

Eq. (2-3) expresses the fact that the net potential around any closed loop of a network is always zero at any time t (see Fig. 2-2). For example, applying Eq. (2-3) to the closed-loop of Fig. 2-2 yields

$$v_1(t) - v_2(t) - v_3(t) = 0 \qquad (2\text{-}4)$$

Eq. (2-4) expresses voltage rises (– to +) as positive quantities if the closed loop in Fig. 2-2 is traversed in the clockwise direction. However, Eq. (2-4) multiplied by – 1 implies either that the closed loop is traversed in the counterclockwise direction with voltage rises as positive quantities or that voltage drops (+ to –) are assumed positive quantities in Eq. (2-4) when traversing the closed loop in the clockwise direction. Again, this implies an arbitrariness about voltage directions, which will be discussed later. However, it will be demonstrated that not all current directions and voltage differences (drops or rises) in a given network are arbitrary.

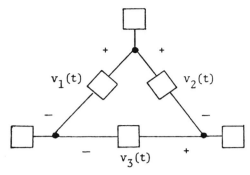

Fig. 2.2 A closed loop.

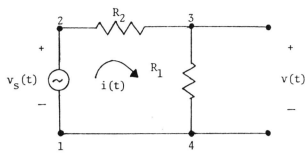

Fig. 2.5 A voltage divider network.

Many of the networks to be studied in this manual will contain resistors, capacitors, and inductors, which will be assumed to be ideal elements. The basic laws describing these ideal elements are given in Experiment 1.

In the following experiments, Kirchhoff's laws will be applied to networks containing resistors, capacitors, and inductors connected together in various ways. One method of generating currents and voltages in these networks is to connect them to what are known as independent voltage or current sources. An independent voltage source is a device whose terminal voltage is independent of the current flowing through it. This voltage source may be a constant for all time (as in the case of an ideal dc battery; see Fig. 2-3a) or it may be an arbitrary function of time (see Fig. 2-3b). When a voltage source $v_s(t)$ or V_s is identically zero, the voltage source is effectively a short circuit.

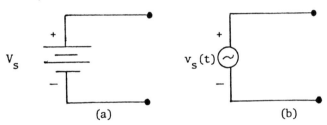

Fig. 2.3 Voltage sources.

An independent current source is a device whose current is independent of the voltage across its terminals. The current source may be a constant for all time, or it may be an arbitrary function of time. The usual notation specifying current direction is given in Fig. 2-4. When the current $i_s(t)$ is identically zero, the current source is effectively an open circuit.

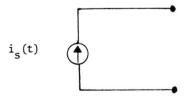

Fig. 2.4 A current source.

Zero-Order Circuits

We will now apply Kirchhoff's laws to a few simple circuits containing resistors and independent sources. These circuits are called zero-order circuits because the KCL and KVL equations describing them are linear algebraic type equations which do not contain derivatives and/or integrals.

Consider the network of Fig. 2-5.

We are interested in solving for the voltage $v(t)$ as a function of $v_s(t), R_1$, and R_2.

Assume that a current $i(t)$ flows in the direction indicated in Fig. 2-5. Apply KVL around the closed loop in the clockwise direction from junctions 1 to 2 to 3 to 4. Assume voltage drops to be positive.

$$-v_s(t) + R_2\, i(t) + R_1 i(t) = 0 \qquad (2\text{-}5)$$

Solve Eq. (2-5) for $i(t)$

$$i(t) = \frac{v_s(t)}{R_1 + R_2} \qquad (2\text{-}6)$$

The voltage $v(t)$ is equal to $R_1 i(t)$. We obtain Eq. (2-7) if we multiply Eq. (2-6) by R_1.

$$\boxed{v(t) = \frac{R_1}{R_1 + R_2}\, v_s(t)} \qquad (2\text{-}7)$$

Eq. (2-7) is called the *voltage divider equation* because the source voltage divides between R_1 and R_2. This equation states that the voltage $v(t)$ is a fraction of the independent source voltage. The fraction is $\dfrac{R_1}{R_1 + R_2}$ and is less than or equal to 1 for all values of $R_2 \geqslant 0$ and $R_1 \geqslant 0$.

$$\frac{R_1}{R_1 + R_2} = \frac{1}{1 + \dfrac{R_2}{R_1}} \leqslant 1 \qquad (2\text{-}8)$$

It is possible to assume at the beginning of this problem that the current $i(t)$ is flowing in the opposite direction. In this case, Eq. (2-5) would be

$$-v_s(t) - R_2 i(t) - R_1 i(t) = 0 \qquad (2\text{-}9)$$

and Eq. (2-6) would be

$$i(t) = - \frac{v_s(t)}{R_1 + R_2} \qquad (2\text{-}10)$$

The voltage $v(t)$ across resistor R_1 would now be $-R_1 i(t)$, and Eq. (2-7) would be the same—that is

$$v(t) = - \left(- \frac{R_1 v_s(t)}{R_1 + R_2} \right) \qquad (2\text{-}11)$$

We can conclude that the assumed direction of the current $i(t)$ is arbitrary. However, KVL is valid regardless of the assumed current direction, and we were careful not to violate Ohm's law across resistor R_1.

The network of Fig. 2-6 is known as a current divider network.

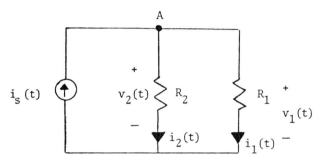

Fig. 2.6 A current divider network.

It is desired to calculate the current $i_1(t)$ as a function of $i_s(t), R_1,$ and R_2. This is accomplished by applying KCL to junction A and assuming that currents entering the junction are negative

$$-i_s(t) + i_1(t) + i_2(t) = 0 \qquad (2\text{-}12)$$

Ohm's laws for resistors R_1 and R_2 are

$$v_1(t) = R_1\, i_1(t) \qquad (2\text{-}13)$$

$$v_2(t) = R_2\, i_2(t) \qquad (2\text{-}14)$$

The KVL equation around the loop containing only R_1 and R_2 yields

$$v_1(t) - v_2(t) = 0 \qquad (2\text{-}15)$$

Therefore, combining Eqs. (2-13), (2-14), and (2-15)

$$i_2(t) = \frac{v_2(t)}{R_2} = \frac{v_1(t)}{R_2} = \frac{R_1}{R_2} i_1(t) \qquad (2\text{-}16)$$

Substituting Eq. (2-16) into (2-12) and solving for $i_1(t)$ yields

$$\boxed{ i_1(t) = \left(\frac{1}{1 + \dfrac{R_1}{R_2}} \right) i_s(t) = \frac{R_2}{R_1 + R_2} i_s(t) } \qquad (2\text{-}17)$$

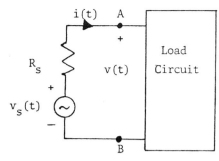

Fig. 2.7 A non-ideal voltage source.

Eq. (2-17) (*current divider equation*) states that the current through resistor R_1 is a fraction of the independent source current $i_s(t)$. The fraction is given by $\dfrac{R_2}{R_1 + R_2}$ and is less than or equal to 1 for $R_1 \geqslant 0$ and $R_2 \geqslant 0$.

Often an independent voltage source has a resistance in series with itself—the voltage across the terminals of a source is not independent of the current through its terminals. This type of nonideal voltage source is shown in Fig. 2-7.

The voltage $v(t)$ across terminals AB can be expressed using KVL as

$$v(t) = v_s(t) - R_s i(t) \qquad (2\text{-}18)$$

The voltage $v(t)$ would be equal to $v_s(t)$ if $i(t)$ were zero or, equivalently, if the load circuit were removed and terminals AB were an open circuit. The terminal voltage $v(t)$, measured from A to B, does depend upon both the current $i(t)$ and the resistance R_s. The series connection of a voltage source and a resistor is called a Thevenin equivalent circuit. If we divide Eq. (2-18) by R_s, we obtain for $i(t)$

$$i(t) = \frac{v_s(t)}{R_s} - \frac{v(t)}{R_s} \qquad (2\text{-}19)$$

We observe that Eq. (2-18) can be represented by a current source in parallel with a resistor R_s. Eq. (2-19) is KCL applied to junction A. The parallel connection of a current source and a resistor R_s is called a Norton equivalent circuit. The networks to the left of terminals AB in Figs. 2-7 and 2-8 are equivalent to each other. The open circuit

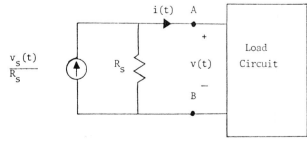

Fig. 2.8 A non-ideal current source.

voltage between terminals AB is $v(t)$ for Figs. 2-7 and 2-8, and the impedance to the left of terminals AB is R_s for both figures.

It will be convenient for the analysis of many of the following experiments to transform an independent voltage source in series with a resistor into a current source in parallel with a resistor, and vice versa.

First-Order Circuits

A first-order circuit is one for which the currents and voltages in it can be described by first-order differential equations.

Eq. (2-20) represents a linear first-order differential equation.

$$a_1(t)\frac{dx}{dt} + a_0(t)x(t) = f(t) \qquad (2\text{-}20)$$

In this experiment, $x(t)$ of Eq. (2-20) can represent a current or a voltage. The coefficients $a_1(t)$ and $a_0(t)$ will be functions of the resistors (R's), inductors (L's) and capacitors (C's). If the R's, L's, and C's are non-time-varying, then the coefficients $a_1(t)$ and $a_0(t)$ will be non-time-varying and denoted a_1 and a_0. The function $f(t)$ is the applied voltage or current usually referred to as the forcing function. The forcing function $f(t)$ can be 0 or an arbitrary function of time. Three important forcing functions are the unit step, the unit impulse, and the unit ramp.

A unit step is defined as

$$f(t) = 0 \ \text{ for } \ t < 0$$
$$= 1 \ \text{ for } \ t > 0 \qquad (2\text{-}21)$$

Its value at $t = 0$ may be taken to be 0, 1/2, or 1. This manual will assume $f(t) = 1$ at $t = 0$. The symbol $u(t)$ is usually used to denote a unit step function. A unit step function beginning at $t = \tau$ is written $u(t - \tau)$ and is called a delayed unit step. Two step functions can be combined to generate a pulse function in the following way. Let $p(t)$ define a pulse which is the difference of two step functions.

$$p(t) = \frac{1}{\Delta} u(t) - \frac{1}{\Delta} u(t - \Delta) \qquad (2\text{-}22)$$

This is a pulse of amplitude $1/\Delta$ starting at $t = 0$ and having 0 amplitude at $t > \Delta$. A pulse is a combination of a step function and a delayed step function. The limit of the pulse as $\Delta \rightarrow 0$ is called the unit impulse and is defined as follows

$$\lim_{\Delta \to 0} p(t) = \lim_{\Delta \to 0} \frac{1}{\Delta} [u(t) - u(t - \Delta)] = \delta(t) \qquad (2\text{-}23)$$

The integral of the unit impulse is the unit step

$$\int_{-\infty}^{t} \delta(t')\,dt' = u(t) \qquad (2\text{-}24)$$

where t' is a dummy variable of integration.

The unit ramp is denoted $r(t)$ and defined as

$$r(t) = tu(t) \qquad (2\text{-}25)$$

The integral of the unit step is the unit ramp function

$$r(t) = \int_{-\infty}^{t} u(t')\,dt' = tu(t) \qquad (2\text{-}26)$$

and the derivative of the unit ramp is the unit step function

$$\frac{dr(t)}{dt} = \frac{d}{dt}\,tu(t) = u(t) \qquad (2\text{-}27)$$

In this experiment we will study the solutions of Eq. (2-20) when the forcing function is either 0 or a unit step function. In order to obtain a complete solution of Eq. (2-20), an initial condition must be specified, usually written $x(t_0)$. That is, $x(t_0)$ is the value of the solution of Eq. (2-20) at some specified initial time, denoted t_0.

Zero-Input Response—Assume that the forcing function $f(t)$ in Eq. (2-20) is equal to zero and that we desire the solution to Eq. (2-20) which represents the response to some initial condition $x(t_0)$. For example, consider the RC circuit of Fig. 2-9, for which there is a voltage on the

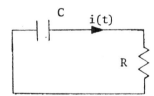

Fig. 2.9 A first-order circuit.

capacitor C at some initial time—say $t_0 = 0$—and we are interested in obtaining the current through resistor R for all time greater than zero.

Kirchhoff's voltage law applied to the circuit of Fig. 2-9 yields

$$Ri - V_0 + \frac{1}{C}\int_{0}^{t} i(t')\,dt' = 0 \ \text{ for } \ t \geqslant 0 \qquad (2\text{-}28)$$

where V_0 is the initial voltage across the capacitor. If we differentiate Eq. (2-28), we obtain

$$R\frac{di}{dt} + \frac{1}{C}i(t) = 0 \ \text{ for } \ t \geqslant 0 \qquad (2\text{-}29)$$

which is similar to Eq. (2-20) with $f(t) = 0$. The initial current through the resistor is $i(0) = V_0/R$, and the solution of Eq. (2-29) is

$$i(t) = i(0)e^{-t/T} \qquad (2\text{-}30)$$

where $T = RC$.

Observe that the solution depends upon the initial condition and $i(t)$ is called the zero input response. The solution given by Eq. (2-30) can be verified by direct substitution into Eq. (2-29).

Zero-State Response—Consider the circuit of Fig. 2-10.

We now have an applied voltage V, a constant for all time greater than time 0. (Time $t_0 = 0$ is that time when the

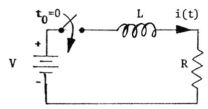

Fig. 2.10 A first-order circuit.

switch is closed.) There is no initial current through the inductor at the instant before the switch is closed. Again, we are interested in obtaining the current through the resistor for all time greater than zero. Kirchhoff's voltage law for this circuit is

$$L\frac{di}{dt} + Ri = Vu(t) \qquad (2\text{-}31)$$

Since we have assumed that there is no current through the inductor at time $t = 0$, there is no current in the resistor at time $t = 0$, according to Kirchhoff's current law. The solution of Eq. (2-31) is

$$i(t) = \frac{V}{R}(1 - e^{-t/T}) \quad t \geqslant 0 \qquad (2\text{-}32)$$

where $T = L/R$. This solution can be verified by direct substitution into Eq. (2-31). The current in this example is called the zero-state response.

Complete Solution—Now consider a first-order RC circuit which responds to both a forcing function input (a step function) and an initial condition (an initial voltage across the capacitor).

Switch T_1 in Fig. 2-11 is closed at the same time ($t_0 = 0$) that switch T_2 is opened. Therefore, the capacitor has a

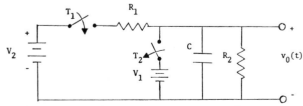

Fig. 2.11 Circuit which responds to input V_2 and an initial condition.

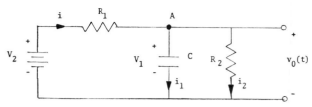

Fig. 2.12 Circuit of Fig. 2.11 redrawn.

voltage across its terminals equal to V_1 at time 0. We are interested in obtaining the voltage $v_0(t)$ for all time greater than zero. The circuit in Fig. 2-11 can be redrawn for time $t > 0$.

Kirchhoff's current law at node A in Fig. 2-12 is

$$i = i_1 + i_2 \qquad (2\text{-}33)$$

The currents i_1 and i_2 can be expressed in terms of voltage $v_0(t)$

$$i_1(t) = C\frac{dv_0}{dt} \quad \text{and} \quad i_2(t) = \frac{v_0(t)}{R_2} \qquad (2\text{-}34)$$

Kirchhoff's voltage law yields

$$-V_2 + R_1 i(t) + v_0(t) = 0 \qquad (2\text{-}35)$$

Substituting Eqs. (2-33) and (2-34) into Eq. (2-35) yields

$$R_1\left[C\frac{dv_0(t)}{dt} + \frac{v_0(t)}{R_2}\right] + v_0(t) = V_2$$

with $v_0(0) = V_1$ the initial voltage across the capacitor. The complete solution for $v_0(t)$ is the sum of the zero input response and the zero-state response and is given by

$$v_0(t) = V_1 e^{-t/T} + \frac{R_2}{R_1 + R_2}V_2(1 - e^{-t/T}) \quad t \geqslant 0$$
$$(2\text{-}36)$$

with

$$T = C\left[\frac{R_1 R_2}{R_1 + R_2}\right].$$

Another circuit in which the initial voltages across the capacitors are not zero is given in Fig. 2-13. The voltages on capacitors C_1 and C_2 for all time up to the instant just before the switch is closed are zero. In particular, the voltage $v_0(0^-)$, with 0^- the instant just before the switch is closed, is zero. The instant just after the switch is closed is denoted 0^+. The voltage $v_0(0^+)$ is a finite value because of the fact that an impulsive current flows in the circuit of Fig. 2-13 when the switch is closed. A finite charge q

$$q = \int_{0^-}^{0^+} i_{C1}(t')\,dt' = \int_{0^-}^{0^+} i_{C2}(t')\,dt' \qquad (2\text{-}37)$$

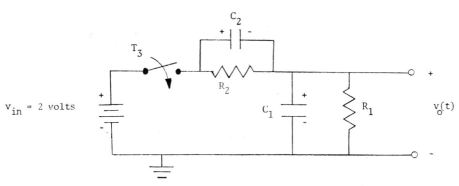

Fig. 2.13 A compensating attenuator circuit.

is delivered to each capacitor because of the impulsive current. Kirchhoff's voltage law at time 0^+ yields

$$v_{in}(0^+) = \frac{q}{C_1} + \frac{q}{C_2} = \frac{C_1 + C_2}{C_1 C_2} q \qquad (2\text{-}38)$$

and the output voltage at time 0^+ is

$$v_0(0^+) = \frac{q}{C_1} = \frac{C_2}{C_1 + C_2} v_{in}(0^+) \qquad (2\text{-}39)$$

This means that the voltage $v_0(t)$ across capacitor C_1 is discontinuous at the instant of the closing of the switch. the voltage $v_0(t)$ changes from 0 at time 0^- to

$$\frac{C_2}{C_1 + C_2} v_{in}(0^+)$$

at time 0^+. Therefore, the voltage across a capacitor can change instantaneously when the current through the capacitor is not finite. More precisely, we define a voltage across capacitor C_2 as $v(t) = v_{in}(t) - v_0(t)$, and Kirchhoff's current law yields

$$C_2 \frac{d}{dt} [v_{in}(t) - v_0(t)] + \frac{1}{R_2} [v_{in}(t) - v_0(t)]$$

$$= \frac{v_0(t)}{R_1} + C_1 \frac{dv_0(t)}{dt} \qquad (2\text{-}40)$$

Eq. (2-40) can be rewritten in the following convenient form

$$\frac{dv_0(t)}{dt} + \frac{1}{R_{eq} C_{eq}} v_0(t) = \frac{C_2}{C_1 + C_2} \frac{dv_{in}(t)}{dt}$$

$$+ \frac{1}{C_{eq} R_2} v_{in}(t) \quad (2\text{-}41)$$

where

$$R_{eq} = \frac{R_1 R_2}{R_1 + R_2} \text{ and } C_{eq} = C_1 + C_2$$

since

$$v_{in}(t) = 2u(t), \text{ then } \frac{dv_{in}(t)}{dt} = 2\delta(t).$$

The solution of Eq. (2-41) consists of two parts. The solution to the impulse which is

$$\left[\frac{2C_2}{C_1 + C_2} e^{-t/R_{eq}C_{eq}} \right] u(t)$$

and the solution to the step input which is

$$\frac{2R_1}{R_1 + R_2} (1 - e^{-t/R_{eq}C_{eq}}) u(t)$$

The complete solution is

$$v_0(t) = \left[\frac{2R_1}{R_1 + R_2} - 2\left(\frac{R_1}{R_1 + R_2} - \frac{C_2}{C_1 + C_2} \right) e^{-t/R_{eq}C_{eq}} \right] u(t)$$
$$(2\text{-}42)$$

Second-Order Circuits

Second-order circuits are those which can be described by second-order differential equations, and are somewhat more complicated than first-order circuits.

A linear second-order differential equation is given by

$$a_2(t) \frac{d^2 x}{dt^2} + a_1(t) \frac{dx}{dt} + a_0(t)x(t) = f(t) \quad (2\text{-}43)$$

where $a_2(t)$, $a_1(t)$, and $a_0(t)$ are time-varying coefficients and $f(t)$ is the forcing function or input. The complete solution of Eq. (2-43), denoted $x(t)$, depends upon two conditions at some initial time denoted t_0. These initial conditions are $x(t_0)$ and $dx(t_0)/dt$. Therefore, the solution of Eq. (2-43) will be completely (and uniquely) specified once the two initial conditions are given.

The quantity $x(t)$ in Eq. (2-43) represents a current $i(t)$ or voltage $v(t)$ in electrical circuits. If resistors, inductors, and capacitors in a circuit are constants independent of time, then the coefficients $a_0(t)$, $a_1(t)$, $a_2(t)$, which depend upon the values of the resistors, inductors, and capacitors, are constants independent of time.

Consider the series RLC circuit of Fig. 2-14.

Kirchhoff's voltage law yields

$$v_L(t) + v_C(t) + v_R(t) = v(t) \qquad (2\text{-}44)$$

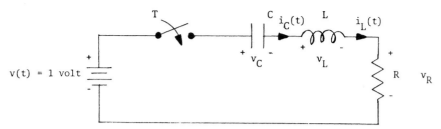

Fig. 2.14 A second-order circuit.

and Kirchhoff's current law yields

$$\frac{v_R}{R} = C \frac{dv_C}{dt} = I_0 + \frac{1}{L} \int_0^t v_L(t')\, dt' \quad (2\text{-}45)$$

where I_0 is the current in the inductor just before the switch is closed and t' is a dummy variable of integration. We obtain Eq. (2-46) by combining Eqs. (2-44) and (2-45)

$$LC \frac{d^2 v_C(t)}{dt^2} + RC \frac{dv_C(t)}{dt} + v_C(t) = u(t) \quad t \geqslant 0 \quad (2\text{-}46)$$

We assume that V_0 is the voltage on the capacitor just before the switch is closed. The instant of time just before and after the switch is closed will be denoted $t_0 = 0^-$ and $t_0 = 0^+$, respectively. We know from experimentation that the voltage across the capacitor is a continuous function of time, which means that the voltage across the capacitor cannot change instantaneously provided there is no impulse of current. This fact is useful in evaluating the initial currents and voltages which occur at the instant just after the switch is closed. These conditions are the initial conditions to be used in solving Eq. (2-46), which is similar to Eq. (2-43). If we integrate Eq. (2-46) from $t_0 = 0^-$ to $t_0 = 0^+$, we obtain

$$LC \left[\frac{dv_C(0^+)}{dt} - \frac{dv_C(0^-)}{dt} \right] + RC \left[v_C(0^+) - v_C(0^-) \right]$$

$$+ \int_{0^-}^{0^+} v_C(t')\, dt' = \int_{0^-}^{0^+} u(t')\, dt' = 0 \quad (2\text{-}47)$$

The integral of $v_C(t)$ from 0^- to 0^+ is zero and $v_C(0^+) = v_C(0^-)$ since $v_C(t)$ is continuous. Eq. (2-47) is reduced to

$$\frac{dv_C(0^+)}{dt} = \frac{dv_C(0^-)}{dt} \quad (2\text{-}48)$$

The current in the capacitor at time $t_0 = 0^-$ is equal to the current in the inductor at time $t_0 = 0^-$, according to Kirchhoff's current law.

$$C \frac{dv_C(0^-)}{dt} = I_0 \quad (2\text{-}49)$$

Hence, the initial conditions become

$$v_C(0^+) = V_0 \quad (2\text{-}50)$$

and

$$\frac{dv_C(0^+)}{dt} = \frac{I_0}{C} \quad (2\text{-}51)$$

Dividing Eq. (2-46) by LC

$$\frac{d^2 v_C(t)}{dt} + \frac{R}{L} \frac{dv_C(t)}{dt} + \frac{1}{LC} v_C(t) = \frac{1}{LC} u(t) \quad (2\text{-}52)$$

the initial conditions are specified by Eqs. (2-50) and (2-51).

Observe that Eq. (2-52) has the same form as Eq. (2-43), with

$$a_2 = 1, a_1 = \frac{R}{L}, a_0 = \frac{1}{LC}, \text{ and } f(t) = \frac{1}{LC} u(t)$$

We will proceed by dividing the complete solution of Eq. (2-10) into two parts. The first part is the so-called homogeneous solution or zero-input response, and the second part is the particular solution.

Suppose, first, that the voltage $v_{Ch}(t)$ satisfies Eq. (2-25) when the battery ($v(t) = 0$) is shorted. That is, $v_{Ch}(t)$ is a response to the initial current in the inductor and initial voltage across the capacitor. For convenience, we will define two parameters α and ω_0.

$$\alpha \triangleq \frac{R}{2L} \text{ and } \omega_0^2 = \frac{1}{LC}$$

Because of the assumptions above, Eq. (2-52) becomes

$$\frac{d^2 v_C(t)}{dt} + 2\alpha \frac{dv_C(t)}{dt} + \omega_0^2 v_C(t) = 0 \quad (2\text{-}53)$$

This is called a homogeneous linear differential equation, and its solution is denoted $v_{Ch}(t)$.

It can be shown that Eq. (2-53) has a unique solution which is the sum of exponentials of the form ke^{st}, where k and s are constants. k depends on the initial conditions, and s is the solution of what is called the "characteristic equation," which depends upon R, L, and C. If ke^{st} is substituted into Eq. (2-53), we obtain

$$s^2 + 2\alpha s + \omega_0^2 = 0 \quad (2\text{-}54)$$

which is the characteristic equation for Eq. (2-53). Eq. (2-54) can be rewritten in factored form

$$(s - s_1)(s - s_2) = 0 \quad (2\text{-}55)$$

s_1 and s_2 are the roots of the characteristic equation (also called the *natural frequencies* of the circuit), and they are

$$s_1 = -\alpha + \sqrt{\alpha^2 - \omega_0^2} \qquad (2\text{-}56)$$

$$s_2 = -\alpha - \sqrt{\alpha^2 - \omega_0^2} \qquad (2\text{-}57)$$

The form of the homogeneous solution $v_{Ch}(t)$ depends upon the roots s_1 and s_2. There are four cases to consider.

1. $\alpha = \omega_0$ (critically damped). In this case, $s_1 = s_2 = -\alpha$, and the solution of Eq. (2-53) becomes

$$v_{Ch}(t) = (k_1 + k_2 t)e^{-\alpha t} \qquad (2\text{-}58)$$

where k_1 and k_2 are constants, depending on the initial conditions.

2. $\alpha > \omega_0$ (overdamped). In this case, s_1 and s_2 are unequal, and the solution of Eq. (2-53) is

$$v_{Ch}(t) = k_1 e^{s_1 t} + k_2 e^{s_2 t} \qquad (2\text{-}59)$$

where k_1 and k_2 depend upon the initial conditions.

3. $\alpha = 0$ (lossless). In this case, $\alpha = 0$ implies $R = 0$ or that the conductance $G(G = 1/R)$ is infinite. The natural frequencies s_1 and s_2 are purely imaginary, and equal to $\pm j\omega_0$. The solution $v_{Ch}(t)$ in this case is

$$v_{Ch}(t) = k_1 \sin \omega_0 t + k_2 \cos \omega_0 t \qquad (2\text{-}60)$$

when k_1 and k_2 depend once more upon the initial conditions. Eq. (2-60) can also be written

$$v_{Ch}(t) = k(k_1,k_2) \cos [\omega_0 t - \phi(k_1,k_2)] \qquad (2\text{-}61)$$

with

$$k(k_1,k_2) = [k_1^2 + k_2^2]^{1/2} \qquad (2\text{-}62)$$

and

$$\phi(k_1,k_2) = \tan^{-1} \frac{k_1}{k_2} \qquad (2\text{-}63)$$

Consequently, k and ϕ depend upon the initial conditions because k_1 and k_2 depend upon the initial conditions.

4. $\alpha < \omega_0$ (underdamped). In this case, the natural frequencies become complex conjugates ($s_2 = \bar{s}_1$)

$$s_1 = -\alpha + j\sqrt{\omega_0^2 - \alpha^2} = -\alpha + j\omega_d \qquad (2\text{-}64)$$

$$s_2 = -\alpha - j\sqrt{\omega_0^2 - \alpha^2} = -\alpha - j\omega_d \qquad (2\text{-}65)$$

Observe that the real part of s_1 and s_2 are equal but that the imaginary part of s_2 is the negative of the imaginary part of s_1. s_2 is called the complex conjugate of s_1. The response $v_{Ch}(t)$ in this case is

$$v_{Ch}(t) = k_1 e^{-\alpha t} \sin \omega_d t + k_2 e^{-\alpha t} \cos \omega_d t \qquad (2\text{-}66)$$

where k_1 and k_2 depend upon the initial conditions. Eq.

(2-66) can be written in the following form

$$v_{Ch}(t) = k(k_1,k_2)e^{-\alpha t} \cos [\omega_d t - \phi(k_1,k_2)] \qquad (2\text{-}67)$$

where k and ϕ depend upon the initial conditions.

The particular solution for Eq. (2-52) is

$$v_{Cp}(t) = u(t) \qquad (2\text{-}68)$$

and the complete solution of Eq. (2-52) is the sum of the homogeneous and particular solutions

$$v_C(t) = v_{Ch}(t) + v_{Cp}(t) \qquad (2\text{-}69)$$

The initial conditions are given by Eqs. (2-50) and (2-51) and the complete solution of the four cases mentioned are

1.

$$\alpha = \omega_0, \quad s_1 = s_2 = -\alpha$$

$$v_C(t) = \left\{ \left[V_0 - 1 - \left(s_1 V_0 - s_1 - \frac{I_0}{C} \right) t \right] e^{s_1 t} + 1 \right\} u(t)$$

$$(2\text{-}70)$$

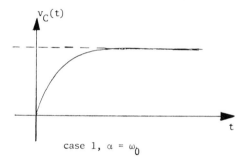

case 1, $\alpha = \omega_0$

Fig. 2.15 Critically damped.

2.

$$\alpha > \omega_0, s_1 = -\alpha + \sqrt{\alpha^2 - \omega_0^2}, s_2 = -\alpha - \sqrt{\alpha^2 - \omega_0^2}$$

$$v_C(t) = \left\{ \frac{1}{(s_2 - s_1)} \left[s_2(V_0 - 1) - \frac{I_0}{C} \right] e^{s_1 t} \right.$$

$$\left. + \frac{1}{(s_1 - s_2)} \left[s_1(V_0 - 1) - \frac{I_0}{C} \right] e^{s_2 t} + 1 \right\} u(t) \quad (2\text{-}71)$$

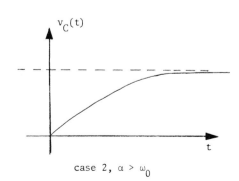

case 2, $\alpha > \omega_0$

Fig. 2.16 Overdamped.

3.

$$\alpha = 0, \quad s_1 = j\omega_0, \quad s_2 = -j\omega_0 = \bar{s}_1$$

$$v_C(t) = \left\{ \left[(V_0 - 1)^2 + \frac{1}{|s_1|^2}\left(\frac{I_0}{C}\right)^2 \right]^{1/2} \right.$$

$$\left. \cdot \cos\left[\omega_0 t + \tan^{-1}\left(\frac{I_0}{|s_1|C(V_0 - 1)}\right) \right] + 1 \right\} u(t) \quad (2\text{-}72)$$

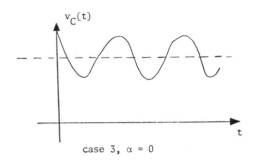

case 3, $\alpha = 0$

Fig. 2.17 Lossless.

4.

$$\alpha < \omega_0, \quad s_1 = -\alpha + j\omega_d, \quad s_2 = -\alpha - j\omega_d = \bar{s}_1$$

$$v_C(t) = \left\{ \left[(V_0 - 1)^2 + \frac{1}{\omega_d^2}\left(\frac{I_0}{C} + \alpha V_0 - \alpha\right)^2 \right]^{1/2} e^{-\alpha t} \right.$$

$$\left. \cdot \cos\left[\omega_d t + \tan^{-1}\left(\frac{\frac{I_0}{C} + \alpha(V_0 - 1)}{\omega_d(V_0 - 1)}\right) \right] + 1 \right\} u(t) \quad (2\text{-}73)$$

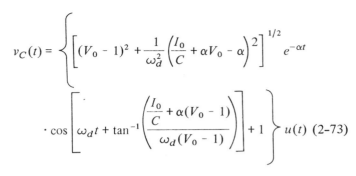

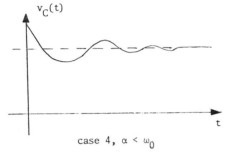

case 4, $\alpha < \omega_0$

Fig. 2.18 Underdamped.

The curves of $v_C(t)$ versus t for the four cases are shown in Figs. 2-15, 2-16, 2-17, and 2-18 when $V_0 = 0 = I_0$.

Part Two

OBJECTIVE

The purpose of this experiment is to apply Kirchhoff's laws to some low-order circuits with independent sources. The solution of the resulting zero, first-, and second-order differential equations will be studied.

REFERENCES

Chirlian, P. M., *Basic Network Theory*. New York: McGraw-Hill, 1969, Chapters 2 and 4.
Cruz, J. B., and Van Valkenburg, M. E., *Introductory Signals and Circuits*. Waltham, Mass.: Blaisdell, 1967, Chapters 5 and 7.
D'Azzo, J. J. and Houpis, C. H., *Principles of Electrical Engineering*. Columbus, Ohio: Merrill, 1968, Chapter 2.
Desoer, C. A., and Kuh, E. S., *Basic Circuit Theory*. New York: McGraw-Hill, 1969, Chapters 3, 4, 5, and 6.
Ghausi, M. S., *Electronic Circuits: Devices, Models, Functions, Analysis, and Design*. New York: Van Nostrand Reinhold, 1971, Chapter 1.
Hayt, W. H., and Kemmerly, J. E., *Engineering Circuit Analysis*. New York: McGraw-Hill, 1971, Chapters 2, 5, 6 and 7.
Romanowitz, H. A., *Electrical Fundamentals and Circuit Analysis*. New York: Wiley, 1966, Chapters 4 and 5.
Skilling, H. H., *Electrical Engineering Circuits*. New York: Wiley, 1968, Chapters 1 and 2.
Smith, R. J., *Circuits, Devices, and Systems*. New York: Wiley, 1968.

LABORATORY PREPARATION

Zero-Order Circuits

1. Kirchhoff's current and voltage laws will be applied to the circuit of Fig. 2-19. Calculate the voltage v_1 across R_1 by first calculating the current i_1 through resistor R_1. In a similar way, calculate the voltage v_4 due to current i_2. Write Kirchhoff's current law at junctions 1, 2, and 3 in terms of currents i_1 and i_2.

2. Calculate voltages v_1 and v_4 for the circuit of Fig. 2-20. Are v_1 and v_4 for the circuit of Fig. 2-20 different from the same voltages for Fig. 2-19? Explain your answer. Apply Kirchhoff's current law to nodes 1, 2, and 3 of Fig. 2-20.

3. Apply the voltage divider equation to the circuit of Fig. 2-21 when R varies between 0 and 100k. Take 5 or 6

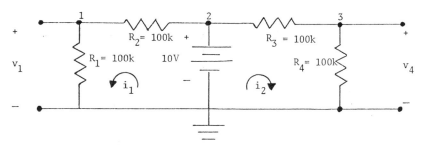

Fig. 2.19 Zero-order circuit.

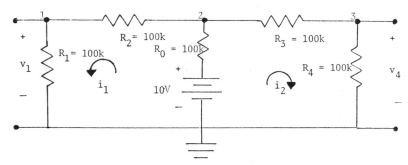

Fig. 2.20 Zero-order circuit.

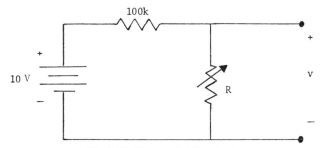

Fig. 2.21 Voltage divider circuit.

values of R in this range and calculate v for each of the values of R chosen.

4. Apply the current divider equation to the circuit of Fig. 2-22 to calculate i.

5. The source resistance R_s of an ac source will be measured in the laboratory. The circuit for performing this measurement is shown in Fig. 2-23. A variable resistance

is placed directly across a sinusoidal source. Set the variable resistor R to a large value (approximately 1 meg ohm). Set the amplitude adjustment of the ac source to a position so that the ac voltage v_{AB} measured across the resistor R is a reasonable value (e.g., 1–10 volts). Use an ac voltmeter to measure the rms value of the voltage v_{AB}. Now R is reduced until voltage v_{AB} is one half its value when R was large. The value of R when v_{AB} is reduced to one half its former value is equal to R_s. Use the voltage divider equation to prove that the value of R obtained in this way is equal to R_s.

First-Order Circuits

6. Derive a differential equation similar to Eq. 2-20 when $x(t)$ is the voltage $v_o(t)$ shown in Fig. 2-24. Calculate the solution of your equation when the initial condition is $v_o(0^+) = 1$. What type of response is $v_o(t)$? Change R to 200 kΩ. How does the solution $v_o(t)$ change?

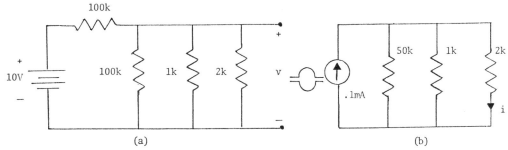

(a)

(b)

Fig. 2.22 Norton equivalence.

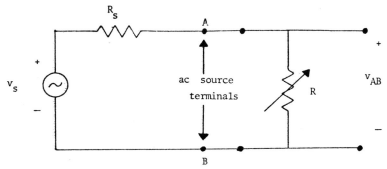

Fig. 2.23 A circuit for measuring source resistance.

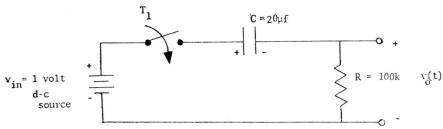

Fig. 2.24 A first-order circuit.

7. Derive the differential equation describing the voltage $v_o(t)$ in Fig. 2-25. What is the solution when $v_o(0^+) = 0$?

8. Suppose another capacitor $C_2 = 10 \mu f$ is added to Fig. 2-25 as shown in Fig. 2-26. Derive a differential equation describing the voltage $v_o(t)$. What is the solution when

$v_o(0^+) = \dfrac{C_2}{C_1 + C_2} v_{in}(0^+)$? What is the time constant for this circuit?

9. Plot the voltage $v_o(t)$ versus t in parts 7 and 8. How do the two answers compare and what is the effect of

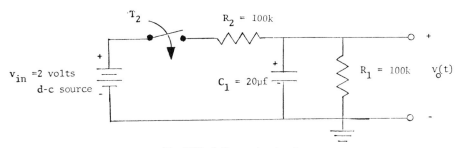

Fig. 2.25 A first-order circuit.

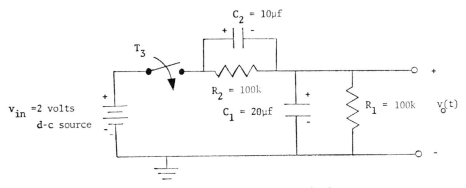

Fig. 2.26 A compensating attenuator circuit.

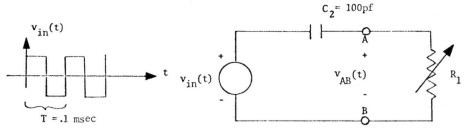

Fig. 2.27a A differentiating circuit.

capacitor C_2? Can you explain why the network of Fig. 2–26 is called a compensating attenuator network? Plot $v_o(t)$ when $R_2 C_2 > R_1 C_1$.

10. The circuit of Fig. 2–27a is called a differentiating circuit. Derive an expression which explicitly shows that the current through R_1 is approximately the derivative of the voltage $v_{in}(t)$. The circuit of Fig. 2–27b is called an integrating circuit. Derive an expression which explicitly

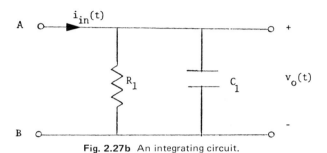

Fig. 2.27b An integrating circuit.

shows that the voltage $v_o(t)$ is approximately the integral of the current $i_{in}(t)$.

Second-Order Circuits

11. The switch T in Fig. 2–28 is closed and allowed to remain closed until the voltage $v_1(t)$ goes to zero. Now the switch is opened, and this time is considered as $t_0 = 0$. Derive a second-order differential equation describing the voltage $v_1(t)$. What are the initial conditions for this circuit? Remember that the initial time is $t_0 = 0$. Solve the second-order differential equation of $v_1(t)$.

12. Write a second-order differential equation for $v_2(t)$ using the initial conditions obtained from opening and closing the switch as described in step 11.

13. Obtain the solution of the second-order differential equation describing the voltage $v_2(t)$ of Fig. 2–29 when the input signal $v(t)$ is a step function of +2 volts, the initial currents are zero, and the initial voltage $v_2(t_0) = -1$ volt.

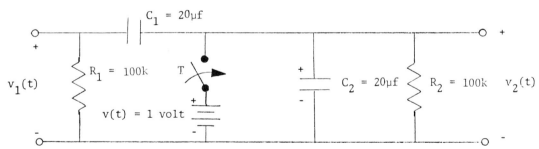

Fig. 2.28 A second-order circuit.

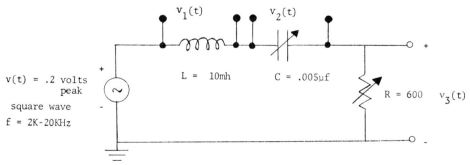

Fig. 2.29 A second-order circuit.

Obtain another solution when $v(t) = -2u(t)$, $v_2(t_0) = +1$ volt and the initial currents are zero.

LABORATORY PROCEDURE

Zero-Order Circuits

1. Construct the circuit of Fig. 2-19 and measure voltages v_1 and v_4 with a dc voltmeter. Compare with calculated values.

2. Construct the circuit of Fig. 2-20. Observe that Fig. 2-20 differs from Fig. 2-19 because of R_0. Measure voltages v_1 and v_4 in Fig. 2-20 and compare to voltages v_1 and v_4 measured in the circuit of Fig. 2-19.

3. Construct the circuit of Fig. 2-21. Measure v for different values of R. Use the values of R calculated in the laboratory preparation. Compare the measured and calculated voltages.

4. Measure voltage v in Fig. 2-22a. Divide this voltage by R_2. You have now calculated the current in resistor R_2. How does this compare with the value calculated in the preparation?

5. Measure the source resistance of an ac oscillator by using the procedure indicated in the laboratory preparation. Check the value of the output resistance given by the manufacturer of the ac source which you are measuring. Explain any difference in the value you measured and the value given by the manufacturer. The laboratory instructor can help you answer this question. If your oscillator has two sinusoidal amplitude ranges, check the output impedance for both of these ranges. Do the output resistances differ for each range? Set the ac source frequency to a reasonable value, like 100 Hz, and leave it set at this frequency for all measurements.

First-Order Circuits

6. Set the vertical sensitivity of the oscilloscope to .2 V/cm and the vertical and horizontal position so that a small dot appears at the middle of the left-edge of the CRO screen. Set the trigger source switch to "internal+" and the sweep time to 1 sec/cm. Now construct the circuit of Fig. 2-24 and apply $v_o(t)$ to the vertical input of the oscilloscope. Be sure that switch T_1 is open and that the polarity of the capacitor is connected as indicated in Fig. 2-24. Close the switch at the instant of time when the dot appears at the middle left-edge of the screen and begins moving from left to right. Measure the time at which the voltage drops to $1/e = 1/2.7183 = .36788$ of its value at the instant just after the switch is closed. How does this time compare with your calculated value? (Be sure to discharge capacitor after opening the switch.)

7. Construct the circuit of Fig. 2-25. Leave the oscilloscope settings at the same positions as in step 6. Close

switch T_2 and measure the time at which the voltage $v_o(t)$ is $1 - 1/e = 1 - .36788 = .63212$ of its maximum value of 1 volt. Compare this time with the calculated value.

8. Construct the circuit of Fig. 2-26. Leave the oscilloscope settings as before and measure the time at which the voltage $v_o(t)$ is .63212 of $[(R_1/(R_1 + R_2)) - (C_2/(C_1 + C_2))] v_{in}(0^+)$. Compare this time with the calculated value. How do the waveforms $v_o(t)$ obtained in this step and in step 7 compare with $\frac{1}{2}v_{in}(t) = u(t)$? Change the battery value to 1 volt and 4 volts and observe the difference in $v_o(t)$. Change C_2 to 20 μf and observe and explain waveform $v_o(t)$.

9. Construct the circuit of Fig. 2-27a. The input signal is a square-wave with an amplitude of 1 volt and a frequency of 10,000 cps. Observe the voltage $v_{AB}(t)$ as R_1 is varied from 100 Ω to 1M Ω. Set R_1 to 10 kΩ. The voltage $v_{AB}(t)$ is a sequence of pulses approximating an impulse with maximum amplitude of $+1$, and $v_{AB}(t)$ is approximately the derivative of the input voltage $v_{in}(t)$. Now connect the circuit of Fig. 2-27b to the circuit of Fig. 2-27a. If an input current is applied to the circuit of Fig. 2-27b, the output voltage $v_o(t)$ is approximately the integral of the input current $i_{in}(t)$ provided $R_1 C_1$ is sufficiently large. In this circumstance, the circuit of Fig. 2-27b is called an integrating circuit. The output $v_o(t)$ is very similar to the input voltage $v_{in}(t)$ if $C_1 = 0.47 \mu f$. The complete circuit can be considered a differentiation followed by an integration whose effects cancel each other so that $v_o(t)$ is a replica of $v_{in}(t)$ but reduced in amplitude.

Second-Order Circuits

10. Construct the circuit of Fig. 2-28. Connect $v_1(t)$ to the vertical input of the CRO(.1 V/cm). Set the trigger source switch to "internal+" and the horizontal sensitivity switch to "internal sweep X1" at 1 sec/cm. The spot should sweep across the screen, starting at the left edge. Close switch T and observe the path that the spot on the screen follows. After $v_1(t)$ reaches 0 and the spot appears at the left edge of the screen, open the switch and observe the path of the spot. Compare this waveform with the predicted results by measuring the slope of $v_1(t)$ for $t \geqslant 0$ and $t > 2$ sec. Measure the maximum amplitude of this waveform. Change $v(t)$ to 2 volts and repeat the procedure.

11. Remove $v_1(t)$ and apply $v_2(t)$ to the vertical input of the CRO. Follow the same procedures as in step 10 with respect to $v_2(t)$.

12. Change R_1 and R_2 to 50 kΩ and repeat steps 10 and 11. Adjust R_1 and R_2 so that $R_1 \neq R_2$ and repeat steps 10 and 11. Compare and comment for the cases when $R_1 = R_2$.

13. Construct the circuit of Fig. 2-29 and set the sweep rate at 50 microsec/cm. Apply $v_1(t)$ to the vertical input of the CRO and *be sure that neither side* of the voltage

$v_1(t)$ is connected to the ground at the scope. In particular, this is accomplished on an oscilloscope with differential inputs by connecting the signal v_1 (or v_2) to the two vertical input terminals on the front of the oscilloscope, neither of which is connected to ground. Make certain that there is no shorting bar connected from ground to either of these terminals. Consult your instructor when making these connections. If your oscilloscope does not have differential type inputs, the measurements of v_1 and v_2 will have to be modified. Consult your instructor in this case.

14. Repeat the entire procedure of step 13 for $v_2(t)$ and $v_3(t)$.

LIST OF EQUIPMENT

1. Cathode-ray oscilloscope
2. General-purpose voltmeter or ac and dc voltmeters
3. Signal sources: function generator or sine- and square-wave oscillators and a dc power supply.
4. Circuit board
5. Components: resistors, capacitors, and inductors

Experiment 3/Nth-Order Circuits: The State-Space Method

Part One

INTRODUCTION

Circuits described by differential equations of high order ($n \geqslant 2$) are certainly more complex than first-order circuits. In addition, more than one response is usually desired in an nth-order circuit. A method of writing nth-order differential equations as n first-order differential equations will be studied in this experiment. The solution of each one of the n first-order differential equations represents, for example, one of the n desired responses.

THEORY

An nth-order nonhomogeneous linear differential equations is given by

$$a_n(t)\frac{d^n x(t)}{dt^n} + a_{n-1}(t)\frac{d^{n-1}x(t)}{dt^{n-1}} + a_{n-2}(t)\frac{d^{n-2}x(t)}{dt^{n-2}}$$

$$+ \cdots + a_1(t)\frac{dx(t)}{dt} + a_0(t)x(t) = f(t) \quad (3\text{-}1)$$

There are n initial conditions which must be specified in order to obtain a unique solution of Eq. (3-1). They are

$$\frac{d^{n-1}x(t_0)}{dt^{n-1}}, \frac{d^{n-2}x(t_0)}{dt^{n-2}}, \frac{d^{n-3}(t_0)}{dt^{n-3}}, \cdots \frac{dx(t_0)}{dt}, x(t_0)$$

with t_0 the initial time.

A simple way of writing Eq. (3-1) as n first-order differential equations is accomplished by first defining two new variables

$$x_1(t) \triangleq x(t) \quad (3\text{-}2)$$

and

$$x_2(t) \triangleq \frac{dx_1(t)}{dt} \quad (3\text{-}3)$$

Eqs. (3-2) and (3-3) imply that

$$x_2(t) = \frac{dx(t)}{dt} \quad (3\text{-}4)$$

We will now use a raised dot ($\dot{}$) to denote an ordinary derivative with respect to time and define another variable, so that

$$\dot{x}_2(t) \triangleq x_3(t) \quad (3\text{-}5)$$

The new variable x_3 defined by (3-5) can also be written

$$x_3(t) = \ddot{x}_1(t) = \ddot{x}(t) \quad (3\text{-}6)$$

from Eqs. (3-2) and (3-3). New variables can continue to be defined, so that

$$x_n = \frac{d^{n-1}x_1(t)}{dt^{n-1}} = \frac{d^{n-1}x(t)}{dt^{n-1}} \quad (3\text{-}7)$$

and

$$\dot{x}_n = \frac{d^n x_1(t)}{dt^n} = \frac{d^n x(t)}{dt^n} \quad (3\text{-}8)$$

Eq. (3-1) can be rewritten in the following form

$$\frac{d^n x(t)}{dt^n} = -\frac{a_{n-1}(t)}{a_n(t)}\frac{d^{n-1}x(t)}{dt^{n-1}} - \frac{a_{n-2}(t)}{a_n(t)}\frac{d^{n-2}x(t)}{dt^{n-2}} \cdots$$

$$\cdots - \frac{a_1(t)}{a_n(t)}\frac{dx(t)}{dt} - \frac{a_0(t)}{a_n(t)}x(t) + \frac{f(t)}{a_n(t)} \quad (3\text{-}9)$$

Observe that the new variables have been defined in terms of successive derivatives of $x(t)$ in Eqs. (3-3), (3-4), (3-5), (3-6), and (3-7). Therefore, Eq. (3-9) can be written as

$$\dot{x}_n = -\frac{a_{n-1}}{a_n}x_n - \frac{a_{n-2}}{a_n}x_{n-1} - \cdots - \frac{a_1}{a_n}x_2 - \frac{a_0}{a_n}x_1 + \frac{f(t)}{a_n}$$

$$(3\text{-}10)$$

A complete system of equations representing nth-order differential Eq. (3-1) can now be written as n first-order differential equations.

$$\dot{x}_1 = x_2$$
$$\dot{x}_2 = x_3$$

$\dot{x}_3 = x_4$

.
.
.

$$\dot{x}_n = -\frac{a_{n-1}}{a_n} x_n - \frac{a_{n-2}}{a_n} x_{n-1} - \cdots - \frac{a_1}{a_n} x_2 - \frac{a_0}{a_n} x_1 + \frac{f(t)}{a_n}$$

(3-11)

If $\underline{x}(t)$ is considered a vector with components $x_1(t), x_2(t),$ ... etc., then the matrix form of Eq. (3-1) will be

$$\underline{\dot{x}} = A\underline{x} + \underline{b}f(t) \qquad (3-12)$$

with the matrix

$$A = \begin{bmatrix} 0 & 1 & 0 & 0 & \cdots & 0 \\ 0 & 0 & 1 & 0 & \cdots & 0 \\ 0 & 0 & 0 & 1 & \cdots & 0 \\ \cdot & \cdot & \cdot & & \ddots & \cdot \\ \cdot & \cdot & \cdot & & & \cdot \\ \cdot & \cdot & \cdot & & & \cdot \\ -\dfrac{a_0}{a_n} & -\dfrac{a_1}{a_n} & \cdots\cdots\cdots & & & -\dfrac{a_{n-1}}{a_n} \end{bmatrix}$$

(3-13)

and

$$\underline{b} = \begin{bmatrix} 0 \\ 0 \\ \cdot \\ \cdot \\ \cdot \\ \cdot \\ 0 \\ \dfrac{1}{a_n} \end{bmatrix}$$

(3-14)

$\underline{x}(t)$ is called the state vector, and the state vector at the initial time t_0 is called the initial state vector. Eq. (3-12) with A specified by Eq. (3-13) is called the normal form of Eq. (3-1).

The discussion up to now has shown that an nth-order differential equation can be written as n first-order differential equations. However, the relationship we have chosen between the variables $x_1(t), x_2(t),$ ... etc. provides us with a very simple A matrix, but it is not the most convenient relationship for the variables (responses) usually desired in RLC type circuits.

Suppose, instead, we chose a relationship between the variables in Eq. (3-12) with

$$A = \begin{bmatrix} a_{11} & a_{12} & \cdots & a_{1n} \\ a_{21} & a_{22} & & a_{2n} \\ \cdot & & \ddots & \cdot \\ \cdot & & & \cdot \\ \cdot & & & \cdot \\ a_{n1} & a_{n2} & \cdots & a_{nn} \end{bmatrix}$$

(3-15)

where the a_{ii}'s are not all zero for $i < n$. Let us consider the series RLC circuit of Fig. 3-1 as an example.

We are interested in obtaining two independent responses of the circuit. (Usually the currents in inductors and the voltage across capacitors are the desired responses in RLC type circuits.) The relationships between the two independent variables ($i_L(t)$ and $v_C(t)$) take the form of two first-order linear differential equations which are coupled. These two first-order equations will now be derived. Kirchhoff's current law for the circuit of Fig. 3-1 is

$$i_L(t) = i_C(t) = i_R(t) \qquad (3-16)$$

Kirchhoff's voltage law applied to Fig. 3-1 yields

$$L\frac{di_L(t)}{dt} + Ri_L(t) + v_C(t) = v(t) \qquad (3-17)$$

Kirchhoff's current law (Eq. [3-16]) can be expressed as

$$i_C(t) = C\frac{dv_C(t)}{dt} = i_L(t) \qquad (3-18)$$

Eqs. (3-17) and (3-18) can be rewritten in matrix form with $i_L(t)$ and $v_C(t)$ as the independent variables

$$\begin{bmatrix} \dfrac{di_L(t)}{dt} \\[2mm] \dfrac{dv_C(t)}{dt} \end{bmatrix} = \begin{bmatrix} -\dfrac{R}{L} & -\dfrac{1}{L} \\[2mm] \dfrac{1}{C} & 0 \end{bmatrix} \begin{bmatrix} i_L(t) \\[2mm] v_C(t) \end{bmatrix} + \begin{bmatrix} \dfrac{1}{L} \\[2mm] 0 \end{bmatrix} v(t)$$

(3-19)

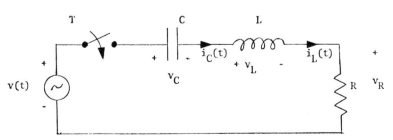

Fig. 3.1 RLC circuit.

The column matrix

$$\underline{x} = \begin{bmatrix} i_L(t) \\ v_C(t) \end{bmatrix} \qquad (3\text{-}20)$$

can be considered the vector $\underline{x}$ with components $i_L(t)$ and $v_C(t)$. This vector at the initial time is given by

$$\begin{bmatrix} i_L(t_0) \\ v_C(t_0) \end{bmatrix} = \begin{bmatrix} I_0 \\ V_0 \end{bmatrix} \qquad (3\text{-}21)$$

The solutions of the linear first-order coupled differential Eq. (3-19) start at the point (I_0, V_0) in the $i_L(t)$ versus $v_C(t)$ plane. As t increases from t_0 to ∞, the point $(i_L(t), v_C(t))$ traces out a curve in the plane. This curve is called the state-space trajectory and represents the solution vector of matrix Eq. (3-19).

The current $i_L(t)$ and the voltage $v_C(t)$ can be thought of as the components of a vector $\underline{x}(t)$.

$$\underline{x}(t) = \begin{bmatrix} x_1(t) \\ x_2(t) \end{bmatrix} = \begin{bmatrix} i_L(t) \\ v_C(t) \end{bmatrix} \qquad (3\text{-}22)$$

The initial state is

$$\underline{x}(t_0) = \begin{bmatrix} i_L(t_0) \\ v_C(t_0) \end{bmatrix} \qquad (3\text{-}23)$$

and matrix Eq. (3-19) can be written

$$\underline{\dot{x}} = A\underline{x} + \underline{b}v(t) \qquad (3\text{-}24)$$

where A is a 2 X 2 matrix in this example

$$A = \begin{bmatrix} -\dfrac{R}{L} & -\dfrac{1}{L} \\ \dfrac{1}{C} & 0 \end{bmatrix} \qquad (3\text{-}25)$$

and $\underline{b}$ is a vector

$$\underline{b} = \begin{bmatrix} \dfrac{1}{L} \\ 0 \end{bmatrix} \qquad (3\text{-}26)$$

The forms of A and $\underline{b}$ are different in this example from those derived for Eq. (3-12). Nevertheless, we have obtained two first-order differential equations whose solutions are the two desired independent responses $i_L(t)$ and $v_C(t)$.

We shall now obtain an approximate solution of vector Eq. (3-24). Consider the definition of $\underline{\dot{x}}(t)$.

$$\underline{\dot{x}} = \begin{bmatrix} \lim_{\Delta t \to 0} \dfrac{x_1(t + \Delta t) - x_1(t)}{\Delta t} \\ \lim_{\Delta t \to 0} \dfrac{x_2(t + \Delta t) - x_2(t)}{\Delta t} \end{bmatrix} \qquad (3\text{-}27)$$

The derivative can be approximated in the following manner if Δt is sufficiently small

$$\underline{\dot{x}} \simeq \begin{bmatrix} \dfrac{x_1(t + \Delta t) - x_1(t)}{\Delta t} \\ \dfrac{x_2(t + \Delta t) - x_2(t)}{\Delta t} \end{bmatrix} \qquad (3\text{-}28)$$

Eq. (3-24) can be rewritten using the approximation of Eq. (3-28)

$$\begin{bmatrix} x_1(t + \Delta t) \\ x_2(t + \Delta t) \end{bmatrix} = \begin{bmatrix} x_1(t) \\ x_2(t) \end{bmatrix} + A\begin{bmatrix} x_1(t) \\ x_2(t) \end{bmatrix}\Delta t + \underline{b}v(t)\Delta t \qquad (3\text{-}29)$$

Let $t = k\Delta t$, with $k = 0, 1, 2, \ldots$ and Eq. (3-29) becomes

$$\underline{x}[(k+1)\Delta t] = \underline{x}[k\Delta t] + A\underline{x}(k\Delta t)\Delta t + \underline{b}v(k\Delta t)\Delta t \qquad (3\text{-}30)$$

Eq. (3-30) represents a straight-line approximation to the state-space trajectory (i.e., the solution of Eq. [3-19]). If $k = 0$, then

$$\underline{x}(\Delta t) = \underline{x}(0) + A\underline{x}(0)\Delta t + \underline{b}v(0)\Delta t \qquad (3\text{-}31)$$

where $\underline{x}(0)$ is the initial condition and if $k = 1$

$$\underline{x}(2\Delta t) = \underline{x}(\Delta t) + A\underline{x}(\Delta t)\Delta t + \underline{b}v(\Delta t)\Delta t \qquad (3\text{-}32)$$

$\underline{x}(\Delta t)$ in Eq. (3-32) is obtained from Eq. (3-31). Similarly, $\underline{x}(3\Delta t)$ involves terms in $\underline{x}(2\Delta t)$ which are obtained from Eq. (3-32) and so on. The value of Δt depends upon many factors including, the terms in matrix A and vector $\underline{b}$, the length of time over which the trajectory is desired, and the accuracy required.

As an example, let $R = 1\,\Omega, L = .5$ h, $C = .05$ f, $v(t) = 1u(t), I_0 = 0 = x_1(0)$ and $x_2(0) = V_0 = -1$. Choose $\Delta t = .002$ sec. When $k = 0$, Eq. (3-30) yields

$$\begin{bmatrix} x_1(.002) \\ x_2(.002) \end{bmatrix} = \begin{bmatrix} x_1(0) \\ x_2(0) \end{bmatrix} + \begin{bmatrix} -2 & -2 \\ 20 & 0 \end{bmatrix}\begin{bmatrix} x_1(0) \\ x_2(0) \end{bmatrix}(.002) + \begin{bmatrix} 2 \\ 0 \end{bmatrix}(1)(.002)$$

and when $k = 1$, Eq. (3-30) yields

$$\begin{bmatrix} x_1(.004) \\ x_2(.004) \end{bmatrix} = \begin{bmatrix} x_1(.002) \\ x_2(.002) \end{bmatrix} + \begin{bmatrix} -2 & -2 \\ 20 & 0 \end{bmatrix}\begin{bmatrix} x_1(.002) \\ x_2(.002) \end{bmatrix}(.002) + \begin{bmatrix} 2 \\ 0 \end{bmatrix}(1)(.002)$$

This process is continued with $\Delta t = .002$ sec. The results are shown in Table 3-1 and plotted in the $(i_L(t), v_C(t))$ plane of Fig. 3-2.

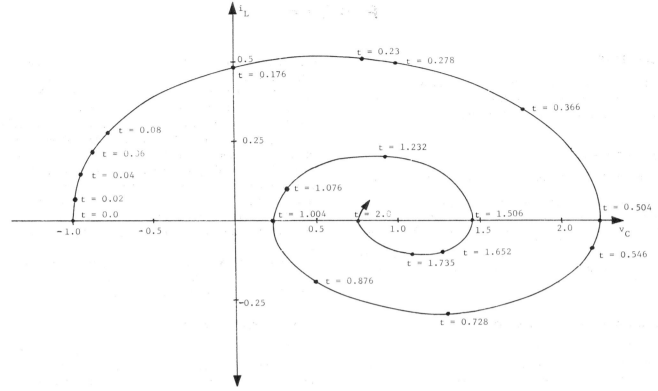

Fig. 3.2 Phase-plane trajectory.

TABLE 3–1

k	$x_1(k\Delta t) = i_L$	$x_2(k\Delta t) = v_C$	k	$x_1(k\Delta t) = i_L$	$x_2(k\Delta t) = v_C$
0	0.000	−1.000	300	−0.207	+2.022
10	0.078	−0.986	400	−0.284	+0.874
20	0.153	−0.941	500	−0.006	+0.234
30	0.222	−0.867	600	0.190	+0.691
40	0.285	−0.767	700	0.102	+1.358
50	0.341	−0.643	800	−0.076	+1.395
100	0.501	+0.231	900	−0.109	+0.961
200	0.260	+1.963	1000	−0.005	+0.710

The number of iterations of Eq. (3–30) required to obtain points along a desired trajectory may be very large. A digital computer can be used to perform a large number of iterations in a reasonably small amount of time. A simple computer program written in FORTRAN which can be used to calculate points along the trajectory for the previous example is given below. The values of k effectively range from 0 to 1000 in the computer program.

```
DIMENSION X1(1001),X2(1001),TIME(1001)
X1(1)=0.0
X2(1)=−1.0
V=1.0
TIME(1)=0.0
DTIME=0.002
DO 5 K=1,1000
X1(K+1)=X1(K) + (−2.0) *X1(K) *DTIME− 2.0*X2(K)
    *DTIME + 2.0*V*DTIME
X2(K+1)=X2(K) + 20.0*X1(K)*DTIME
TIME(K+1)=TIME(K) + DTIME
5 CONTINUE
DO 7 K=1,1001
WRITE (6,100) TIME(K),X1(K),X2(K)
100 FORMAT (10X,5HTIME=,F8.4,10X,3HX1=,F10.4,
    10X,3HX2=,F10.4)
7 CONTINUE
STOP
END
```

Part Two

OBJECTIVE

The state-space method will be used to analyze some second-order circuits. The solution vectors of some simple second-order circuits will be generated.

REFERENCES

Chirlian, P. M., *Basic Network Theory*. New York: McGraw-Hill, 1969, Chapter 7.

Cruz, J. B., and Van Valkenburg, M. E., *Introductory Signals and Circuits*. Waltham, Mass.: Blaisdell, 1967, Chapter 13.

Desoer, C. A., and Kuh, E. S., *Basic Circuit Theory*. New York: McGraw-Hill, 1969, Chapter 12.

Ghausi, M. S., *Electronic Circuits: Devices, Models, Functions, Analysis, and Design*. New York: Van Nostrand Reinhold, 1971, Chapter 2.

LABORATORY PREPARATION

1. The switch T in Fig. 3-3 is closed and allowed to remain closed until the voltage $v_1(t)$ goes to zero. Now the switch is opened, and this time is considered as $t_0 = 0$. What are the initial conditions for this circuit? Derive two first-order differential equations valid for $t \geq t_0$ whose independent variables are $v_1(t)$ and $v_2(t)$.

2. The switch T is initially open. If $v_1(t)$ is applied to the vertical input and $v_2(t)$ to the horizontal input of the CRO, describe the path or trajectory that the spot will follow after T is closed. Assume that the spot is in the center of the screen of the CRT before T is closed. Describe the trajectory as a function of time after the switch is opened again. (The instant the switch is opened again was denoted as $t_0 = 0$ in step 1.) The trajectory is described by solving for the state vector whose components are $v_1(t)$ and $v_2(t)$. Pick $\Delta t = .1$ and start at $v_1(t_0) = 0$ and $v_2(t_0) = 1.0$ volt. Plot the results of $v_1(t)$ versus $v_2(t)$ from when the switch is open ($t \ll t_0$), then closed ($t < t_0$), and opened again ($t \geq t_0$).

3. Consider Fig. 3-3 with $C_1 = C_2 = 10 \,\mu f$ and $R_1 = R_2 = 1 \,k\Omega$. If the switch remains closed for $t \geq t_0$ and the initial conditions for the circuit are $v_1(t_0) = 0$, $v_2(t_0) = -1$, and $v(t) = +1$, what is the trajectory for $t \geq t_0$? If $v_1(t_0) = 0$, $v_2(t_0) = +1$ and $v(t) = -1$, what is the trajectory? Plot the results for both trajectories on the same page.

4. Plot the trajectory of the current $i_R(t)$ versus the voltage $L(di_L(t)/dt)$ for the RLC circuit of Fig. 3-4 by the approximate method given in this experiment with $k \,\Delta t \ll (k/10)(2\pi/\omega_d)$. Allow k to be 0, 1, 2, and 3. What do you expect to occur for $k > 3$? Consider the two cases when $v(t) = 1$ volt, $v_C(t_0) = -1$ volt, $i_L(t_0) = 0$, and when $v(t) = -1$ volt, $v_C(t_0) = +1$ volt and $i_L(t_0) = 0$. Also plot $i_R(t)$ versus $v_C(t)$ and $L(di_L/dt)$ versus $v_C(t)$ for the two cases given.

5. (optional) Write some digital computer programs to obtain trajectories similar to those of step 4, with $\Delta t = 5 \times 10^{-6}$ sec, $k = 1$ to 400, and $f = 10$ kHz.

LABORATORY PROCEDURE

1. Construct the circuit of Fig. 3-3. Connect $v_1(t)$ and $v_2(t)$ to the vertical and horizontal inputs of the CRO. Set the vertical sensitivity to .2 V/cm and the horizontal sensitivity to .2 V/cm. Close switch T and observe the path that the spot on the screen follows. After $v_1(t)$ reaches 0 volts, open switch T and observe the path of the spot. How does this compare with your predicted results? Change R_1 and R_2 to 50 k and compare the trajectory to the case for $R_1 = R_2 = 100$ k. Adjust R_1 and R_2 so that $R_1 \neq R_2$ and compare with $R_1 = R_2$.

2. Set $C_1 = C_2 = 10 \,\mu f$ and $R_1 = R_2 = 1 \,k\Omega$ in Fig. 3-3. Replace $v(t)$ with a square-wave signal with an amplitude of 1 volt peak and a frequency of 20 cps. The voltages $v_1(t)$ and $v_2(t)$ are still applied to the vertical and horizontal inputs of the CRO. The vertical and horizontal sensitivities of the CRO should be set to .2 V/cm. How do the trajectories on the screen of the CRO compare to your preparation (step 3)? Why are they different?

3. Change R_1 and R_2 as well as the amplitude of the square-wave voltage $v(t)$. Observe and explain the changes in the trajectory.

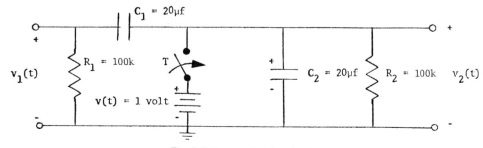

Fig. 3.3 A second-order circuit.

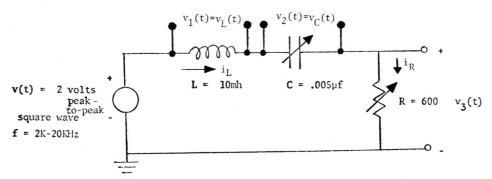

Fig. 3.4 RLC circuit.

4. Set $R = 600\ \Omega$, $C = .005\ \mu f$, and $L = 10$ mh in Fig. 3-4. Connect $v_1(t)$ to the vertical input and $v_2(t)$ to the horizontal input of the CRO. Set the horizontal sensitivity to 50 mV/cm and the vertical sensitivity to 50 mV/cm. Vary the frequency of the input square wave from 2 to 20 kHz and observe the changes in the trajectory. Explain the changes. Also change the amplitude of the square-wave and observe the changes in the trajectory. In addition, simultaneously vary the capacitor C and resistor R and observe the changes in the trajectory. Note that this part of the experiment requires an oscilloscope with differential inputs. For example, the signal $v_1(t)$ is connected to the two vertical input terminals on the front of the scope, neither of which is connected to ground. Consult your instructor when making these connections. If your oscilloscope does not have differential type inputs, the measure-

ments of $v_1(t)$ and $v_2(t)$ will have to be modified. Consult your instructor in this case.

5. Now apply $v_2(t)$ to the horizontal input of the CRO and observe and explain the trajectory. Make necessary adjustments on horizontal and vertical sensitivity so that the complete trajectory appears on the screen. Change various parameters as was done in step 4.

LIST OF EQUIPMENT

1. Cathode-ray oscilloscope
2. Signal sources: function generator or sine- and square-wave oscillators and a dc power supply
3. Circuit board
4. Components: resistors, capacitors, and inductors

Experiment 4/Frequency Response: Phasors, Transforms, and Bode Plots

Part One

INTRODUCTION

The response of RLC circuits to various inputs can be obtained as a function of frequency (frequency response) or as a function of time (time response) from the solution of ordinary linear differential equations. However, when the input or forcing function of a differential equation belongs to the special class of sinusoidal signals, then the response (time or frequency) can be obtained by the phasor method. The phasor method is based on the property that a sinusoidal-input to a time-invariant (constant coefficient) differential equation produces a steady-state solution of the same frequency but of a different amplitude and phase than the sinusoidal input.

Another method for solving linear differential equations when the input signal or forcing function is not sinusoidal or even periodic is to transform the original differential equation into an algebraic equation by means of Laplace transforms. The solution of the resulting algebraic equation is then used to obtain the desired frequency or time response.

THEORY

The Phasor Method

Complex numbers are used extensively in the phasor method of analysis, and a short discussion of the basic properties of these numbers will be presented. First of all, a complex number is an ordered pair of real numbers. A complex number is written in terms of the imaginary number $j (j = \sqrt{-1})$ as $a + jb$ or sometimes simply (a, b). Therefore, a complex number $s(s = a + jb)$ has two parts associated with it: the number a, called the real part of s and denoted $\text{Re } s = a$; and a number b, called the imaginary part of s and denoted $\text{Im } s = b$.

An ordering has taken place by associating a with the real part of s and b with the imaginary part of s. We can now write

$$s = \text{Re } s + j \text{ Im } s = a + jb \qquad (4\text{-}1)$$

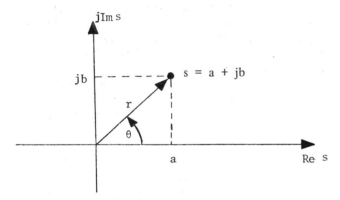

Fig. 4.1 Complex plane.

The complex conjugate of s is defined as

$$\bar{s} = \text{Re } s - j \text{ Im } s = a - jb$$

That is, the complex conjugate of s is obtained by changing the sign of the imaginary part of s.

Complex numbers have many useful properties and can be written in a number of useful forms. These forms and their uses will now be studied.

The complex number $s = a + jb$ represents a point in the complex plane, as shown in Fig. 4–1.

The point s has coordinates (a, b). This point can also be described by two other numbers r and θ. In fact, if

$$a = r \cos \theta$$
$$b = r \sin \theta \qquad (4\text{-}2)$$

then

$$s = a + jb = r (\cos \theta + j \sin \theta)$$

The complex number $\cos \theta + j \sin \theta$ can also be written as $e^{j\theta}$, which is called Euler's form. That is,

$$e^{j\theta} = \cos \theta + j \sin \theta \qquad (4\text{-}3)$$

and the complex number s as

$$s = re^{j\theta} = \text{Re } [re^{j\theta}] + j \text{ Im } [re^{j\theta}] = r \cos \theta + jr \sin \theta \qquad (4\text{-}4)$$

The number r is called the magnitude of s and written

$$r = |s| = \sqrt{a^2 + b^2} \qquad (4\text{-}5)$$

The quantity θ is the phase angle of s, and it equals

$$\theta = \tan^{-1} \frac{b}{a} = \tan^{-1} \left(\frac{\text{Im } s}{\text{Re } s} \right) \qquad (4\text{-}6)$$

Two complex numbers s_1 and s_2 are equal if

$$\text{Re } s_1 = \text{Re } s_2$$

and

$$\text{Im } s_1 = \text{Im } s_2 \qquad (4\text{-}7)$$

which implies, using Euler's form, that if

$$s_1 = r_1 e^{j\theta_1} \quad \text{and} \quad s_2 = r_2 e^{j\theta_2}$$

then

$$r_1 = r_2 \qquad (4\text{-}8)$$

and

$$\theta_1 = \theta_2 + 2k\pi \quad \text{with} \quad k = 0, \pm 1, \pm 2, \ldots$$

Euler's form is particularly useful when multiplying and dividing two complex numbers. For example, if

$$s_1 = a + jb = r_1 e^{j\theta_1} \quad \text{and} \quad s_2 = c + jd = r_2 e^{j\theta_2} \qquad (4\text{-}9)$$

then

$$s_1 s_2 = (a + jb)(c + jd) = ac - bd + j(bc + ad) \qquad (4\text{-}10)$$

and

$$\frac{s_1}{s_2} = \frac{a + jb}{c + jd} = \frac{a + jb}{c + jd} \cdot \frac{(c - jd)}{(c - jd)} = \frac{ac + bd}{c^2 + d^2} + j \frac{(bc - ad)}{c^2 + d^2} \qquad (4\text{-}11)$$

However, Euler's form yields

$$s_1 s_2 = \left(r_1 e^{j\theta_1} \right) \left(r_2 e^{j\theta_2} \right) = r_1 r_2 e^{j(\theta_1 + \theta_2)} \qquad (4\text{-}12)$$

and

$$\frac{s_1}{s_2} = \frac{r_1 e^{j\theta_1}}{r_2 e^{j\theta_2}} = \frac{r_1}{r_2} e^{j(\theta_1 - \theta_2)} \qquad (4\text{-}13)$$

Euler's form is also convenient in obtaining the roots of a complex number. A complex number can be written as

$$s = r e^{j\theta} \quad \text{and also as} \quad s = r e^{j(\theta + 2k\pi)} \qquad (4\text{-}14)$$

with $k = 0, \pm 1, \pm 2, \ldots$ In order to obtain the nth root of a complex number s, we use Euler's form

$$s^{1/n} = (a + jb)^{1/n} = \left[r e^{j(\theta + 2k\pi)} \right]^{1/n} = r^{1/n} e^{j(\theta + 2k\pi)/n} \qquad (4\text{-}15)$$

The first step in the phasor method of analysis of linear differential equations is to express the sinusoidal input in

Euler's form. In particular, assume that

$$f(t) = A_m \cos(\omega t + \phi) \qquad (4\text{-}16)$$

with A_m the maximum amplitude of $f(t)$ and ϕ the phase of $f(t)$. Eq. (4-14) yields

$$f(t) = \text{Re } [A_m e^{j(\omega t + \phi)}] = \text{Re } [A_m e^{j\phi} e^{j\omega t}] \qquad (4\text{-}17)$$

Define

$$A = A_m e^{j\phi} \quad \text{(a complex number)}$$

Very often A_m and ϕ are functions of ω, and, consequently, A is written $A(j\omega)$. Eq. (4-17) becomes

$$f(t) = \text{Re } [A(j\omega) e^{j\omega t}] \qquad (4\text{-}18)$$

Thus the phasor $A(j\omega)$ is a complex number which contains information concerning the amplitude and phase angle of $f(t)$. It can also be shown that the following two propositions are valid and especially useful in the phasor method of analysis.

(1)
$$\frac{d}{dt} \{ \text{Re } [\alpha_1 A_1(j\omega) e^{j\omega t}] \} + \frac{d}{dt} \{ \text{Re } [\alpha_2 A_2(j\omega) e^{j\omega t}] \}$$

$$= \alpha_1 \text{ Re } [j\omega A_1(j\omega) e^{j\omega t}] + \alpha_2 \text{ Re } [j\omega A_2(j\omega) e^{j\omega t}] \qquad (4\text{-}19)$$

for α_1 and α_2 any real numbers and

$$A_1(j\omega) = A_{m1} e^{j\phi_1} \qquad (4\text{-}20)$$

$$A_2(j\omega) = A_{m2} e^{j\phi_2} \qquad (4\text{-}21)$$

(2)
$$A_1(j\omega) = A_2(j\omega) \quad \text{if and only if}$$

$$\text{Re } [A_1(j\omega) e^{j\omega t}] = \text{Re } [A_2(j\omega) e^{j\omega t}] \quad \text{for all } t$$

Proposition (1) can be shown to be valid by considering the following derivative.

$$\frac{d}{dt} \text{ Re } [\alpha_1 A_1(j\omega) e^{j\omega t}] = \frac{d}{dt} [\alpha_1 A_{m1} \cos(\omega t + \phi_1)]$$

$$= -\omega \alpha_1 A_{m1} \sin(\omega t + \phi_1)$$

$$= \alpha_1 \text{ Re } [j\omega A_{m1} e^{j(\omega t + \phi_1)}]$$

$$= \alpha_1 \text{ Re } [j\omega A_1(j\omega) e^{j\omega t}] \qquad (4\text{-}22)$$

Apply the same steps to the second term in Eq. (4-19) involving α_2 and $A_2(j\omega)$; adding the results concludes the argument. Proposition (2) can be shown to be valid if we first assume that

$$\text{Re } [A_1(j\omega) e^{j\omega t}] = \text{Re } [A_2(j\omega) e^{j\omega t}] \quad \text{for all } t \qquad (4\text{-}23)$$

We need to show from Eq. (4-23) that

$$A_{m1} \cos(\omega t + \phi_1) = A_{m2} \cos(\omega t + \phi_2) \quad \text{for all } t \qquad (4\text{-}24)$$

since A_1 and A_2 are defined by Eqs. (4-20) and (4-21).

Suppose that $t = 0$, $\phi_1 = 45°$, $\phi_2 = 0$, $A_{m1} = 2$, and $A_{m2} = \sqrt{2}$. Eq. (4-24) is satisfied at $\omega t = 0, \pm\pi, \pm 2\pi, \ldots$ but not for all time t. On the other hand, Eq. (4-24) is satisfied for all t provided that

$$A_{m1} = A_{m2} \quad \text{and} \quad \phi_1 = \phi_2 + 2k\pi, k = 0, \pm 1, \pm 2, \ldots$$

Conversely, if we assume that

$$A_1(j\omega) = A_2(j\omega)$$

then we want to show that

$$\text{Re } [A_1(j\omega) e^{j\omega t}] = \text{Re } [A_2(j\omega) e^{j\omega t}] \quad \text{for all } t$$

It is true from Eqs. (4-20) and (4-21) that

$$A_1(j\omega) = A_{m1} \cos (\omega t + \phi_1) + jA_{m1} \sin (\omega t + \phi_1)$$

and

$$A_2(j\omega) = A_{m2} \cos (\omega t + \phi_2) + jA_{m2} \sin (\omega t + \phi_2)$$

$$(4\text{-}25)$$

These two complex numbers will be equal if their real and imaginary parts are equal, and, consequently, the proposition is valid.

Complex numbers and these propositions will now be used in the phasor method to generate the particular solution to linear time-invariant differential equations with sinusoidal inputs. Consider the series RLC circuit of

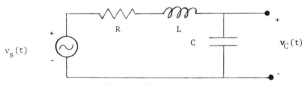

Fig. 4.2 RLC circuit.

Fig. 4-2. The second-order differential equation describing the voltage $v_C(t)$ is

$$\frac{d^2 v_C(t)}{dt^2} + \frac{R}{L} \frac{dv_C(t)}{dt} + \frac{1}{LC} v_C(t) = \frac{1}{LC} v_s(t) \quad (4\text{-}26)$$

Assume that the solution of Eq. (4-26) represents a response of the series RLC circuit in the steady state. That is, the effects of an initial current in the inductor and/or an initial voltage across the capacitor have been reduced to zero. More precisely, the homogeneous solution to Eq. (4-26) is zero, and the only solution is the particular solution. Let the applied voltage $v_s(t)$ be

$$v_s(t) = V_m \cos (\omega t + \theta) \quad (4\text{-}27)$$

with V_m the amplitude of the voltage $v_s(t)$, θ the phase angle and ω the applied angular frequency ($\omega = 2\pi f$). Now the sinusoidal-input voltage $v_s(t)$ can be written as

$$v_s(t) = V_m \cos (\omega t + \theta) = \text{Re } [V_m e^{j\theta} e^{j\omega t}]$$

$$= \text{Re } [V(j\omega) e^{j\omega t}] \quad (4\text{-}28)$$

where

$$V(j\omega) = V_m e^{j\theta}$$

The particular solution can be conveniently obtained by the phasor method. The particular solution of Eq. (4-26) will be a sinusoid since the forcing function (input) $v_s(t)$ is a sinusoid. Assume then that

$$v_C(t) = \text{Re } [V_C(j\omega) e^{j\omega t}] \quad (4\text{-}29)$$

where $V_C(j\omega)$ is a complex number.

We must calculate $V_C(j\omega)$ in order to obtain $v_C(t)$. Substituting for $v_C(t)$ in Eq. (4-26) yields

$$\frac{d^2}{dt^2} [\text{Re } (V_C e^{j\omega t})] + \frac{R}{L} \frac{d}{dt} [\text{Re } (V_C e^{j\omega t})]$$

$$+ \frac{1}{LC} \text{Re } [V_C e^{j\omega t}] = \text{Re } [V_m e^{j\theta} e^{j\omega t}] \quad (4\text{-}30)$$

If proposition (1) is repeatedly applied to Eq. (4-30), we obtain

$$\text{Re} \left\{ \left[(j\omega)^2 + \frac{R}{L} (j\omega) + \frac{1}{LC} \right] [V_C e^{j\omega t}] \right\}$$

$$= \frac{1}{LC} \text{Re } [V_m e^{j\theta} e^{j\omega t}] \quad (4\text{-}31)$$

We can now solve for V_C by applying proposition (2).

$$V_C(j\omega) = \frac{V(j\omega)}{LC \left[(j\omega)^2 + \frac{R}{L} (j\omega) + \frac{1}{LC} \right]} = \frac{V(j\omega)}{1 - \omega^2 LC + j\omega RC}$$

$$(4\text{-}32)$$

The voltage $V_C(j\omega)$ can be rewritten in polar form

$$V_C(j\omega) = |V_C(j\omega)| e^{+j\psi} \quad (4\text{-}33)$$

where

$$|V_C(j\omega)| = \frac{V_m}{[(1 - \omega^2 LC)^2 + (\omega RC)^2]^{1/2}} \quad (4\text{-}34)$$

is the amplitude of $v_C(t)$ or magnitude of $V_C(j\omega)$ and $\psi(\omega) = \theta - \tan^{-1} \omega RC/(1 - \omega^2 LC)$ is the phase of $V_C(j\omega)$. The particular solution or, in this case, the complete solution is

$$v_C(t) = |V_C| \cos (\omega t + \psi) \quad (4\text{-}35)$$

The amplitude $|V_C(j\omega)|$ and phase $\psi(\omega)$ of $V_C(j\omega)$ are plotted as functions of frequency in Figs. 4-3 and 4-4.

In general, the particular solution of an nth-order differential equation with a sinusoidal input has the following form

$$x(t) = \text{Re } [X(j\omega) e^{j\omega t}]$$

The nth-order differential linear time-invariant equation is of the form

$$a_n \frac{d^n x(t)}{dt^n} + a_{n-1} \frac{d^{n-1} x(t)}{dt^{n-1}} + \cdots + a_1 \frac{dx(t)}{dt} + a_0 x(t) = f(t)$$

$$(4\text{-}36)$$

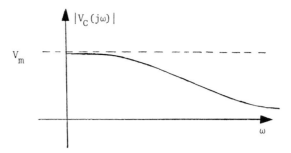

Fig. 4.3 Magnitude response.

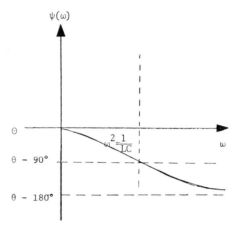

Fig. 4.4 Phase response.

with $f(t) = \text{Re}\,[F(j\omega)\,e^{j\omega t}]$. The application of propositions (1) and (2) result in the following expression for $X(j\omega)$

$$X(j\omega) = \frac{F(j\omega)}{a_n(j\omega)^n + a_{n-1}(j\omega)^{n-1} + \cdots + a_1 j\omega + a_0} \quad (4\text{-}37)$$

Note that the solution $x(t)$ depends upon $X(j\omega)$; the method we have discussed for obtaining $X(j\omega)$ is called the phasor method. The particular solution $x(t)$ in this case is called the steady-state solution.

Laplace Transform Method

We would now like to obtain the solution of Eq. (4-36) for a general type input not necessarily sinusoidal. The method we will employ uses the Laplace transform.

The Laplace transform $F(s)$ of the time function $f(t)$ is defined to be

$$F(s) \triangleq \int_{0^-}^{\infty} f(t)\,e^{-st}dt \quad (4\text{-}38)$$

where s is a complex number given by

$$s = \text{Re}\,s + j\,\text{Im}\,s = \sigma + j\omega \quad (4\text{-}39)$$

The Laplace transform of $f(t)$ is sometimes written as $\mathcal{L}[f(t)]$. Observe that in Eq. (4-38) the time function $f(t)$

is first multiplied by e^{-st} and then integrated from $t = 0^-$ to $t = \infty$. Since the integral is definite, $F(s)$ does not depend upon t, but only on the complex number s and only on those values of s for which the integral is defined.

The following two examples illustrate the reason for the definition of $F(s)$ given in Eq. (4-38).

Suppose $f(t) = u(t)$, the unit step, then by Eq. (4-38)

$$\mathcal{L}[u(t)] = \int_{0^-}^{\infty} u(t)e^{-st}dt = \int_{0^-}^{\infty} 1e^{-(\sigma+j\omega)t}dt = \frac{-e^{-(\sigma+j\omega)t}}{(\sigma+j\omega)}\bigg|_{0^-}^{\infty}$$

$$(4\text{-}40)$$

The evaluation of Eq. (4-40) at the upper and lower limits of integration yields

$$\mathcal{L}[u(t)] = \frac{1}{\sigma + j\omega} = \frac{1}{s} \quad (4\text{-}41)$$

provided $\sigma > 0$. That is, the integral is well defined if $\text{Re}\,s > 0$.

Now suppose $f(t) = \delta(t)$, the impulse function, then by Eq. (4-38)

$$\int_{0^-}^{\infty} \delta(t)e^{-st}dt = \int_{0^-}^{0^+} \delta(t)e^0\,dt = \int_{0^-}^{0^+} \delta(t)dt = 1 \quad (4\text{-}42)$$

Therefore, the lower limit 0^- of the integral of Eq. (4-38) is chosen to include in the transform the effect of discontinuities and/or impulses of $f(t)$ occurring at time $t = 0$.

Table 4-1 is a collection of useful transforms where each $F(s)$ can be verified by using the definition given in Eq. (4-38).

The Laplace transform method can be used to solve linear differential equations similar to Eq. (4-36). The Laplace transform method converts a differential equation into an algebraic equation. The solution of the algebraic equation then yields the frequency response. For example, consider Eq. (4-26) derived for the circuit of Fig. 4-2. The Laplace transform of Eq. (4-26) is

$$\mathcal{L}\left[\frac{d^2 v_C}{dt^2} + \frac{R}{L}\frac{dv_C(t)}{dt} + \frac{1}{LC}v_C(t)\right] = \frac{1}{LC}\mathcal{L}[v_s(t)] \quad (4\text{-}43)$$

Using Table 4-1 and defining the transforms of $v_C(t)$ and $v_s(t)$ as

$$\mathcal{L}[v_C(t)] \triangleq V_C(s) \quad \text{and} \quad \mathcal{L}[v_s(t)] = V(s)$$

Eq. (4-43) is equivalent to

$$s^2 V_C(s) - s\frac{dv_C(0^-)}{dt} - v_C(0^-) + \frac{R}{L}[sV_C(s) - v_C(0^-)]$$

$$+ \frac{1}{LC}V_C(s) = \frac{1}{LC}V(s)$$

$$(4\text{-}44)$$

TABLE 4-1 LAPLACE TRANSFORMS.

$f(t)$	$F(s) = \int_{0^-}^{\infty} f(t)e^{-st}dt$
$\delta(t)$	1
$u(t)$	$\dfrac{1}{s}$
$\dfrac{t^n}{n!}$	$\dfrac{1}{s^{n+1}}$
e^{-at}	$\dfrac{1}{s+a}$
te^{-at}	$\dfrac{1}{(s+a)^2}$
$\cos \omega t$	$\dfrac{s}{s^2 + \omega^2}$
$\sin \omega t$	$\dfrac{\omega}{s^2 + \omega^2}$
$\dfrac{df}{dt}$	$sF(s) - f(0^-)$
$\dfrac{d^n f}{dt^n}$	$s^n F(s) - \sum_{k=0}^{n-1} s^k \dfrac{d^{(n-1-k)}f(t)}{dt^{(n-1-k)}}\bigg|_{t=0^-}$
$\displaystyle\int_{0^-}^{t} g(t)dt$	$\dfrac{G(s)}{s}$
$\alpha_1 f_2(t) + \alpha_2 f_2(t)$	$\alpha_1 F_1(s) + \alpha_2 F_2(s)$

The ratio of output to input, assuming that all the initial conditions are zero, is called the transfer function $H(s)$.

$$H(s) = \frac{V_C(s)}{V(s)} = \frac{1}{LC\left[s^2 + \dfrac{R}{L}s + \dfrac{1}{LC}\right]} \quad (4\text{-}45)$$

We obtain the same transfer function as obtained from Eq. (4-32) if we let $s = j\omega$ in Eq. (4-45). It is important to note that if the output (desired response) and input (forcing function) are related through a linear differential equation, then the ratio of the transforms of the output to the input is represented by a ratio of polynomials in s. This ratio is valid regardless of the type of input, and represents an algebraic relationship between output and input. The ratio $H(s)$ yields the frequency response for a sinusoidal input (Eq. [4-32]).

This experiment deals mainly with the frequency response $H(j\omega)$, but the transfer function $H(s)$ also yields the zero-state response for a general type input. As an example of how the zero-state time response could be obtained from

the transfer function, consider the example of Eq. (4-45) with $R = 0$, $L = C = 1$ and the input $v(t) = \delta(t)$, a unit impulse function. The transform of $v(t)$ is

$$\mathcal{L}[v(t)] = \mathcal{L}[\delta(t)] = 1 \quad (4\text{-}46)$$

and Eq. (4-45) reduces to

$$V_C(s) = \frac{1}{s^2 + 1} \quad (4\text{-}47)$$

Table 4-1 shows that the zero-state time response (impulse response) corresponding to the transform given by Eq. (4-47) is $\sin t$. Thus the output $v_C(t)$ is $\sin t$ when $R = 0$, $L = C = 1$, and the input is an impulse function.

The output-input relationship given by $H(s)$ is also conveniently described by Fig. 4-5. $H(s)$ is sometimes called the network function or impulse response. Thus, the transfer function can be used to determine the frequency or time response of a circuit.

Fig. 4.5 Linear system.

Bode Plots

In the design of linear electronic circuits we are generally concerned with analyzing or synthesizing a given transfer function which is the ratio of polynomials in s. For example, a general transfer function $H(s)$ can be written as

$$H(s) = \frac{a_m s^m + a_{m-1}s^{m-1} + a_{m-2}s^{m-2} + \cdots + a_0}{b_n s^n + b_{n-1}s^{n-1} + b_{n-2}s^{n-2} + \cdots b_0} \quad (4\text{-}48)$$

and in factored form as

$$H(s) = \frac{K(s+z_1)(s+z_2)(\quad) \cdots (s+z_m)}{(s+p_1)(s+p_2)(\quad) \cdots (s+p_n)} \quad (4\text{-}49)$$

where K is a constant and $-z_1, -z, \ldots -z_m$ are defined as zeros, and $-p_1, -p_2, \ldots -p_m$ are defined as poles of $H(s)$. If there is only one pole at one location, say $s = -p_k$, then the *pole is simple*. If there is more than one pole at one location, say $-p_1 = -p_2 = -p_3$, then the *pole is multiple* and of order 3. For example, if we have a factor $(s+p_k)^2$ in the denominator of $H(s)$, then we have a pole at $s = -p_k$ of order 2. Similarly for zeros. Consider the following example

$$H(s) = \frac{K(s+z_1)^2 (s+z_2)(s+z_3)(s+\bar{z}_3)}{(s+p_1)(s+p_2)^3 (s+p_3)(s+\bar{p}_3)} \quad (4\text{-}50)$$

where z_1, p_2 are negative real numbers; p_1, z_2 are positive real numbers; z_3, p_3 are complex numbers; $\bar{z}_3, \bar{p}_3$ are the

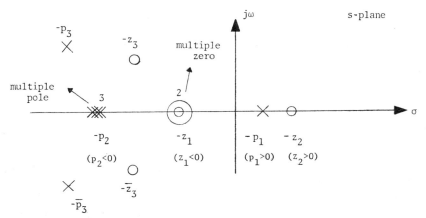

Fig. 4.6 A pole-zero diagram.

complex conjugates of z_3 and p_3, and

$$K = \frac{H(0)p_1 p_2{}^3 |p_3|^2}{(z_1)^2 (z_2)|z_3|^2} \qquad (4\text{-}51)$$

The transfer function $H(s)$ can be represented in the s-plane by what is called the pole-zero diagram. The poles of $H(s)$ are indicated by the symbol "x," and the zeros of $H(s)$ by the symbol "o." The pole-zero diagram of $H(s)$ of Eq. 4–50 is shown in Fig. 4–6.

Note that if we are given a pole-zero diagram, we can write $H(s)$ to within an arbitrary constant K. That is, the value of K is not specified in the pole-zero diagram of the transfer function.

The pole-zero diagram is a helpful guide in determining the frequency and time response of electronic circuits. The frequency response in particular, which is characterized by the magnitude and phase angle of the transfer function, can usually be sketched as a function of the input frequency from inspection of the pole-zero diagram.

Suppose that we are given the transfer function of Eq. (4–48) in factored form. The magnitude of the transfer function is

$$|H(j\omega)| = |H(s)|_{s=j\omega} = \frac{|K|\,|j\omega + z_1|\,|j\omega + z_2|\cdots\cdots|j\omega + z_m|}{|j\omega + p_1|\,|j\omega + p_2|\cdots\cdots\cdots|j\omega + p_n|}$$

$$(4\text{-}52)$$

and the phase angle of the transfer function is

$$\phi = \angle H(s)|_{s=j\omega} = + \left[\tan^{-1}\frac{\omega}{z_1} + \tan^{-1}\frac{\omega}{z_2} + \cdots + \tan^{-1}\frac{\omega}{z_m}\right]$$

$$- \left[\tan^{-1}\frac{\omega}{p_1} + \tan^{-1}\frac{\omega}{p_2} + \cdots + \tan^{-1}\frac{\omega}{p_n}\right]$$

$$(4\text{-}53)$$

The frequency response consists of the magnitude of $H(j\omega)$ and the phase angle ϕ of $H(j\omega)$, both of which depend upon the frequency of the sinusoidal input.

It will be useful to correlate the pole-zero diagram of the transfer function with straight-line approximations to the frequency response. In this way, an inspection of the pole-zero diagram will quickly reveal important portions of the frequency response. We will also be able to predict how changes in the pole-zero diagram will effect the response, and vice versa. Typical frequency responses are shown in Fig. 4–7.

$H(j\omega)$ is called a voltage or current gain when it represents a ratio of voltages or currents respectively. The dc value of the gain is that value of $H(j\omega)$ where $\omega = 0$. The midband gain ($|H(j\omega)|_{\text{mid}}$) is usually defined as the value of $|H(j\omega)|$ in a frequency band where $|H(j\omega)|$ has zero slope (flat). The dc gain and midband gain are identical for

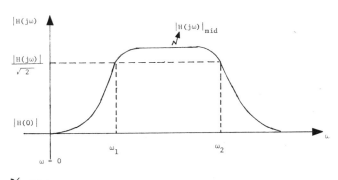

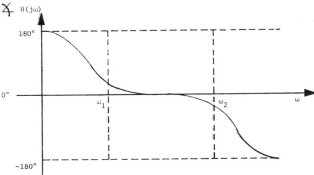

Fig. 4.7 Typical magnitude and phase responses.

some transfer functions. The *lower 3 dbv frequency* or half power frequency is the lower value of frequency f_1 ($f_1 = \omega_1/2\pi$) at which the gain falls to .707 of its midband value (i.e., $\dfrac{|H(j\omega)|_{mid}}{\sqrt{2}} = |H(j\omega_1)|$). The *upper 3 dbv frequency* or upper half power frequency is the larger value of frequency f_2 ($f_2 = \omega_2/2\pi$) at which the gain falls to .707 of its midband gain. For example, the values of ω_1 and ω_2 (i.e., $\dfrac{|H(j\omega)|_{mid}}{\sqrt{2}} = |H(j\omega_1)| = |H(j\omega_2)|$) are shown in Fig. 4-7.

We will now show that straight-line approximations to $|H(j\omega)|$ can be obtained by inspection of the pole-zero diagram. These straight-line approximations are called Bode plots. In a Bode plot, one generally plots the voltage gain (or current gain) in decibels versus log ω. For example, a transfer function with a single pole is

$$H(s) = \frac{H(0)p_1}{s + p_1} = \frac{K}{s + p_1} \qquad (4\text{-}54)$$

where p_1 is assumed to be a real positive number and $K = H(0)p_1$.

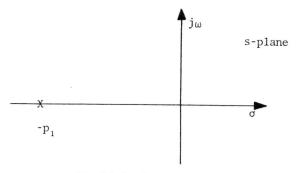

Fig. 4.8 A pole-zero diagram.

The pole-zero diagram is given in Fig. 4-8. The magnitude of $H(j\omega)$ is simply

$$|H(j\omega)| = \frac{|H(0)||p_1|}{[\omega^2 + p_1^2]^{1/2}} \qquad (4\text{-}55)$$

and expressed in decibels is

$$20 \log_{10} |H(j\omega)| = 20 \log_{10}|H(0)| \, |p_1|$$
$$- 20 \log_{10} [\omega^2 + p_1^2]^{1/2} \quad (4\text{-}56)$$

The term $-20 \log_{10} [\omega^2 + p_1^2]^{1/2}$ is plotted considering the low-frequency and high-frequency behavior (low- and high-frequency asymptotes). Thus the magnitude of the gain for $\omega \ll p_1$ is

$$20 \log_{10}|H(j\omega)| \cong 20 \log_{10}|H(0)|p_1 - 20 \log_{10}p_1$$
$$= 20 \log_{10}|H(0)| \qquad (4\text{-}57)$$

The asymptote for this frequency range in a straight line, as

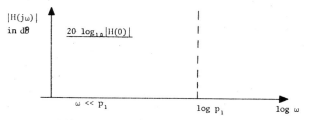

Fig. 4.9 Low-frequency asymptote.

shown in Fig. 4-9. The gain $\omega \gg p_1$ is approximately

$$20 \log_{10}|H(j\omega)| \simeq 20 \log_{10}|H(0)|p_1 - 20 \log \omega \quad (4\text{-}58)$$

Eq. (4-58) is a straight line when plotted on semilog paper and has a value of $20 \log_{10}|H(0)|p_1$ when $\omega = 1$. The slope of this straight line can be obtained by considering two frequencies: ω and 2ω.

db change in $|H(j\omega)| = -20 \log_{10} 2\omega + 20 \log_{10} \omega =$
$$-20 \log_{10} \frac{2\omega}{\omega} = -20 \log_{10} 2 \cong -6 \text{ db}$$
$$(4\text{-}59)$$

Two frequencies which are in the ratio of 2 to 1 are called octaves, and the slope of the straight line is -6 db/octave. Another frequency range is a decade (10ω and ω are a decade apart). The slope of Eq. 4-58 in this case is -20 db/decade. That is,

db change in $|H(j\omega)| = -20 \log_{10} \dfrac{10\omega}{\omega}$
$$= -20 \log_{10} 10 \cong -20 \text{ db} \qquad (4\text{-}60)$$

The asymptotes of Eq. 4-56 are made of two straight lines. The intersection of these straight lines is shown in Fig. 4-10 and is determined from Eqs. (4-57) and (4-58).

$$20 \log_{10}|H(0)| = 20 \log_{10}|H(0)|p_1 - 20 \log \omega. \quad (4\text{-}61)$$

Eq. (4-61) implies that $\omega = p_1$.

The frequency at which the asymptotes intersect is called the break or corner frequency.

A similar argument will reveal that a zero in the transfer function will contribute a $+6$ db/octave or $+20$ db/decade slope to the frequency response.

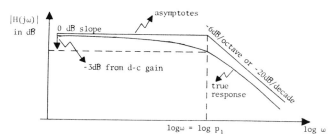

Fig. 4.10 Asymptotic plot of magnitude vs log ω.

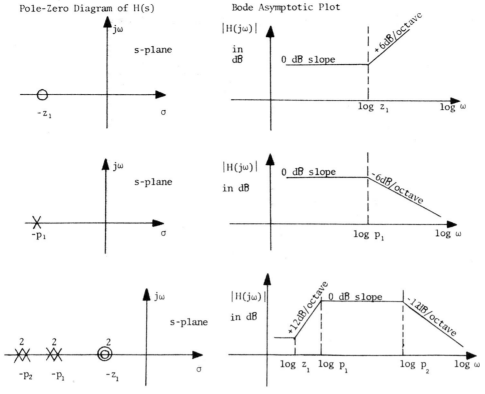

Fig. 4.11 Pole-zero diagrams and Bode plots.

The frequency ω_2 for the transfer function of Eq. (4-54) is calculated in the following way

$$|H(j\omega_2)| = \frac{|H(0)|}{\sqrt{2}} = \frac{|H(0)|p_1}{[\omega_2^2 + p_1^2]^{1/2}} \qquad (4\text{-}62)$$

The band width ($\omega_2 - \omega_1 \cong p_1 - 0$) for this transfer function is simply the pole location.

Some pole-zero diagrams and Bode plots are shown in Fig. 4-11.

Finally, consider the case of a pair of complex poles $-p$ and $-\bar{p}$. The transfer function is

$$H(s) = \frac{H(0)|p_1|^2}{(s + p_1)(s + \bar{p}_1)} = \frac{H(0)|p_1|^2}{s^2 + (p_1 + \bar{p}_1)s + |p_1|^2} \qquad (4\text{-}63)$$

The low-frequency asymptote is again a constant with 0 db slope, while the high-frequency asymptote occurs when $\omega \gg |p_1|$, i.e.,

$$20 \log_{10}|H(j\omega)| = 20 \log_{10}|H(0)| \, |p_1|^2 - 20 \log \omega^2$$

$$(4\text{-}64)$$

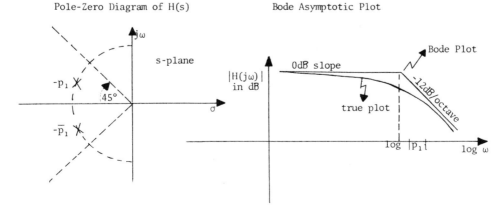

Fig. 4.12 Pole-zero diagram and Bode plot.

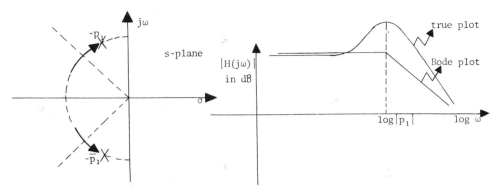

Fig. 4.13 Pole-zero diagram and Bode plot.

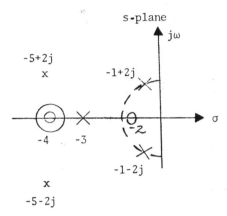

Fig. 4.14 Pole-zero diagram.

The pole-zero diagram and Bode plot for this case are shown in Fig. 4–12.

Suppose we were to move the poles p_1 and $\bar{p}_1$ along the circle in the direction indicated in Fig. 4–13. We know the true frequency response would change as we change the pole locations, but the Bode asymptotic plot would remain the same. This inconsistency is due to the fact that the approximation used does not give good results near the corner frequency $\omega = |p_1|$ (i.e., the approximation required ω to be much larger or much smaller than $|p_1|$).

Fig. 4–14 is an example of a pole-zero diagram and Bode plot, including all of the cases mentioned.

The transfer function $H(s)$ for this example is

and the slope is -12 db/octave or -40 db/decade. The break frequency occurs at

$$20 \log_{10}|H(0)| \, |p_1|^2 - 20 \log_{10}\omega^2 = 20 \log_{10}|H(0)| \quad (4\text{-}65)$$

or $\omega = |p_1|$.

$$\frac{H(0)\,(s+2)\,(s+4)^2 \left[\dfrac{(3)\,(5)\,(29)}{(2)\,(4)^2}\right]}{(s+1+2j)\,(s+1-2j)\,(s+3)\,(s+5+2j)\,(s+5-2j)}$$

$$(4\text{-}66)$$

and the Bode asymptotic plot of the magnitude is shown in Fig. 4–15.

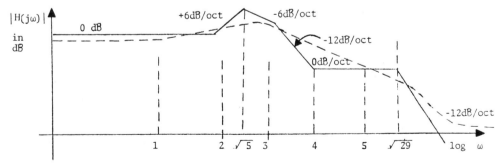

Fig. 4.15 Bode asymptotic plot of the magnitude of Equation 4-66.

Part Two

OBJECTIVE

The purpose of this experiment is to study the frequency response of various RLC circuits. The phasor method, pole-zero diagrams, and Bode plots will be used to predict the frequency behavior of these circuits.

REFERENCES

Chirlian, P. M., *Basic Network Theory*. New York: McGraw-Hill, 1969, Chapters 5 and 6.

Cruz, J. B., and Van Valkenburg, M. E., *Introductory Signals and Circuits*. Waltham, Mass.: Blaisdell, 1967, Chapters 9, 10, and 11.

D'Azzo, J. J., and Houpis, C. H., *Principles of Electrical Engineering*. Columbus, Ohio: Merrill, 1968, Chapters 3, 5, and 14.

Desoer, C. A., and Kuh, E. S., *Basic Circuit Theory*. New York: McGraw-Hill, 1969, Chapters 7, 13, 14, and 15.

Ghausi, M. S., *Electronic Circuits: Devices, Models, Functions, Analysis, and Design*. New York: Van Nostrand Reinhold, 1971, Chapters 1 and 2.

Hayt, W. H., and Kemmerly, J. E., *Engineering Circuit Analysis*. New York: McGraw-Hill, 1971, Chapters 8, 9, 10, 13, and 19.

Romanowitz, H. A., *Electrical Fundamentals and Circuit Analysis*. New York: Wiley, 1966, Chapter 9.

Skilling, H. H., *Electrical Engineering Circuits*. New York: Wiley, 1968, Chapters 3, 4, and 16.

Smith, R. J., *Circuits, Devices, and Systems*. New York: Wiley, 1968, Chapters 3, 4, 5, 6, 7, and 22.

LABORATORY PREPARATION

1. The circuit of Fig. 4-16 consists of three parts. What is $\dfrac{V_{01}(j\omega)}{V_{in}(j\omega)}$ at $f = 4000$ Hz? What is the theoretical maximum phase shift which can be achieved by adjusting R and C in Fig. 4-16a? The circuit of Fig. 4-16b is connected to that of Fig. 4-16a. What is the magnitude and phase of $\dfrac{V_{02}(j\omega)}{V_{in}(j\omega)}$ at $f = 10,000$ Hz? Fig. 4-16c is connected to Fig. 4-16b, which is connected to Fig. 4-16a. What is the magnitude and phase of $\dfrac{V_{03}(j\omega)}{V_{in}(j\omega)}$? Plot the magnitude and

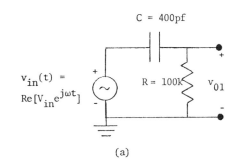

(a)

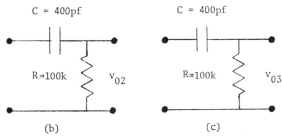

(b)   (c)

Fig. 4.16 Cascading R-C circuits.

phase of $\dfrac{V_{03}(j\omega)}{V_{in}(j\omega)}$ as a function of frequency as f varies from 20 to 200,000 Hz.

2. Observe that the circuit of Fig. 4-17 is similar to the circuit of Fig. 4-16 with a, b, and c connected together. These circuits are similar because both circuits contain three resistors and three capacitors. Calculate the magnitude and phase of $\dfrac{V_0(j\omega)}{V_{in}(j\omega)}$ for the circuit of Fig. 4-17 at $f = 4000$ Hz. Note that $V_0(j\omega) = -V_{03} + V_{in}$ with V_{03} defined in Fig. 4-16. Plot the phase and magnitude of $\dfrac{V_0(j\omega)}{V_{in}(j\omega)}$ as a function of f as f varies from 20 to 10,000 Hz.

3. What are the magnitude and phase of $\dfrac{V_3(j\omega)}{V_{in}(j\omega)}$ at $f =$

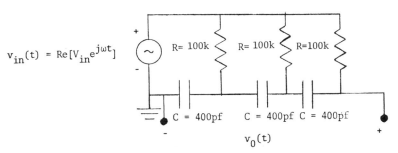

Fig. 4.17 Cascaded R-C circuit.

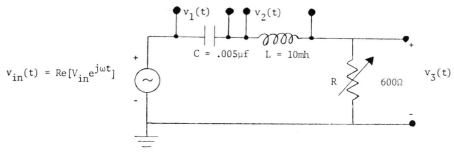

Fig. 4.18 RLC Circuit.

4×10^4 Hz in Fig. 4-18? Plot the magnitude and phase of $\dfrac{V_2(j\omega)}{V_{in}(j\omega)}$, $\dfrac{V_3(j\omega)}{V_{in}(j\omega)}$ and $\dfrac{V_1(j\omega)}{V_{in}(j\omega)}$ as f varies from 20 to 100 kHz. Pick only several important values of f over this range.

Transforms and Bode Plots

4. Calculate $\dfrac{V_0(s)}{V_{in}(s)}$ for the circuits of Fig. 4-19a and 4-19b. Plot the pole-zero diagrams and Bode asymptotic plots of gain. What is $|V_0(j\omega)|$ when $|V_{in}| = 1$ volt and $\omega = 2\pi 100\, r/s$, $2\pi 1000\, r/s$ and $2\pi 10{,}000\, r/s$ for the circuits of Fig. 4-19a and b?

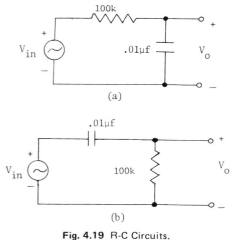

(a)

(b)

Fig. 4.19 R-C Circuits.

5. Calculate $\dfrac{V_0(s)}{V_{in}(s)}$ for the circuits of Fig. 4-20a and b.
Plot the pole-zero diagram and asymptotic plots of gain for these circuits. Compare the pole-zero diagrams and Bode plots for the circuits of Fig. 4-20a and 4-20b. Compare these results with your answers in step 4. Calculate $|V_0(j\omega)|$ for $|V_{in}| = 1$ volt and $f = 20$, 100, 1000, 100,000, and 500,000 Hz for the circuits in Fig. 4-20a and b.

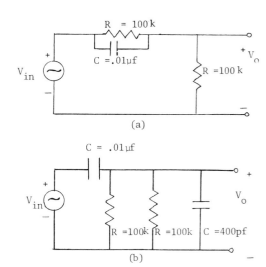

(a)

(b)

Fig. 4.20 Some more R-C circuits.

6. Calculate $\dfrac{V_0(s)}{V_{in}}$ for the circuits of Fig. 4-21a and b and plot the pole-zero diagram and Bode asymptotic plots of gain. Calculate $V_0(j\omega)$ for $V_{in} = 1$ volt, and $f = 100$, 1000, 10,000, 100,000, 300,000, and 500,000 Hz. Compare the pole-zero diagrams and Bode plots for these circuits. Vary R in Fig. 4-21b from 0 to 100 kΩ and explain the effect on the pole-zero diagram and Bode asymptotic plot of gain.

7. Plot the pole-zero diagram and Bode asymptotic plot of gain for the circuit of Fig. 4-22. Compare these results with those of steps 5 and 6.

8. (optional) Place a 400 pf capacitor in series with the 10 mh inductor and 1 kΩ resistor of Fig. 4-21a. Also place a 10 mh inductor in parallel with the 400 pf capacitor of Fig. 4-21a. Plot the pole-zero diagram and Bode asymptotic plot of gain. Compare these results with those of step 6. Place a 400 pf capacitor in series with the 500 Ω resistor and 10 mh inductor and place another 10 mh inductor in parallel with the 400 pf capacitor of Fig. 4-21b. Compare these results with those of step 6. Can you explain the effect of adding a capacitor in series with the inductors and an inductor in parallel with the capacitors of the circuits of Fig. 4-21a and b?

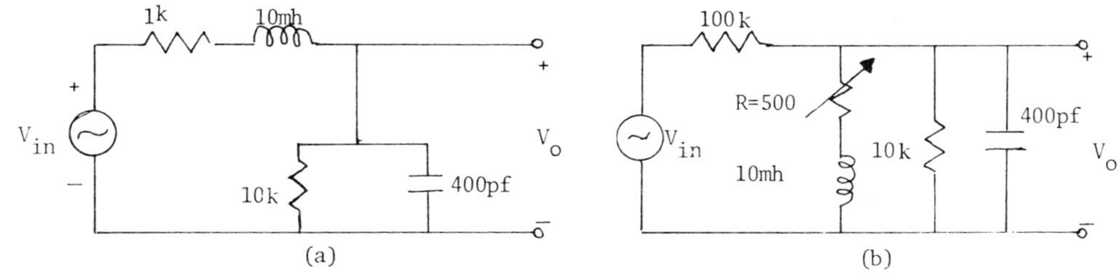

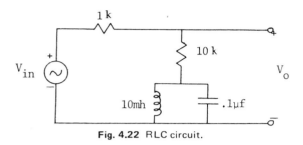

Fig. 4.21 RLC circuits.

Fig. 4.22 RLC circuit.

LABORATORY PROCEDURE

The Phasor Method

1. Construct the circuit of Fig. 4-16a, and set V_{in} = 1 volt. Vary f from 120 to 500,000 Hz, and measure the output voltage $|V_{01}|$ with a sensitive ac voltmeter. At the same time, apply $v_{01}(t)$ to the vertical input of the oscilloscope and $v_{in}(t)$ to the horizontal input, and measure the phase angle between these two voltages as f is varied. Follow the procedure for measuring phase angle described in Experiment 1. Connect the circuit of Fig. 4-16b to that of Fig. 4-16a, and perform the same measurements with respect to v_{02} and v_{in}. Finally, connect the circuit of Fig. 4-16c to that of Fig. 4-16b, which is connected to Fig. 4-16a. Perform the same measurements with respect to v_{03} and v_{in}.

2. Construct the circuit of Fig. 4-17. Set V_{in} = 1 volt, and measure $V_0(j\omega)$, the amplitude of $v_0(t)$, as f is varied from 120 to 10,000 Hz, and also the phase angle between $V_0(j\omega)$ and V_{in}. In particular, measure the amplitude and phase of the voltage $v_0(t)$ close to f = 4000 Hz. The gain should be slightly greater than 1 close to f = 4000 Hz.

3. Construct the circuit of Fig. 4-18. Apply $v_{in}(t)$ to the horizontal input of the oscilloscope and $v_3(t)$ to the vertical input. Since $v_3(t)$ is proportional to the current $i(t)$ (i.e., $v_3 = Ri(t)$), the phase angle between $v_{in}(t)$ and $i(t)$ will be measured as the frequency of the sinusoidal input is varied from 2 k to 200 kHz. ($f = \omega/2\pi$). Remove v_3 and apply v_2 and v_1, respectively, to the vertical input of the CRO. Measure the phase angles between v_1 and v_{in} and v_2 and v_{in}. At the same time, the voltages v_1 and v_2 should be measured with an ac voltmeter as ω is varied. Make certain that throughout these measurements the amplitude of the input

oscillator remains constant as the oscillator frequency is varied. This can be accomplished by monitoring the voltage $v_{in}(t)$ with a second ac voltmeter or by monitoring the maximum horizontal deflection on the CRO. In addition, make certain that neither side of voltages v_1 or v_2 is connected to the ground of the oscilloscope input, by using an oscilloscope with differential type inputs. Consult your instructor if such a CRO is not available.

Transforms and Bode Plots

4. Construct the circuits of Fig. 4-19a and b. Measure the frequency response of the gain as f is varied from 100 to 10,000 Hz. Compare with your calculated values and Bode asymptotic plots.

5. Test the circuits of Fig. 4-20a and b by measuring the frequency response of the gains. Compare these experimental results with your Bode plots. Compare the bandwidth at the circuit of Fig. 4-20b with the predicted results.

6. Test the circuits of Fig. 4-21a and b as f is varied from 100 to 300,000 Hz. Compare with your predicted results. Vary R in Fig. 4-21b and observe the effect on the frequency response.

7. Test the circuit of Fig. 4-22 over the complete frequency range of your input ac oscillator. Explain the results. How do they compare with your predicted results?

8. (optional) Place 400 pf capacitors in series with the 10 mh inductors and 10 mh inductors in parallel with the 400 pf capacitors of the circuits in Fig. 4-21a and b. Measure the frequency response of gain. What is the primary effect of adding these capacitors and inductors to the circuits. Now vary R in the circuit of Fig. 4-21b and measure the frequency response of gain. What is the primary effect of changing R?

LIST OF EQUIPMENT

1. Cathode-ray oscilloscope
2. General-purpose voltmeters or ac voltmeters
3. Signal source: function generator or sine-wave oscillator
4. Circuit board
5. Components: resistors, capacitors, and inductors

Experiment 5/Resonant Circuits

Part One

INTRODUCTION

The response of a circuit containing inductors, capacitors, and resistors to a sinusoidal input will vary depending upon the frequency of the sinusoidal input. The response of RLC type circuits to an input sinusoid at a particular frequency known as resonance can be significantly different from the response to essentially the same sinusoidal input but with a frequency different from the resonant frequency. Three types of RLC circuits responding to sinusoidal inputs will be studied in this experiment. In particular, the responses of a series resonant, parallel resonant, and a hybrid resonant circuit will be investigated.

THEORY

Assume that the voltage applied to a resistor is sinusoidal and given by

$$V_R(t) = V \cos(\omega t + \phi) = \mathrm{Re}[Ve^{j\phi}e^{j\omega t}]$$
$$= \mathrm{Re}[V_R(j\omega)e^{j\omega t}] \qquad (5\text{-}1)$$

with $V_R(j\omega)$ the phasor voltage across the resistor. The current in the resistor by Ohm's law is

$$i_R(t) = \frac{V}{R}\cos(\omega t + \phi) = \mathrm{Re}\left[\frac{V_R(j\omega)}{R}e^{j\omega t}\right]$$
$$= \mathrm{Re}\left[I_R e^{j\omega t}\right] \qquad (5\text{-}2)$$

with the phasor current through the resistor defined by

$$I_R(j\omega) = \frac{V_R(j\omega)}{R} \qquad (5\text{-}3)$$

Assume that a sinusoidal voltage is applied across an inductor

$$v_L(t) = V \cos(\omega t + \phi) = \mathrm{Re}[V_L(j\omega)e^{j\omega t}] \qquad (5\text{-}4)$$

The current in the inductor is given by the solution of the following differential equation

$$L\frac{di_L(t)}{dt} = \mathrm{Re}[V_L(j\omega)e^{j\omega t}] \qquad (5\text{-}5)$$

with a prescribed initial condition. Assume that we are interested only in the steady-state solution. That is, the response $i_L(t)$ to zero initial conditions or the so-called zero-state response (see Experiment 2) has the following form

$$i_L(t) = \mathrm{Re}[I_L(j\omega)e^{j\omega t}] \qquad (5\text{-}6)$$

Substituting Eq. (5-6) into Eq. (5-5) yields

$$\mathrm{Re}[j\omega L\, I_L(j\omega)e^{j\omega t}] = \mathrm{Re}[V_L(j\omega)e^{j\omega t}] \qquad (5\text{-}7)$$

This last equation implies that

$$j\omega L\, I_L(j\omega) = V_L(j\omega) \qquad (5\text{-}8)$$

when we apply proposition (2) of Experiment 4. Define

$$V_L(j\omega) \triangleq Z_L(j\omega)\, I_L(j\omega) \qquad (5\text{-}9)$$

and we obtain that

$$Z_L(j\omega) = j\omega L \qquad (5\text{-}10)$$

Now consider a single capacitor and assume that the applied voltage across the capacitor is a sinusoid given by

$$v_C(t) = V \cos(\omega t + \phi) = \mathrm{Re}[V_C(j\omega)e^{j\omega t}] \qquad (5\text{-}11)$$

then

$$i_C(t) = C\frac{dv_C}{dt} = C\frac{d}{dt}\{\mathrm{Re}[V_C(j\omega)e^{j\omega t}]\} \qquad (5\text{-}12)$$

Apply proposition (1) of Experiment 4 to Eq. (5-12) and assume that the current $i_C(t)$ has the following form

$$i_C(t) = \mathrm{Re}[I_C(j\omega)e^{j\omega t}] \qquad (5\text{-}13)$$

Eq. (5-12) becomes

$$\mathrm{Re}[j\omega C\, V_C(j\omega)e^{j\omega t}] = \mathrm{Re}[I_C(j\omega)e^{j\omega t}] \qquad (5\text{-}14)$$

which implies from proposition (2) that

$$I_C(j\omega) = j\omega C\, V_C(j\omega) \qquad (5\text{-}15)$$

and that

$$Z_C(j\omega) \triangleq \frac{1}{j\omega C} \qquad (5\text{-}16)$$

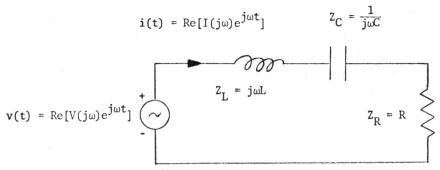

$$i(t) = \mathrm{Re}[I(j\omega)e^{j\omega t}] \qquad Z_C = \frac{1}{j\omega C}$$

$$Z_L = j\omega L$$

$$v(t) = \mathrm{Re}[V(j\omega)e^{j\omega t}] \qquad Z_R = R$$

Fig. 5.1 Series resonant RLC circuit.

Now consider the series RLC circuit shown in Fig. 5-1, which has a total impedance

$$\frac{V(j\omega)}{I(j\omega)} = R + j\omega L + \frac{1}{j\omega C} \qquad (5\text{-}17)$$

This is exactly the same result as obtained in the previous experiment.

The resonant frequency is defined to be that frequency ω_0 for which the imaginary part of the impedance or the admittance is zero. Rewrite the impedance of the circuit of Fig. 5-1 as

$$Z(j\omega) = R + j\left(\omega L - \frac{1}{\omega C}\right) = \mathrm{Re}\, Z(j\omega) + j\,\mathrm{Im}\, Z(j\omega) \qquad (5\text{-}18)$$

and the imaginary part is zero at

$$\omega^2 = \frac{1}{LC}$$

This frequency is denoted $\omega = \omega_0$. Observe that at $\omega = \omega_0$, the impedance has only a real part

$$Z(j\omega_0) = R \quad \text{and} \quad Y(j\omega_0) = \frac{1}{Z(j\omega_0)} = \frac{1}{R}$$

Another important quantity in resonant circuits is the quality factor (Q) of the circuit. A definition of the Q of a circuit is

$$Q = \frac{\omega \cdot (\text{maximum energy stored in the circuit})}{(\text{average power dissipated by the circuit})} \qquad (5\text{-}19)$$

Assume that the current $i(t)$ due to $v(t)$ in the series RLC circuit of Fig. 5-1 is

$$i(t) = I \cos \omega t \qquad (5\text{-}20)$$

The energy stored in the inductor is

$$W_L(t) = \tfrac{1}{2} Li^2(t) = \tfrac{1}{2} LI^2 \cos^2 \omega t \qquad (5\text{-}21)$$

and the energy stored in the capacitor is

$$W_C(t) = \tfrac{1}{2} Cv_C^2(t) \qquad (5\text{-}22)$$

The voltage across the capacitor can be calculated by integrating the current through the capacitor

$$v_C(t) = \frac{1}{C} \int_0^t I \cos \omega t\, dt = +\frac{I}{\omega C} \sin \omega t \qquad (5\text{-}23)$$

Eq. (5-22) reveals that the energy stored in the capacitor is

$$W_C(t) = \frac{1}{2} \frac{I^2}{\omega^2 C} \sin^2 \omega t \qquad (5\text{-}24)$$

The total energy stored in the series RLC circuit is W_T

$$W_T(t) = W_L(t) + W_C(t) = \frac{1}{2} LI^2 \left(\cos^2 \omega t + \frac{1}{\omega^2 LC} \sin^2 \omega t\right) \qquad (5\text{-}25)$$

The maximum energy stored occurs at those times when $\omega t = \pm k\pi$ for $k = 0, 1, 2, \ldots$. These times are obtained by setting the derivative of Eq. (5-25) with respect to t equal to zero and solving for t. The maximum value of $W_T(t)$ is

$$W_T(t) = \tfrac{1}{2} LI^2 \qquad (5\text{-}26)$$

The average power dissipated in this circuit is

$$P_{AV} = \frac{1}{T} \int_0^T Ri^2(t)\, dt = \frac{RI^2}{T} \int_0^T \cos^2 \omega t\, dt \qquad (5\text{-}27)$$

with $T = 2\pi/\omega$.

The integrand $\cos^2 \omega t$ can be replaced if the following trigonometric identity is used

$$\cos^2 \omega t = \tfrac{1}{2} + \tfrac{1}{2} \cos^2 \omega t \qquad (5\text{-}28)$$

Hence, the average power dissipated is

$$P_{AV} = \tfrac{1}{2} RI^2 \qquad (5\text{-}29)$$

The Q of the series resonant circuit denoted Q_s can now be calculated using the definition

$$Q_s = \frac{\omega(\tfrac{1}{2} LI^2)}{\tfrac{1}{2} RI^2} = \frac{\omega L}{R} \qquad (5\text{-}30)$$

Q_s can be written in alternate forms if $\omega = \omega_0$

$$Q_{so} = \frac{1}{\omega_0 RC} = \frac{1}{R}\sqrt{\frac{L}{C}} \qquad (5\text{-}31)$$

The admittance of the series RLC circuit can now be written using the expressions for ω_0 and Q_{so}

$$Y(j\omega) = \frac{1}{Z(j\omega)} = \frac{1}{R + j\left(\omega L - \dfrac{1}{\omega C}\right)}$$

$$= \frac{1}{R\left[1 + jQ_{so}\left(\dfrac{\omega}{\omega_0} - \dfrac{\omega_0}{\omega}\right)\right]} \qquad (5\text{-}32)$$

with

$$Y(j\omega_0) = \frac{1}{R} \quad \text{and} \quad \delta \triangleq \frac{\omega - \omega_0}{\omega}$$

then

$$\frac{Y(j\omega)}{Y(j\omega_0)} = \frac{1}{1 + jQ_{so}\delta\left(\dfrac{2 + \delta}{1 + \delta}\right)} \qquad (5\text{-}33)$$

The magnitude and phase of Eq. (5-33) are

$$\left|\frac{Y(j\omega)}{Y(j\omega_0)}\right| = \frac{1}{\left[1 + Q_{so}^2\left(\dfrac{\omega}{\omega_0} - \dfrac{\omega_0}{\omega}\right)^2\right]^{1/2}}$$

$$= \frac{1}{\left[1 + (Q_{so}\delta)^2\left(\dfrac{2 + \delta}{1 + \delta}\right)^2\right]^{1/2}} \qquad (5\text{-}34)$$

and

$$\angle\frac{Y(j\omega)}{Y(j\omega_0)} = -\tan^{-1}Q_{so}\delta\left(\frac{2 + \delta}{1 + \delta}\right) \qquad (5\text{-}35)$$

The magnitude and phase can be plotted as functions of the frequency ω or equivalently as functions of $Q_{so}\delta$, as shown in Figs. 5-2 and 5-3.

A convenient frequency is the value of ω at which the magnitude of the admittance ($|Y(j\omega)|$) is $1/\sqrt{2} = .707$ of

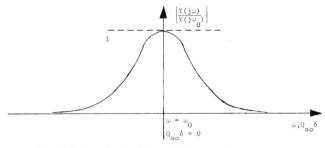

Fig. 5.2 Magnitude of the admittance about $\omega = \omega_0$.

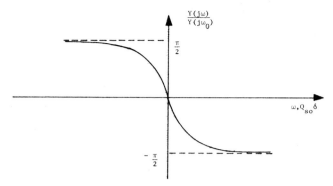

Fig. 5.3 Phase of the admittance about $\omega = \omega_0$.

its value at resonant ($\omega = \omega_0$). That is,

$$\left|\frac{Y(j\omega)}{Y(j\omega_0)}\right| = \frac{1}{\sqrt{2}} \qquad (5\text{-}36)$$

This frequency is called the half-power frequency or 3 dbv frequency. It is equivalent to the frequency where $Q_{so}\delta = \pm 1/2$. In the series resonant circuit, there can be two half-power frequencies ω_1 and ω_2. These two frequencies are obtained by setting Eq. (5-34) equal to $1/\sqrt{2} = .707$, and then

$$\left|1 + jQ_{so}\left(\frac{\omega}{\omega_0} - \frac{\omega_0}{\omega}\right)\right| = \sqrt{2} \qquad (5\text{-}37)$$

or

$$1 + Q_{so}^2\left(\frac{\omega}{\omega_0} - \frac{\omega_0}{\omega}\right)^2 = 2 \qquad (5\text{-}38)$$

Eq. (5-38) yields

$$\frac{\omega}{\omega_0} - \frac{\omega_0}{\omega} = \pm\frac{1}{Q_{so}} \qquad (5\text{-}39)$$

depending upon whether the positive or negative square root is chosen. Eq. (5-39) is reduced to the following equation

$$\omega^2 \pm \frac{\omega_0}{Q_{so}}\omega - \omega_0^2 = 0 \qquad (5\text{-}40)$$

The roots of Eq. (5-40) (ω_2 and ω_1) are called the upper and lower half-power frequencies. Define $\dfrac{\omega_0}{Q_{so}} = 2\alpha$, and we obtain

$$\omega^2 \pm 2\alpha\omega - \omega_0^2 = 0 \qquad (5\text{-}41)$$

We choose only the positive real roots of Eq. (5-40) corresponding to the true physical situation

$$\omega_2 = \alpha + \sqrt{\alpha^2 + \omega_0^2}$$

$$\omega_1 = -\alpha + \sqrt{\alpha^2 + \omega_0^2} \qquad (5\text{-}42)$$

The bandwidth is defined to be the difference between

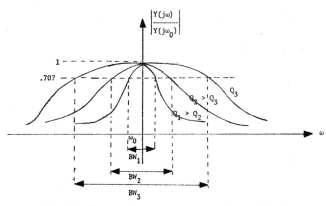

Fig. 5.4 Magnitude responses as a function of Q_{so}?

ω_2 and ω_1

$$BW = \omega_2 - \omega_1 = 2\alpha = \frac{\omega_0}{Q_{so}} \qquad (5\text{-}43)$$

and also note that

$$\omega_1 \omega_2 = \omega_0^2 \qquad (5\text{-}44)$$

The larger the Q_{so}, the narrower the bandwidth, as shown in Fig. 5-4.

Now let us turn our attention to the circuit of Fig. 5-5, known as a parallel resonant circuit. The impedance of this circuit has the same form as the admittance of the series

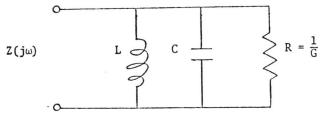

Fig. 5.5 Parallel resonant RLC circuit.

resonant circuit of Fig. 5-1

$$Z(j\omega) = \frac{1}{G + j\omega C + \dfrac{1}{j\omega L}} = \frac{1}{G + j\left(\omega C - \dfrac{1}{\omega L}\right)} \qquad (5\text{-}45)$$

If $\omega_0^2 = \dfrac{1}{LC}$, then

$$Q_{po} = \frac{1}{Q_{so}} = \omega_0 RC = \frac{R}{\omega_0 L} = R\sqrt{\frac{C}{L}} \qquad (5\text{-}46)$$

and $Z(j\omega_0) = R$, then

$$\frac{Z(j\omega)}{Z(j\omega_0)} = \frac{1}{1 + jQ_{po}\left(\dfrac{\omega}{\omega_0} - \dfrac{\omega_0}{\omega}\right)} \qquad (5\text{-}47)$$

Observe that the form of the expression for the admittance $Y(j\omega)$ of the series resonant circuit is equivalent to

the form of the impedance expression of the parallel resonant circuit except that the Q_{so} of the former circuit is the reciprocal of the Q_{po} for the latter circuit. The same comments and figures concerning phase and magnitude of the admittance of the series resonant circuit apply to the impedance of the parallel resonant circuit, and vice versa.

Another important resonant circuit is the hybrid circuit shown in Fig. 5-6. The impedance of this circuit is

$$Z(j\omega) = \frac{(R + j\omega L)\left(\dfrac{1}{j\omega C}\right)}{R + j\omega L + \dfrac{1}{j\omega C}} = \frac{\dfrac{L}{C}\left(1 - j\dfrac{R}{\omega L}\right)}{R + j\left(\omega L - \dfrac{1}{\omega C}\right)} \qquad (5\text{-}48)$$

The impedance $Z(j\omega)$ can be rewritten in terms of its real and imaginary parts

$$Z(j\omega) = \frac{\dfrac{R}{\omega^2 C^2} - j\left(\dfrac{R^2 C + \omega^2 L^2 C - L}{\omega C^2}\right)}{R^2\left[1 + \omega^2\left(\dfrac{L}{R} - \dfrac{1}{\omega^2 CR}\right)^2\right]} \qquad (5\text{-}49)$$

The resonant frequency is calculated by setting the imaginary part of $Z(j\omega)$ to zero. Thereupon

$$R^2 C + \omega^2 L^2 C - L = 0 \qquad (5\text{-}50)$$

implies that the resonant frequency ω_0 for this hybrid circuit is

$$\omega_0^2 = \frac{1}{LC} - \left(\frac{R}{L}\right)^2 \qquad (5\text{-}51)$$

and at this frequency the real part of $Z(j\omega)$ is

$$Z(j\omega_0) = \frac{L}{CR} \qquad (5\text{-}52)$$

The Q of this hybrid circuit is more difficult to calculate than the Q of the series circuit. The total energy stored is given by

$$W_T(t) = \frac{I^2}{2}\left[L + CR^2 + L^2 C\omega^2\right]$$

$$+ I\left\{\frac{1}{4}\left[L + CR^2 - L^2 C\omega^2\right]^2\right.$$

$$\left. + \left[RLC\omega\right]^2\right\}^{1/2} \cdot \cos(2\omega t + \phi) \qquad (5\text{-}53)$$

where

$$\phi = \tan^{-1}\frac{2RLC\omega}{L + CR^2 - L^2 C\omega} \qquad (5\text{-}54)$$

The maximum energy stored can be obtained as before, and since the average power dissipated by this circuit is $\frac{1}{2}RI^2$, the Q of the hybrid circuit can be obtained from Eq. (5-19) in terms of the series resonant circuit Q_{so} at

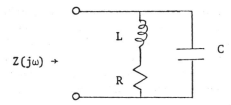

Fig. 5.6 Hybrid resonant RLC circuit.

$$\omega^2 = \omega_0^2 = \frac{1}{LC} - \left(\frac{R}{L}\right)^2 \quad \text{as}$$

$$Q_{ho} = (Q_{so} + 1)\left[1 - \frac{1}{Q_{so}^2}\right]^{1/2} \qquad (5\text{-}55)$$

Note that as Q_{so} increases, Q_{ho} first approaches $Q_{so} + 1$ and then approaches Q_{so}. Also for ω close to ω_0

$$Q_{so}^2 = \left(\frac{\omega L}{R}\right)^2 \cong \left(\frac{\omega_0 L}{R}\right) = \left(\frac{L}{R}\right)^2\left[\frac{1}{LC} - \left(\frac{R}{L}\right)^2\right] = \frac{L}{CR^2} - 1$$

$$(5\text{-}56)$$

and the impedance for the hybrid circuit near resonance becomes

$$Z(j\omega_0) = \frac{L}{CR} = R(1 + Q_{so}^2) \qquad (5\text{-}57)$$

This relationship implies that at $\omega \cong \omega_0$, the two-branch hybrid circuit can be replaced by the three-branch parallel circuit shown in Fig. 5-7. If in addition to ω approximately

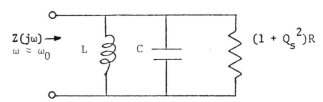

Fig. 5.7 Equivalent parallel resonant circuit.

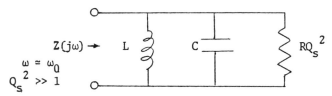

Fig. 5.8 Another equivalent parallel resonant circuit.

ω_0 we assume that $Q_{so}^2 \gg 1$, then the following circuit is equivalent to the hybrid circuit of Fig. 5-8.

Another resonant circuit which has many applications is shown in Fig. 5-9. This circuit is also the equivalent circuit representation of a piezoelectric crystal.

The admittance of the circuit in Fig. 5-9 is

$$Y(j\omega) = j\omega C_p + \cfrac{1}{R + j\left(\omega L - \cfrac{1}{\omega C_s}\right)} \qquad (5\text{-}58)$$

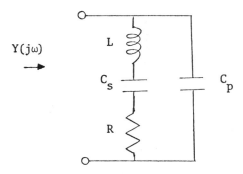

Fig. 5.9 Hybrid resonant circuit with two resonant frequencies.

Assume that the resistance R is small compared to $\omega L - \dfrac{1}{\omega C_s}$. The admittance under this condition is given approximately by

$$Y(j\omega) \cong \frac{j^2 \omega C_p \left(\omega L - \dfrac{1}{\omega C_s}\right) + 1}{j\left(\omega L - \dfrac{1}{\omega C_s}\right)}$$

$$= \frac{j^2 \omega C_p \left(\omega^2 L C_s - 1 - \dfrac{C_s}{C_p}\right)}{j\left(\omega L - \dfrac{1}{\omega C_s}\right)\omega C_s} \qquad (5\text{-}59)$$

$\omega_s = \dfrac{1}{\sqrt{LC_s}}$ is the series resonant frequency and $\omega_p = \sqrt{\dfrac{1}{L}\left(\dfrac{1}{C_s} + \dfrac{1}{C_p}\right)}$ is the parallel resonant frequency.

The magnitude of the admittance when R is neglected is plotted as a function of frequency in Fig. 5-10.

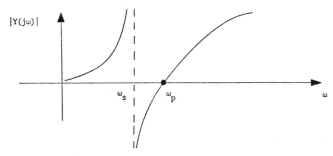

Fig. 5.10 Magnitude of admittance vs frequency.

The resonant circuits considered in this experiment are primarily synthesized with passive RLC type elements. Resonant circuits can also be synthesized by the use of active RC elements. In fact, for frequencies below 1 kHz, active RC circuits are very often used because of their size, performance, and relatively low cost. Experiments 14 and 15 deal with the synthesis of resonant circuits by means of active filters.

Part Two

OBJECTIVE

The purpose of this experiment is to study the response of RLC type circuits when excited by sinusoidal inputs and when the frequency of the sinusoidal inputs varies. In particular, some series, parallel, and hybrid circuits will be studied.

REFERENCES

Chirlian, P. M., *Basic Network Theory*. New York: McGraw-Hill, 1969, Chapters 5 and 6.

Cruz, J. B., and Van Valkenburg, M. E., *Introductory Signals and Circuits*. Waltham, Mass.: Blaisdell, 1967, Chapter 11.

D'Azzo, J. J., and Houpis, C. H., *Principles of Electrical Engineering*. Columbus, Ohio: Merrill, 1968, Chapter 3.

Desoer, C. A., and Kuh, E. S., *Basic Circuit Theory*. New York: McGraw-Hill, 1969, Chapter 7.

Ghausi, M. S., *Electronic Circuits: Devices, Models, Functions, Analysis, and Design*. New York: Van Nostrand Reinhold, 1971, Chapters 2 and 7.

Hayt, W. H., and Kemmerly, J. E., *Engineering Circuit Analysis*. New York: McGraw-Hill, 1971, Chapters 4 and 17.

Romanowitz, H. A., *Electrical Fundamentals and Circuit Analysis*. New York: Wiley, 1966, Chapters 11 and 12.

Skilling, H. H., *Electrical Engineering Circuits*. New York: Wiley, 1968, Chapters 2 and 16.

Smith, R. J., *Circuits, Devices, and Systems*. New York: Wiley, 1968, Chapter 7.

LABORATORY PREPARATION

1. The circuit to the right of terminals BG of Fig. 5–11 represents a series resonant RLC circuit. The admittance between terminals B and G is given by Eq. 5–32. Calculate

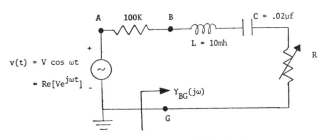

Fig. 5.11 Series resonant RLC circuit.

the resonant frequency ω_0 and the Q_{so} of this circuit when R varies between 1 and 1500 ohms. Sketch the magnitude and phase of the impedance $Z_{BG}(j\omega)$ as a function of frequency when $R = 120$ ohms. Calculate the bandwidth for this circuit.

2. The circuit between terminals B and G of Fig. 5–12 represents a parallel resonant circuit. Calculate the resonant frequency and Q_p for this circuit as R varies from 1 k to

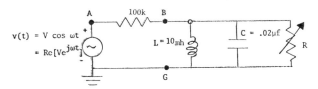

Fig. 5.12 Parallel resonant RLC circuit.

200 k ohms. Sketch the magnitude and phase of the admittance $Y_{BG}(j\omega)$ as a function of frequency ω when $R = 4$ k ohms. Calculate the bandwidth.

3. The circuit of Fig. 5–13 between terminals B and G represents a hybrid circuit. Find the resonant frequency

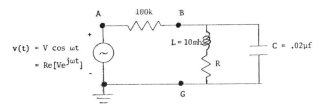

Fig. 5.13 Hybrid resonant RLC circuit.

and the Q_{so} for $R = 500$ ohms. Sketch the magnitude and phase of the admittance $Y_{BG}(j\omega)$ as a function of frequency ω when $R = 500$ ohms and when $R = 120$ ohms. Calculate the bandwidth for $R = 500$ ohms and for $R = 120$ ohms.

4. The circuit for Fig. 5–14 between terminals B and G represents a hybrid resonant circuit with two resonant fre-

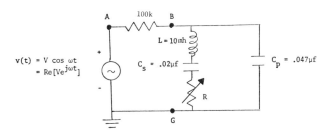

Fig. 5.14 Hybrid resonant circuit with two resonant frequencies.

quencies. Calculate the resonant frequencies when $R = 120$ ohms. Sketch the magnitude and phase of $Y_{BG}(j\omega)$ as a function of frequency ω when $R = 120$ and 500 ohms.

LABORATORY PROCEDURE

1. A 100 k resistor is placed in series with all the resonant circuits under test. This is done to maintain a constant output amplitude from the audio oscillator as the frequency of the audio oscillator is varied. The impedance of the

resonant circuits will vary with frequency, causing the amplitude of the oscillator output to change if the 100 k resistor was not placed in series with the resonating circuits. Construct the circuit of Fig. 5-11. The admittance between B and G will be measured as the frequency ω of the audio oscillator is varied. The ac voltage from B to G will be monitored with an ac voltmeter having millivolt ranges. The magnitude of voltage v_{AG} will be maintained at a constant value of 1 volt as the frequency ω is varied. This voltage can be monitored with an oscilloscope or another ac voltmeter. Assume that v_{AG} in Fig. 5-11 remains constant as ω is varied. The current through the 100 k resistor is a maximum at resonance due to the impedance Z_{BG} being a minimum at resonance. The voltage v_{AB} will be a maximum at resonance since it is proportional to the current from A to B, which is a maximum. Since v_{AG} is constant and v_{AB} is a maximum, the voltage v_{BG} must be a minimum at resonance. Measure the magnitude and phase of $Y_{BG}(j\omega)$ as ω is varied at $R = 120$ ohms. Compare the resonant frequency and Q_{so} of this circuit with the calculated values when R varies between 1 and 1500 ohms. Discuss any discrepancies between calculated and measured values. The measurements of $Y_{BG}(j\omega)$ are to be made in the following way. Measure the rms value of v_{BG} with a sensitive ac voltmeter. The current in the series circuit is obtained from the equation $i = \dfrac{v_{AG} - v_{BG}}{100 \text{ k}}$

The ratio of i to v_{BG} is the admittance Y_{BG}. The phase of $Y_{BG}(j\omega)$ is measured on the CRO by connecting voltage v_{BG} to the vertical input and the voltage across the resistor R to the horizontal input. Q_s is obtained from

Eq. 5-30. It can be conveniently measured by measuring the resonant frequency and the 3 dbv bandwidth with a voltmeter having a db scale.

2. Construct the circuit of Fig. 5-12. Measure the resonant frequency and Q_{po} as R varies from 1 k to 200 k ohms. Measure the magnitude of the impedance $Z_{BG}(j\omega)$ as a function of frequency ω when $R = 4$ k ohms. What is the bandwidth? This can be done, as in step 1 by keeping v_{AG} constant and making only one voltage measurement (i.e., v_{BG}). Also measure the phase of Y as ω is varied with $R = 4$ k ohms.

3. Construct the circuit of Fig. 5-13. Measure the resonant frequency and Q_h when R is zero. Vary R from 0 to 600 ohms and measure the Q_{ho} and the bandwidth.

4. Construct the circuit of Fig. 5-14. Measure the series and parallel resonant frequencies as R is varied from 0 to 100 ohms in steps of 20 ohms and from 100 to 500 ohms in steps of 100 ohms. What can be said about the resistance associated with the inductor from measurements made in steps 3 and 4. Discuss the bandwidth of the circuit of Fig. 5-14 from the measurements made in this step.

LIST OF EQUIPMENT

1. Cathode-ray oscilloscope
2. General-purpose voltmeters or ac voltmeters
3. Signal sources: function generator or sine-wave oscillator
4. Circuit board
5. Discrete circuit elements: resistors, capacitors, and inductors

Experiment 6/Diode Characteristics and Some Applications

Part One

INTRODUCTION

Many different types of diodes are suited to a large variety of applications. The application of specific diodes to signal wave shaping depends upon the unique electrical properties of these devices. Semiconductor diodes derive their properties from the *pn* junction. The essential electrical characteristic of the *pn* junction is that it operates as a rectifier in permitting the easy flow of current in one direction but restrains the flow in the opposite direction. The flow of current across the junction can be altered by controlling the nature, concentration, and distribution of activating impurities in both the *p*- and *n*-type materials. In addition, an applied positive or negative voltage (biasing) will be a major factor in controlling the current flow across a junction.

This experiment will study the *pn* junction as a two-terminal nonlinear device. As a nonlinear device, a single set of parameters cannot adequately describe the electrical performance of the device; instead, a graphical display will be employed to represent the volt-ampere (V-I) characteristics of the diode. Once its characteristics have been determined, the diode will be used in a specific signal wave-shaping circuit which is dependent upon the diode's V-I characteristics.

In particular, this experiment will study some commonly used diodes: the germanium, silicon, zener, varactor, tunnel, and photo diodes.

THEORY

The *pn* Junction

Two opposite types of germanium or silicon in contact form a *pn* or *np* junction where the two faces meet, as shown in Fig. 6-1.

The *n*-type material is produced, for example, by doping germanium with antimony. This produces negative charges (electrons), which are free to drift from atom to atom. The *p*-type material is formed, for example, by doping germanium with gallium, producing covalence bonds between atoms which have missing electrons. These missing electrons are called "holes." A hole is a free positive charge which can drift from atom to atom.

Some free electrons in the *n*-type material can diffuse through the junction to the *p*-type material, while at the same time some hole charges move in the opposite direction. Very little charge is redistributed, however, before a potential barrier (contact potential) forms at the junction to prevent any more current from flowing. The amount of

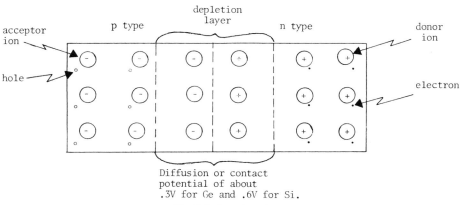

Fig. 6.1 A *pn* junction.

this barrier potential is approximately .2 volt for germanium or .6 volt for silicon at room temperature.

It is important to realize that the contact potential makes the junction useful since its effects can be controlled by an externally applied voltage. An external dc voltage of opposite polarity from the contact potential (barrier voltage) neutralizes the contact potential and allows more current through the junction. This situation is called forward biasing, and causes an easy flow of current (forward current). An external dc voltage of the same polarity as the contact potential increases the barrier voltage. This situation is called reverse biasing, and restrains the flow of current (reverse current).

In summary, then, two types of current flow across a *pn* junction: a diffusion current, resulting from a difference in concentration of charge carriers in adjacent areas of a diode; and a drift current, resulting from the motion of charged carriers forced to move by the electric field of a potential difference. It should be noted that the primary current inside the *p*- and *n*-type materials is a drift current.

The majority of the charged carriers in *p*-type materials are holes, and in *n*-type materials are electrons. In a forward bias condition, the externally applied voltage neutralizes the barrier voltage, causing majority charge carriers to flow through the junction. In a reverse bias condition, there still is some current flowing through the junction, because of the diffusion of minority carriers across the junction. Because of thermal energy, some minority carriers on each side of the junction are in random motion, and are able to diffuse through the junction. Since the minority carriers have polarities opposite to the majority carriers, the

current is in the reverse direction compared with the forward drift of majority carriers with forward bias. This diffusion current is called reverse leakage current. The equation approximately describing the current-voltage relationship in a diode is

$$i_D = I_0 \left(e^{qv_D/\eta kT} - 1\right) \qquad (6\text{-}1)$$

I_o is the reverse saturation current, v_D is the applied voltage, kT/q = .026 volts at room temperature, and η is unity for germanium and approximately 2 for silicon.

The V-I characteristics (Eq. [6-1]) for germanium and silicon *pn* junction diodes are shown in Fig. 6-2.

An important voltage, known as the threshold voltage V_γ, is shown in Fig. 6-2. This is the voltage below which the diode current is very small and above which the current rises very rapidly. Silicon diodes can be divided into three broad categories: low-current or switching diodes, dissipating up to approximately 1 watt; medium-power or medium-current cells, handling up to 20 amps with dissipations of several watts; and, finally, silicon rectifiers or high-current cells, handling hundreds of amps and dissipating some tens of watts.

Fig. 6-2 indicates that a diode could be biased in the forward direction, reverse direction, or switched from the forward-bias to the reverse-bias regions. The following electronic circuits have been carefully chosen to exhibit forward-bias, reverse-bias, and switching operations of diodes. However, new diode types and new diode applications are currently being discovered, and the reader is encouraged to study those diodes and circuits which are useful to him and perhaps not covered in this short experiment.

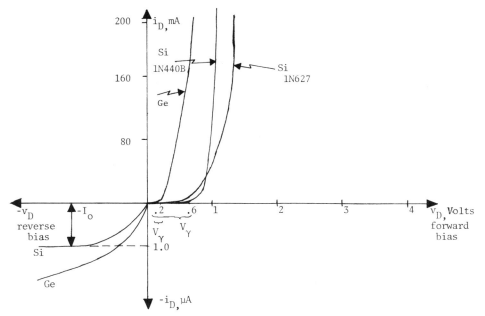

Fig. 6.2 Diode characteristics.

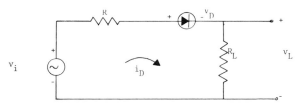

Fig. 6.3 Half-wave rectifier.

Germanium and Silicon Diode Applications

Consider the circuit of Fig. 6–3, containing a silicon diode.

We know that the silicon diode is a nonlinear device ($i_D = f(v_D)$) whose V-I characteristics are shown in Fig. 6–2. Now applying KVL around the loop of Fig. 6–3 yields

$$v_D = v_i - (R + R_L)i_D = v_i - R_T i_D \quad \text{(load line equation)}$$

$$(6-2)$$

The intersection of the V-I characteristics with the load line equation gives the operating point for this circuit. The operating point (quiescent or Q point) are the values of v_D and i_D for a particular diode and a set of values v_i and R_T.

If v_i is a dc voltage of 2 volts, then the load line and Q point are shown in Fig. 6–4a.

If $v_i = V_1 \sin \omega t$, then the diode current i_D is shown in Fig. 6–4b, and the circuit of Fig. 6–3 is called a half-wave rectifier. The dc value of the half-rectified sine-wave cur-

rent is I_m/Π. If $v_i = V_D + V_2 \sin \omega t$, then i_D is shown in Fig. 6–4c. The total peak-to-peak variation of the ac signal v_i in this case is usually a small fraction of the dc voltage V_D. The effective resistance that this small ac signal sees is assumed to be constant, and is called the dynamic resistance of the diode. It is evaluated by determining the inverse slope of the diode characteristic at the Q point. Hence

$$r_d = \frac{\Delta v_D}{\Delta i_D} \bigg|_{Q \text{ point}} \quad (6-3)$$

and a simple ac equivalent circuit valid about a dc quiescent point in the forward-bias region is shown in Fig. 6–5.

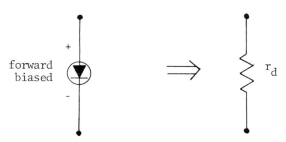

Fig. 6.5 Simple equivalent circuit for a diode.

An interesting situation arises if we add a capacitor C_L to the output of a half-wave rectifier, as shown in Fig. 6–6. When the time constant $T_L = R_L C_L$ is large in comparison to the period $T = 2\pi/\omega$ of the input signal ($T_L > T$), the

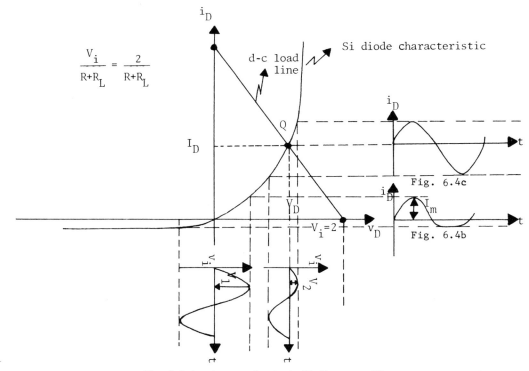

Figs. 6-4a,b,c Input and output of half-wave rectifier.

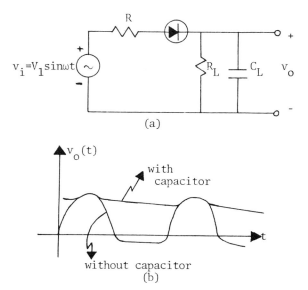

Fig. 6.6 Half-wave rectifier with output capacitor.

Breakdown Diodes

Zener, avalanche, and breakdown diodes are semiconductor *pn* junction devices with controlled reverse-biased properties. The forward characteristics are similar to those of the standard germanium or silicon diode discussed previously. The reverse characteristics, however, exhibit a region in which the diode's terminal voltage is almost independent of the diode's current. Zener breakdown usually occurs at small reverse voltages, and avalanche breakdown at large reverse voltages. Neither breakdown phenomenon is damaging to the junction provided that the power dissipation and operating temperature of the diode are kept low.

Two distinct mechanisms explain breakdown. Zener breakdown occurs across a relatively narrow junction where the electric field of the junction becomes large even for a small reverse-bias voltage and conduction by tunneling occurs (see "Tunnel Diode," below). Avalanche breakdown occurs when a large critical reverse bias causes a large critical electric field to impart sufficient energy to electrons to collide with and break valence bonds of electrons. Each collision creates a new electron hole pair, and the cumulative result is an avalanche discharge. The reverse voltage necessary for avalanche breakdown (usually larger than Zener breakdown voltages) depends upon the resistivity and temperature of the materials. The symbol and typical V-I characteristics for a Zener diode are shown in Fig. 6–8*a* and *b*.

capacitor C_L cannot discharge through R_L completely in one period of the input signal. Consequently, the dc value of the output voltage has increased above $I_m R_L / \pi$ (no capacitor). This circuit produces an output signal whose dc value depends upon the amplitude of the ac input signal.

Another circuit using four diodes is shown in Fig. 6–7*a*, and is called a full-wave rectifier. The dc value of v_L is $2 I_m R_L / \pi = 2 V_m / \pi$.

The connection shown in Fig. 6–7*a* can be made from a single integrated circuit diode array. Diode arrays are available with four or more diodes on a single silicon chip.

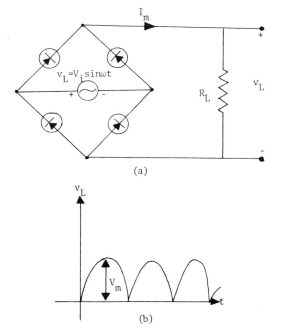

(a)

(b)

Fig. 6.7 Full-wave rectifier.

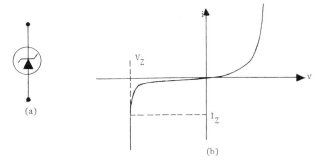

Fig. 6.8 Zener diode with V-I characteristic.

In most applications, the Zener diode operates in the reverse-biased region. A simple application is the voltage-regulator circuit shown in Fig. 6-9.

The current i_L can vary over a wide range because of variations of R_L, but the load voltage v_L will remain al-

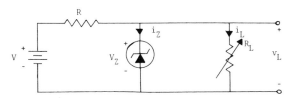

Fig. 6.9 Zener diode voltage regulator circuit.

most constant. Suppose that $V = 16$ volts, $R = 50\,\Omega$, and the load current i_L can vary from 10 to 100 mA. The load line equation is

$$v_Z = 16 - 50\,(i_Z + i_L) \qquad (6\text{-}4)$$

or

$$v_Z + 50i_Z = 16 - 50i_L \qquad (6\text{-}5)$$

Note that when $i_L = 10$ mA, the load line is

$$v_Z + 50i_Z = 15.5 \qquad (6\text{-}6)$$

and when $i_L = 100$ mA, the load line is

$$v_Z + 50i_Z = 11 \qquad (6\text{-}7)$$

These two load line curves are drawn in Fig. 6-10.

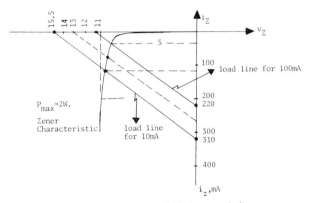

Fig. 6.10 Load lines on V-I characteristics.

The voltage v_Z varies from 9.3 to 9.8. The Zener diode has provided voltage regulation with respect to changes in load current. This occurs since the impedance seen by the load (r_d, the resistance of the diode) is small compared with the load resistance $R_L > 9.8/100$ mA $= 98\,\Omega$.

Another form of voltage regulation is obtained with a Zener diode. The circuit of Fig. 6-11 maintains almost

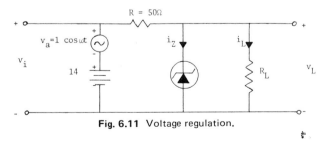

Fig. 6.11 Voltage regulation.

constant voltage v_L even though the input voltage v_i represents a slowly varying dc source. ($v_i = 14 + 1 \cos \omega t$)

Assuming that R_L draws 100 mA of current, the load line equation is

$$v_Z + 50i_Z = 14 + 1 \cos \omega t - 50i_L \qquad (6\text{-}8)$$

which is shown as a dotted line in Fig. 6-10. The output ac voltage across the load varies between 9.5 and 9.75. This represents a .25 peak-to-peak voltage, which is small compared to the 2 volt peak-to-peak ac signal associated with v_i.

Varactor Diode

A varactor diode is a voltage variable capacitor whose behavior is dependent upon a *pn* junction. As discussed previously, there is a cross-migration of charges between the *p*-type and *n*-type materials. Electrons from the *n*-region cross the junction to neutralize positive carriers near the junction in the *p*-region, and holes from the *p*-region cross the junction to neutralize the excess electrons near the junction of the *n*-region. The result of the migration is that all free charged particles are swept out of the immediate vicinity of the junction area, and a contact potential or space charge of about .6 volt for silicon appears across the junction. This area about the junction is called the depletion layer. The total *pn* structure acts very much like a slightly charged capacitor, with the depletion layer representing the dielectric, and the semiconductor material adjacent to the depletion layer representing the two conductive plates.

The depletion layer increases, resulting in a capacitance decrease, if an external voltage reinforces the contact potential of a reverse biased *pn* junction. The depletion layer decreases, resulting in a capacitor increase, if an external forward voltage is applied to a reverse-biased junction. However, if the external voltage is made large enough to overcome the contact potential, forward conduction occurs and the capacitance effect is destroyed. Therefore, the capacitance of a reverse-biased varactor diode is a function of the total applied voltage. This relationship is

$$C(v) = \frac{C_o}{\left(1 + \dfrac{v(t)}{\phi}\right)^{\gamma}} \qquad (6\text{-}9)$$

where $v(t)$ is the magnitude of the total applied voltage ($v(t) = |V + v_a(t)|$ and $V + v_a(t) < 0$). V is the reverse-bias voltage and $v_a(t)$ is the time-varying applied voltage. C_o is

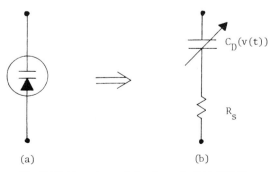

Fig. 6.12 Varactor and simple equivalent circuit.

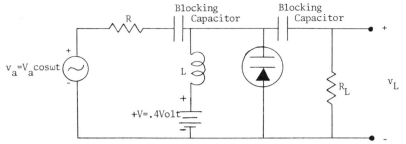

Fig. 6.13 Variable tuned parallel resonant circuit.

the capacitance for zero total applied voltage. γ is the law of the diode (.5 for abrupt junction silicon varicap diodes), and ϕ is the contact potential of approximately .6 for silicon varactors.

The varactor symbol and a simple equivalent circuit are given in Figure 6–12a and b. R_s is the bulk resistance of the diode, which is about 8 to 10 Ω.

The varactor is used in tuning circuits and parametric amplifiers. A simple example of a variable tuned parallel resonant circuit is shown in Fig. 6–13.

The voltage across the diode is maintained at -4 volts dc as long as the magnitude of the ac signal across the diode is less than 4 volts because of KVL. This is certainly the case if $V_a < |V| = 4$. The ac voltage across the load at resonance is

$$v_L = \frac{R_L}{R + R_L}\, V_a \cos \omega_o t \qquad (6\text{--}10)$$

and the resonance frequency is

$$f_o = \frac{1}{2\pi \sqrt{LC_D}} \qquad (6\text{--}11)$$

Note, however, that the resonant frequency will change if the bias voltage V is changed, because C_D depends upon the reverse-bias voltage. This type of variable tuning circuit can be used to produce a variable resonant frequency (frequency modulation).

Tunnel Diode

The tunnel diode is a two-terminal *pn* junction device which has a negative resistance characteristic. There is intentionally high doping in both the *n*-type and *p*-type materials, while the junction has a very narrow width. This causes a current to tunnel through the junction for small applied forward voltages. Heavy doping and small applied voltage cause electrons on one side of the junction to be at higher energy levels than allowed energy states in the valence band on the other side of the junction. The tunneling current reaches a maximum when all the electrons in a conduction band see empty states just across the junction. Diffusion type currents described earlier predominate as the

applied forward voltage is increased. The V-I characteristics of a typical tunnel diode are shown in Fig. 6–14.

The V-I characteristics of a tunnel diode exhibit a negative resistance in a region of forward voltage, from a few hundredths of a volt to a few tenths of a volt. In addition,

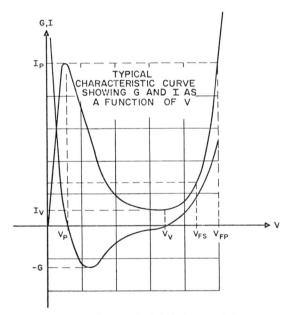

Fig. 6.14 Tunnel diode V-I characteristic.

the tunneling effect is carried by very mobile minority carriers (electrons), which makes tunnel diodes useful in high-frequency circuits. Low- and high-frequency equivalent electrical circuits of the tunnel diode in the negative conductance region are shown in Fig. 6–15b and c. The resistor $-R$ has a typical value of $-50\,\Omega$; C is the transition capacitance, which varies as $v_{TD}^{-1/2}$, and has a typical value of 5 pf; L_s is lead inductance (typically 1nh); and R_s is the bulk resistance (.5 Ω).

The negative resistance of the tunnel diode enables the device to be used as either an astable, monostable, or bistable switch, as well as a relaxation oscillator or microwave amplifier.

The relaxation oscillator is an interesting application of

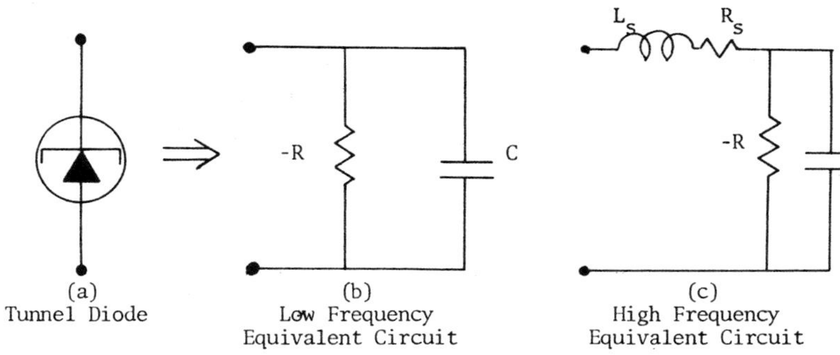

Fig. 6.15 Tunnel diode and equivalent circuits.

the tunnel diode. The operation of a relaxation oscillator can be understood by considering the input impedance of the high-frequency equivalent circuit shown in Fig. 6-15c. The input impedance $Z(s)$ of the tunnel diode when it is biased in the negative conductance region is

$$Z(s) = R_s + sL_s + \frac{\frac{1}{sC}(-R)}{\frac{1}{sC}+(-R)} \qquad (6\text{-}12)$$

The impedance $Z(s)$ represents the ratio of input voltage to input current. The input voltage is zero when the input is short-circuited, and a current will flow provided $Z(s) = 0$. That is, if

$$Z(s)I(s) = V(s) = 0 \qquad (6\text{-}13)$$

and if $Z(s) = 0$, then $I(s)$ can be nonzero. Therefore, we are looking for the zeros of the driving point impedance which characterizes the small signal behavior of the tunnel diode. The zeros of $Z(s)$ are called the natural frequencies. We know that if the zeros are purely imaginary, the time response is sinusoidal. If the zeros are in the left half of the s-plane, the response to an impulse is a damped exponential, and the response is a growing exponential if the zeros are in the right half of the s-plane.

The zeros of $Z(s)$ are the roots of the following equation

$$s^2 - \left(\frac{1}{RC} - \frac{R_s}{L_s}\right)s + \frac{1}{L_sC}\left(1 - \frac{R_s}{R}\right) = 0 = (s - s_1)(s - s_2) \qquad (6\text{-}14)$$

The roots are

$$s_1, s_2 = \frac{1}{2}\left(\frac{1}{RC} - \frac{R_s}{L_s}\right) \pm \frac{j}{2}\sqrt{\frac{4}{L_sC}\left(1 - \frac{R_s}{R}\right) - \left(\frac{1}{RC} - \frac{R_s}{L_s}\right)^2} \qquad (6\text{-}15)$$

1. A steady oscillation occurs when the roots s_1 and s_2 are purely imaginary—that is, when

$$\frac{1}{RC} - \frac{R_s}{L_s} = 0$$

and

$$1 - \frac{R_s}{R} > 0$$

The expression $1 - (R_s/R) \leqslant 0$ $(R_s \geqslant |R|)$ is the condition for switching because the effect of the diode's negative resistance is canceled by the positive resistance R_s.

The frequency of oscillation with purely imaginary roots is

$$f_{TD} = \frac{1}{2\pi}\sqrt{\frac{1}{L_sC}\left(1 - \frac{R_s}{R}\right)} \qquad (6\text{-}16)$$

2. If $R_s < |R|$, a condition for growing oscillations (roots in right half s-plane), occurs with

$$\frac{1}{RC} - \frac{R_s}{L_s} > 0 \qquad \text{or} \qquad \frac{1}{RC} > \frac{R_s}{L_s}$$

For the special case where $R_s \ll |R|$ and $1/RC \gg R_s/L_s$, it is possible that Eq. (6-15) has no imaginary part. That is,

$$\sqrt{\frac{4}{L_sC}\left(1 - \frac{R_s}{R}\right) - \left(\frac{1}{RC} - \frac{R_s}{L_s}\right)^2} \cong \sqrt{\frac{4}{L_sC} - \left(\frac{1}{RC}\right)^2} < 0 \qquad (6\text{-}17)$$

This type of behavior is called relaxation oscillation. The domain of relaxation oscillation occurs for

$$R_s \ll |R|, \frac{R_s}{L_s} \ll \frac{1}{RC}$$

and

$$\frac{4}{L_sC} - \left(\frac{1}{RC}\right)^2 < 0$$

The roots s_1, s_2 have positive real values for this case.

Note that the response is a growing exponential which is limited by the nonlinear characteristics of the diode once it exceeds small signal behavior.

3. If $R_s \leqslant R$, a condition for damped oscillation (roots in left-half s-plane), occurs when

$$\frac{1}{RC} - \frac{R_s}{L_s} < 0 \qquad \text{or} \qquad \frac{1}{RC} < \frac{R_s}{L_s}$$

For the special case when $R_s \ll R$ and $1/RC \ll R_s/L_s$, it is possible that Eq. (6-15) has no imaginary part. That is,

$$\sqrt{\frac{4}{L_sC}\left(1 - \frac{R_s}{R}\right) - \left(\frac{1}{RC} - \frac{R_s}{L_s}\right)^2} \cong \sqrt{\frac{4}{L_sC} - \left(\frac{R_s}{L_s}\right)^2} < 0$$

(6-18)

This represents a decaying exponential response with no oscillation at all. The domain of this decaying response occurs for

$$R_s \ll |R|, \frac{1}{RC} \ll \frac{R_s}{L_s}$$

and

$$\frac{4}{LC} - \left(\frac{R_s}{L_s}\right)^2 < 0$$

The roots s_1, s_2 have negative real values for this case. A completely stable trace of the V-I characteristics of a tunnel diode can be achieved if these last conditions are met.

Photodiode

If a reverse voltage in excess of a few tenths of a volt is applied to a semiconductor junction diode, an almost constant current independent of the magnitude of the reverse bias is obtained. If in addition, a light spot is allowed to shine upon one surface across the junction, the current will now vary depending upon the light intensity and the distance from the junction at which the light spot is focused.

The number of hole electron pairs created by the illumination of a reverse-biased *pn* junction is proportional to the number of incident electrons. The V-I equation for a photodiode is

$$i_{PD} = I_s + I_o(1 - e^{v_{PD}q/\eta kT})$$

(6-19)

where I_s is the short-circuit current, which is proportional to the light intensity, v_{PD} is the applied voltage, and η is a parameter which is unity for germanium and two for silicon. A typical photodiode reverse bias V-I characteristic is shown in Fig. 6-16.

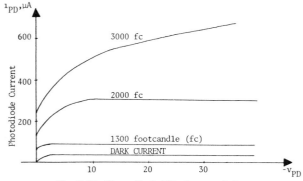

Fig. 6.16 Photodiode V-I characteristics.

A reverse-bias small-signal equivalent circuit for a photodiode is shown in Fig. 6-17. R is the reverse resistance, r is the bulk ohmic resistance, C is the barrier capacitance, L is the light flux in lumens, and K is a proportionality constant in the range of 10 to 50 mA/lumen.

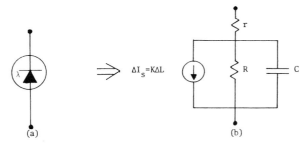

Fig. 6.17 Photodiode and simple equivalent circuit.

Important use of the photodiode is made in "electric eye" circuits, where the photodiode is used in conjunction with a relay. A few examples are: counters or sorters of objects, automatic door openers and fire-burglar alarm systems. We will study the photodiode in a circuit to detect the presence or absence of a light source. The photodiode circuit converts a dc signal into an ac signal. This conversion is sometimes called "chopping."

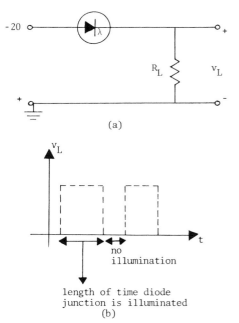

Fig. 6.18 Photodiode chopping circuit.

The circuit of Fig. 6-18a is a photodiode chopper. The output voltage v_L (Fig. 6-18b) is time-varying, and the shape of this waveform will depend upon how long the diode is illuminated, the intensity of the illumination, and the distance that the light spot falls from the junction.

Part Two

OBJECTIVE

The purpose of this experiment is to study the V-I characteristics of several diodes and to use these diodes in several signal wave shaping circuits.

REFERENCES

Alley, C. L., and Atwood, K. W., *Electronic Engineering.* New York: Wiley, 1966, Chapters 2 and 3.

Angelo, E. J., *Electronics: BJTs, FETs, and Microcircuits.* New York: McGraw-Hill, 1969, Chapter 3.

Chirlian, P. M., *Electronic Circuits: Physical Principles, Analysis, and Design.* New York: McGraw-Hill, 1971, Chapters 1 and 3.

Fitchen, F. C., *Transistor Circuit Analysis and Design.* New York: Van Nostrand Reinhold, 1966, Chapters 1 and 2.

Ghausi, M. S., *Electronic Circuits: Devices, Models, Functions, Analysis, and Design.* New York: Van Nostrand Reinhold, 1971, Chapter 3.

Gray, P. E., and Searle, C. L., *Electronic Principles: Physics, Models, and Circuits.* New York: Wiley, 1967, Chapter 6.

Millman, J., and Halkias, C. C., *Electronic Devices and Circuits.* New York: McGraw-Hill, 1967, Chapters 2, 5 and 6.

Schilling, D. L., and Belove, C., *Electronic Circuits: Discrete and Integrated.* New York: McGraw-Hill, 1968, Chapter 2.

LABORATORY PREPARATION

Silicon and Germanium Diodes

1. Select a few germanium and silicon diodes and obtain the manufacturer's maximum ratings for your diodes. If possible, obtain the V-I characteristics from the manufacturers or from your laboratory instructor. Some typical germanium diodes are the 1N34A, 1N270, and 1N2326. The 1N34A has a peak inverse voltage of 60 V and a maximum dc forward voltage of 1 V at rated current 5.0 mA. Some typical silicon diodes are 1N627, 1N440B, 1N2615, and 1N4004. The 1N440B has a peak inverse voltage of 100 V and a maximum dc forward current of .75 A at 1.5 V and 50° C. The 1N627 has a peak inverse voltage of 75 V and a dc forward current of 30 mA with a power dissipation of 250 mW.

2. Determine the resistances R and R_L and the dc voltage source (see Fig. 6-3) required to be put in series with your silicon and germanium diodes in order that the Q points of your diodes be at one half their maximum dc forward current ratings. The V-I characteristics are required for these designs.

3. Design a half-wave rectifier circuit using a silicon diode such as the 1N647, a 60 Hz ac input signal, and a load resistor R_L to yield an average value of load voltage that is anywhere between $\frac{1}{20}$ and $\frac{1}{10}$ of the peak amplitude of the ac input signal (Set $R = 0$ in Fig. 6-3).

4. Select a capacitor value for C_L in Fig. 6-6a such that

$T = R_L C_L = \frac{1}{60}$ and a larger value of C_L such that $R_L C_L > \frac{1}{60}$.

5. (optional) Select an integrated circuit (IC) diode array such as CA3019 and design a full-wave rectifier circuit as shown in Fig. 6-7a. Use an oscillator as the input signal, and sketch the output waveform across R_L when the input frequency and amplitude vary. In addition, design some other circuits which make use of IC diode arrays in electronic circuits other than those described in this experiment.

Breakdown Diodes

6. Select a few breakdown diodes such as the 1N714, 1N747, and 1N758. Obtain maximum ratings and V-I characteristics for your diodes. The ratings for Zener diode 1N758 are: Zener breakdown voltage V_Z of 10 V at $I_Z = 20$ mA dc, with maximum dc forward current of 230 mA at 25° C and a power dissipation of 400 mW.

7. Design a voltage regulator circuit as shown in Fig. 6-9 for a load current variation of 10 to 1 (i.e., calculate R, R_L, and V). Be sure that you do not exceed the power dissipation limits of your Zener diode.

8. Select a Zener diode (1N714, for example) and design the voltage regulator circuit of Fig. 6-11 so that the peak-to-peak variation of the output signal v_L is less than 1/10 of the peak-to-peak input voltage v_a.

9. Two other interesting applications of Zener diodes are the impedance compensating circuit shown in Fig. 6-19b

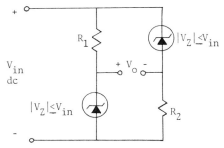

Fig. 6.19a Short circuit proof low voltage power supply circuit.

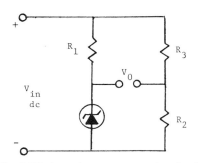

Fig. 6.19b Impedance compensating circuit.

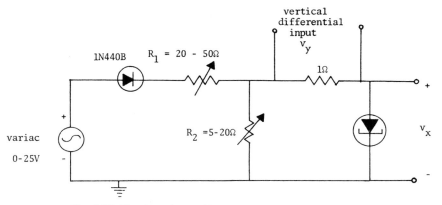

Fig. 6.20 Circuit to display V-I characteristics of tunnel diode.

and the short-circuit-proof low-voltage power supply circuit shown in Fig. 6-19a.

Describe the operation of these two circuits, and design resistors R_1, R_2, and R_3 which will operate with some Zener diodes such as 1N714 or 1N758.

Varactor Diodes

10. Select a varactor diode such as MV1650 or MV1720 to MV1750 and obtain characteristics for your device.

11. If $\gamma = .5$, $\phi = .6$, and C_o ranges from 10 pf to 300 pf, estimate the range of capacitance of a diode which has -4 volts reverse bias applied to it. Estimate the maximum and minimum capacitance of this diode when biased at -4 volts and an ac voltage v_a is applied which varies between -2 and $+2$ volts.

12. Calculate the resonant frequency f_o for the circuit of Fig. 6-13 when $L = 10$ mh and $C_o = 275$ pf. Calculate the output voltage v_L at resonance when $R = R_L = 100$ k. Calculate the change in the resonant frequency as $|V|$ varies from $+2$ to $+8$ volts.

Tunnel Diodes

13. Select a tunnel diode in the series from 1N3712 to 1N3721, such as 1N3718, or 1N3853 in the series from 1N3847 to 1N3860. The 1N3718 (TD718) is a germanium tunnel diode with $I_P = 10$ mA, $I_V = 2.43$ mA, $V_P = 65$ mV, a junction capacitance C of 90 pf, $R_s = 1\ \Omega$, and $L_s = .5$ nh.

14. The circuit of Fig. 6-20 can be used to display the V-I characteristics of a tunnel diode. Discuss the purpose of the silicon diode 1N440B and the reason for small values of R_1 and R_2 shown in Fig. 6-20.

15. The circuit of Fig. 6-21 is a harmonic oscillator. Select the values of L, R_1, and R_2 for your tunnel diode so that this circuit will oscillate.

Photodiode

16. (optional) Select a photodiode (e.g., a photo duo-diode, such as the T-11) and design a circuit which will dis-

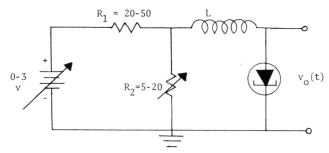

Fig. 6.21 Harmonic oscillator.

play the reverse characteristics of the photodiode. Pay careful attention to the maximum power ratings and type of light source recommended by the manufacturer.

LABORATORY PROCEDURE

Diode Characteristics

1. The circuits of Fig. 6-22a, b, and c can be used to display the V-I characteristics of diodes.*

Observe that each circuit of Fig. 6-22 has a resistor R which is to be carefully chosen to limit the amount of current flowing through the diode. In addition, each circuit of Fig. 6-22 serves a special purpose. The circuit of Fig. 6-22a does not require a scope with differential type inputs, but note that the voltage applied to the horizontal (X) input of the scope is the sum of the voltage across the diode and the 1 Ω resistor. If the voltage drop across the 1 Ω resistor is small compared with the voltage drop across the diode, then the voltage applied to the X input of the scope is a good approximation to the diode voltage. However, some distortion is always present in v_x because of the current through the 1 Ω resistor. Next, note that the voltage across the 1 Ω resistor which is applied to the vertical input (Y) of the scope is equal to the current through the diode. The 1 Ω resistor should be adjusted to a higher value whenever v_y is small compared to v_x.

---

*Set all oscilloscope input switches to dc setting.

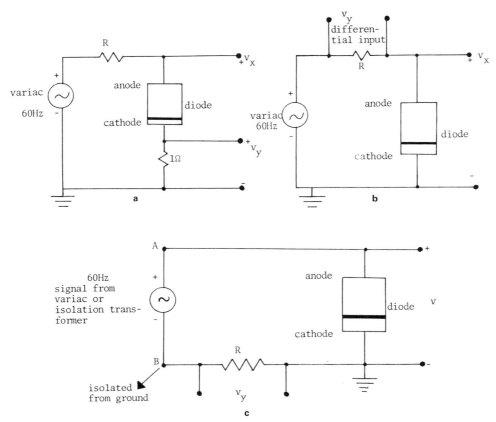

Fig. 6.22 Display circuits.

The circuit of Fig. 6–22b does not introduce the distortion that the circuit of Fig. 6–22a does, but an oscilloscope with a differential type input is required to measure v_y. Similarly, the circuit of Fig. 6–22c does not suffer from the type of distortion produced by the circuit of Fig. 6–22a, but requires that the input signal be isolated from ground (check with ohmmeter). The variac should be fed into an isolation transformer whose output is connected to terminals AB.

When using any one of the circuits, it is important to distinguish a phase angle difference between voltage and current introduced by the diode under test, a phase angle difference due to the type of circuit being used to measure the V-I characteristics of the diodes, and a possible phase difference between the horizontal (X) and the vertical (Y) amplifiers of your oscilloscope. If a low-frequency signal (60 Hz) from a variac is used, there is negligible phase difference due to the diode alone or other circuits elements. If the oscilloscope has identical X, Y amplifiers, then normally the phase difference introduced by the amplifiers themselves is negligible. A phase difference between X and Y amplifiers can be measured, if necessary, by displaying the V-I characteristics of a resistor. If the resistor's V-I characteristic appears as an ellipse and not a straight line, then there is a phase difference in the oscilloscope amplifiers. However, it is essential that the input coupling be the same

for both amplifiers, because if one is set to ac and the other to dc, a significant phase shift between X and Y inputs will result. Fig. 6–23 shows a typical V-I characteristic displayed on an oscilloscope where there is a phase difference between V and I.

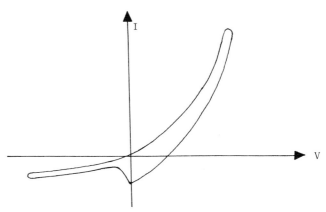

Fig. 6.23 Phase shift in V-I characteristics.

Germanium and Silicon

1. Use the circuit of Fig. 6–22a to display the V-I characteristics of some germanium and silicon diodes. Discuss any distortions which are observed in the oscilloscope displays. Measure important quantities such as V_γ and I_o for

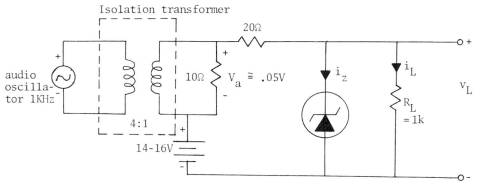

Fig. 6.24 Modification of the circuit of Fig. 6.11.

each of your diodes. (Use the circuit of Fig. 6–22c and an isolation transformer if your characteristics display an undesirable amount of phase shifting.)

2. Construct the half-wave rectifier circuit of Fig. 6–3 using the values of R and R_L which you designed for your diode. Observe the waveform across R_L. Measure the period, and observe any nonsymmetrical properties of the waveform. Place a variable capacitor ($0 - 1\ \mu f$) across R_L. Observe and discuss the waveform now appearing across R_L. Observe how changes in R_L, C_L, and v_i effect v_L.

3. (optional) Construct a full-wave rectifier circuit as shown in Fig. 6–7. Use an integrated circuit diode array as a full-wave rectifier circuit, and observe the output waveform when the input signal comes from an audio oscillator. Vary the audio oscillator frequency, and observe the output waveform.

Zener Diodes

4. Display the V-I characteristics of some Zener diodes. Carefully measure V_γ, V_z, and I_o.

5. Construct the voltage regulator circuit of Fig. 6–9 for a diode similar to 1N714. Vary R_L so that the load current varies over a range of 10 to 1 with the diode remaining within its power dissipation limits.

6. Construct the circuit of Fig. 6–11 with the modification shown in Fig. 6–24. Measure v_L as R_L is varied from 1 k to 10 kΩ.

7. (optional) Construct and test some impedance compensating circuits and short-circuit-proof circuits as shown in Fig. 6–19.

Varactor Diodes

8. Display the V-I characteristics of some varactor diodes.

9. Construct and test the circuit of Fig. 6–13. Use blocking capacitors of 1 μf or larger and $L = 10$ mh, $R_L = R = 100$ k. A typical varactor would be MV1650. Vary V_a

from 1 to 5 volts and V from 2 to 8 volts, and note changes in the resonant frequency. Monitor the output voltage v_L with an oscilloscope.

Tunnel Diodes

10. Display the V-I characteristics of some tunnel diodes using the circuit of Fig. 6–20. Measure important quantities such as I_P, V_P, V_V, I_V, etc. What errors in these values are introduced by using the circuit of Fig. 6–20? If oscillation breaks out in the negative conductance region, carefully adjust R_1 and R_2 to reduce the oscillation.

11. Construct the harmonic oscillator circuit shown in Fig. 6–21. Keep the leads as short as possible and monitor v_o with an oscilloscope. Adjust R_1 and R_2 until a periodic waveform appears across the tunnel diode. Measure the frequency or period of this waveform. If you are having difficulty making this circuit oscillate, discuss it with your instructor.

Photodiode

12. (optional) Construct your circuit which displays the reverse V-I characteristics of some photodiodes.

13. Build a photodiode circuit which chops a dc input signal into an ac signal whose frequency depends upon the frequency at which the light source strikes the photodiode.

LIST OF EQUIPMENT

1. Cathode-ray oscilloscope
2. General-purpose voltmeters or ac and dc voltmeters
3. Signal sources: function generator or sine-wave oscillator, dc power supply, and a 60 Hz variac.
4. Circuit board
5. Isolation transformer
6. Components: resistors, capacitor, inductors, and various diodes

Experiment 7/Transistor Characteristics and Biasing

Part One

INTRODUCTION

This experiment is concerned with the determination of the characteristics of the three-terminal device known as a transistor. These characteristics are useful in establishing an operating point (Q point). The exact location of the Q point is determined by the transistor characteristics and the external elements and power supplies which are connected to the transistor. The placement of the Q point at a particular position on the transistor's characteristic curves is necessary if a transistor circuit is to operate as a small or large signal amplifier or as a switching circuit.

It is also desirable that the operating point remain in a relatively fixed position (stable) with changes in temperature. The proper choice of transistor type and the design of external elements will provide the desired dc stability for a given application.

THEORY

Numerous techniques and materials are used in constructing the various types of transistors which are commercially available. One of the most important is the bipolar junction transistor. A bipolar transistor is one in which both minority and majority carriers participate in current conduction. A bipolar transistor consists of two pn junctions placed back to back forming either a pnp- or an npn-type device. Physically the transistor consists of three parts: emitter, base, and collector. The emitter-to-base and collector-to-base junctions are biased in the appropriate directions to establish desired junction behavior. A pnp transistor with biasing is shown in Fig. 7–1a and 7–1b.

The battery V_{EB} forward biases the emitter-base pn junction, while the battery V_{CB} reverse biases the collector-base pn junction. The emitter-base junction acts as a forward-biased diode with low impedance to current flow while the collector-base junction acts essentially as a reverse-biased diode with high impedance to current flow. The current flow in the collector consists of two currents. The predominant one is due to emitter current which reaches the

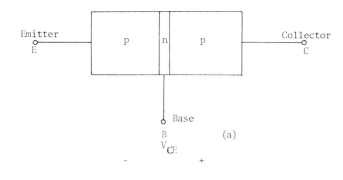

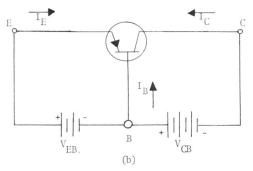

Fig. 7.1 A transistor.

collector. The amount of emitter current which reaches the collector depends mainly on the construction and temperature of the transistor. The ratio of this collector current to emitter current is defined as h_{FB} or $-\alpha$. The second and smaller current flowing in the collector is due to the reverse-biased collector-base junction when the emitter is open-circuited ($I_E = 0$). This current is called I_{CBO} (I_O for a diode), and is usually small compared to I_E. Therefore, the total collector current is

$$I_C = -\alpha I_E + I_{CBO} \qquad (7\text{–}1)$$

If we now apply KCL to the transistor we obtain

$$I_C + I_B + I_E = 0 \ \text{ or } \ I_E = -I_C - I_B \qquad (7\text{–}2)$$

65

and, substituting Eq. (7-2) into Eq. (7-1), we obtain for I_C

$$I_C = \frac{\alpha}{1-\alpha} I_B + \frac{1}{1-\alpha} I_{CBO} \qquad (7\text{-}3)$$

The quantity $\alpha/(1-\alpha)$ is defined as h_{FE} or β. In addition to current flow in the collector and emitter, there is current flow in the base of a transistor. The cross-sectional area for current flow in the collector (or emitter) is usually very much larger than in the base. Therefore, a large bulk resistance can be attributed to the base because of its small cross-sectional area. (Bulk or ohmic resistance is proportional to resistivity, and length and inversely proportional to cross-sectional area.) This dc ohmic resistance is called the base-spreading resistance, and denoted $r_{bb'}$. Fig. 7-1 can be redrawn to include the effect of $r_{bb'}$, and a new node B' is created, as shown in Fig. 7-2.

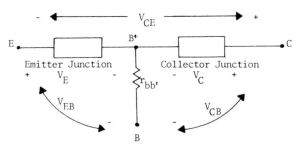

Fig. 7.2 Transistor model with base-spreading resistance.

Now, remembering that the collector-base junction is nothing more than a *pn* junction diode, we can generalize Eq. (7-1) by replacing I_{CBO} by the ideal diode voltage-current equation (see Experiment 6)

$$I_C = -\alpha I_E - I_{CO}(e^{V_{CB'}/\eta V_T} - 1) \qquad (7\text{-}4)$$

where $V_T = kT/q = +.025$ at $T = 300°$ K, and η is the factor associated with recombination within the depletion layer and is 1 for germanium and 1.5 to 2 for silicon type diodes. Observe that if $V_{CB'}$ is negative, as shown in Fig. 7-1, and has a magnitude which is large compared to V_T, then Eq. (7-4) reduces to Eq. (7-1). We can use a similar argument concerning the emitter-base junction in order to replace I_E in Eq. (7-1) by an ideal diode equation so that it can be written in the following general form

$$I_C = I_{EC}(e^{V_{EB'}/\eta V_T} - 1) + I_{CC}(e^{V_{CB'}/\eta V_T} - 1) \quad (7\text{-}5)$$

I_{EC} and I_{CC} are called the current coefficients, and are similar to the saturation current for a diode. In the *pnp* transistor shown in Fig. 7-1, I_{EC} is a small negative current, and I_{CC} is a small positive current. An equation similar to Eq. (7-5) for the emitter current can be obtained

$$I_E = I_{EE}(e^{V_{EB'}/\eta V_T} - 1) + I_{EC}(e^{V_{CB'}/\eta V_T} - 1) \quad (7\text{-}6)$$

where I_{EE} is a small positive current for a *pnp* transistor.

Eqs. (7-5) and (7-6) are called the Ebers-Moll equations, and are valid for both forward- and reverse-biasing voltages. If we are interested in solving Eqs. (7-5) and (7-6) for $V_{CB'}$ and $V_{EB'}$, we obtain complicated logarithmic expressions, which will be written for simplicity in the following form

$$V_{CB'} = \eta V_T \ln f_1(I_E, I_C) \qquad (7\text{-}7)$$

$$V_{EB'} = \eta V_T \ln f_2(I_E, I_C) \qquad (7\text{-}8)$$

where f_1 and f_2 are complicated functions of I_{EC}, I_{CC}, etc. The difference between $V_{CB'}$ and $V_{EB'}$ is expressed as

$$V_{CE} = V_{CB'} - V_{EB'} = \eta V_T \ln \frac{f_1(I_E, I_C)}{f_2(I_E, I_C)} \qquad (7\text{-}9)$$

I_E can be eliminated from Eq. (7-9) by using Eq. (7-2) so that

$$V_{CE} = \eta V_T \ln \frac{f_1(I_B, I_C)}{f_2(I_B, I_C)} \qquad (7\text{-}10)$$

It becomes obvious at this point that if, for example, we wanted to accurately plot V_{CE} versus I_C with I_B equal to a constant value in Eq. (7-10), we would have to know all the other constants in the Ebers-Moll equations. Not only are a large number of constants required, but Eq. (7-10) represents only an approximate mathematical model for the behavior of the transistor. Consequently, instead of plotting curves of I_C versus V_{CE} with I_B constant (common-emitter characteristic) or any other combination of variables using the Ebers-Moll equations, we are usually given a set of typical characteristics by a transistor manufacturer. The transistor, being a three-terminal device, requires only two sets of parametric curves to completely describe its terminal behavior.

Suppose we consider the *pnp* configuration in Fig. 7-3.

A characteristic curve will be defined as a plot of two terminal variables, with a third terminal variable held constant. The circuit of Fig. 7-3 has four terminal variables and twelve characteristic curves. Obtaining all twelve characteristic curves would result in an overspecification since only two characteristic curves are sufficient. The choice of which two characteristic curves are used depends upon the properties of the transistor and the circuit application of the device. However, for most applications, curves of I_C

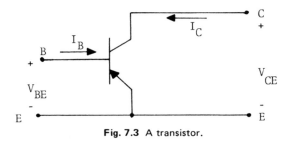

Fig. 7.3 A transistor.

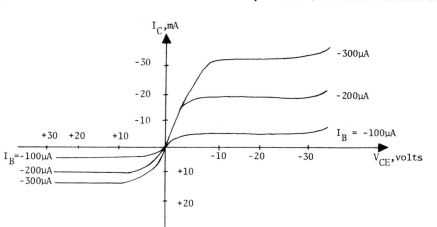

Fig. 7.4 Transistor output V–I characteristics.

versus V_{CE} with I_B held constant are given. These characteristics are called common-emitter or output curves. Fig. 7–4 shows a set of *pnp* transistor output curves in both the first and third quadrants.

Manufacturers normally give only the first quadrant characteristics because the transistor provides maximum amplification or gain in this region. This is clear by noting that a 100 μA change in I_B corresponds to a 10 mA change in I_C in the first quadrant and only a 5 mA change in the third quadrant of Fig. 7–4. In addition, manufacturers do not always indicate a current sign convention on the characteristics curves. The manufacturer specifies either an *npn* or *pnp* transistor. It is up to the user to recognize that if a *pnp* transistor is to be biased in the first quadrant, called the normal active region, then a negative power supply is required for collector bias, and that if I_C is defined as flowing into the collector terminal, then the true direction of positive current flow will be out of the collector terminal.

The foregoing discussion has revolved around the common-emitter configuration, but it can be readily adapted to other transistor circuit configurations. Since the common-emitter configuration is used most often, it is more likely that curves of I_C versus V_{CE} will be available than, for example, I_C versus V_{CB}. It is possible, however, to construct necessary curves, given one set, should this be required. Another important set of characteristics for the common-emitter (*CE*) configuration are called the input curves (I_C versus V_{BE} with V_{CE} = constant), which are shown in Fig. 7–5.

The maximum voltage which may be applied to a transistor under normal circumstances is determined by breakdown or punch-through (except where these phenomena are used to produce special circuit effects). Most manufacturers indicate the maximum permissible collector-emitter voltage in their data sheets in addition to the maximum collector-base voltage. Another important limitation of transistor operation is the maximum permissible power dis-

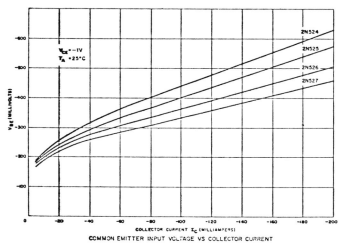

Fig. 7.5 Transistor input V–I characteristics.

sipation. For most practical purposes, it is equal to the product of dc collector current and voltage minus the output power. This power is dissipated at the collector junction, and causes the device to heat up. The maximum permissible power dissipation is often indicated in the plot of the output curves, or a derating curve is supplied which shows the maximum power dissipation as a function of ambient temperature. An example of a maximum power dissipation curve and a temperature derating curve for a power transistor are shown in Fig. 7–6*a* and *b*, respectively.

Other parameters in addition to the output curves and power limitations are specified by the manufacturer. Some of these will be described in the next experiment. However, since h_{FE} and h_{FB} are such important parameters, a manufacturer will often specify the temperature and current dependence of one of these parameters, as shown in Fig. 7–7.

Once a transistor circuit is chosen and the transistor characteristics are given, we can determine the dc operating or

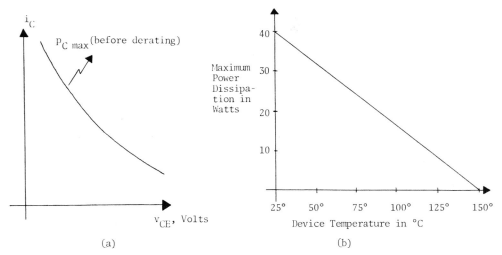

Fig. 7.6 Power dissipation and temperature derating curves.

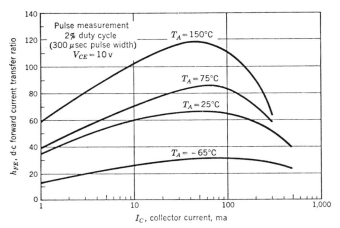

Fig. 7.7 Temperature and current dependence of h_{FE}.

quiescent point. It is important to recognize that a semi-graphical technique will be employed since characteristic curves are given, and that the technique for determining the Q point should be general enough to apply to a large class of transistor circuits.

As an illustrative example, let us consider the fixed-bias

transistor circuit of Fig. 7-8a and b. The circuit of Fig. 7-8b is easily derived by splitting the power supply V_{CC} shown in Fig. 7-8a. The final dc circuit shown in Fig. 7-8b has two loop equations: one for the collector-emitter loop, and one for the base-emitter loop.

$$I_C = -\frac{V_{CE}}{R_L} + \frac{V_{CC}}{R_L} \quad \text{(collector loop)} \quad (7\text{-}11)$$

$$I_B = -\frac{V_{BE}}{R_B} + \frac{V_{CC}}{R_B} \quad \text{(base loop)} \quad (7\text{-}12)$$

Eq. (7-11) represents a straight line with a negative slope. A plot of Eq. (7-11) on the characteristic curves is known as a "dc load line," and is shown in Fig. 7-9. Eq. (7-12) may also be related to the characteristics by noting that for V_{BE} = constant, this equation represents a fixed value of I_B for fixed values of V_{CC}, R_B, and R_L. Eqs. (7-11) and (7-12) represent two conditions which must be simultaneously satisfied. The intersection of the dc load line (Eq. [7-11]) and the bias curve (Eq. [7-12]) determines the Q point, as shown in Fig. 7-9.

The value of V_{BE} is required in order to determine the quiescent point. V_{BE} either is small enough to be neglected

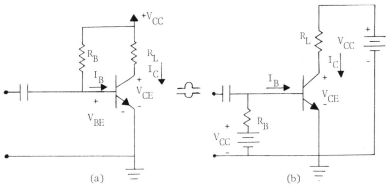

Fig. 7.8 Fixed-biased transistor circuit.

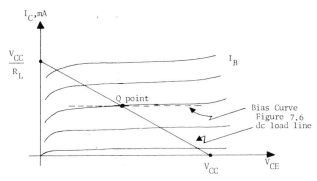

Fig. 7.9 Bias curve and d-c load line.

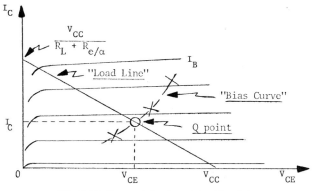

Fig. 7.11 Determining transistor Q point.

in Eq. (7-12) or is furnished by the manufacturer as a nominal value or as a characteristic curve of common-emitter input voltage (V_{BE}) versus collector current for constant values of V_{CE}.

Another important dc biasing scheme is shown in Fig. 7-10a and b, and is called a self-biasing circuit.

The procedure used for the circuit of Fig. 7-8 will be used again. The voltage supply V_{CC} is split, and a Thevenin equivalent circuit is obtained to the left of terminals AB in Fig. 7-10b (see Experiment 2). Once again, the circuit of Fig. 7-10b has two KVL (loop) equations, and, by using $I_C \cong -\alpha I_E$, we obtain

$$I_C = -\frac{V_{CE}}{R_L + \dfrac{R_E}{\alpha}} + \frac{V_{CC}}{R_L + \dfrac{R_E}{\alpha}} \quad \text{(collector loop)} \quad (7\text{-}13)$$

$$I_C = -\frac{R_{EQ}}{\dfrac{R_E}{\alpha}} I_B + \frac{V_{EQ} - V_{BE}}{\dfrac{R_E}{\alpha}} \quad \text{(base loop)} \quad (7\text{-}14)$$

The intersection of Eqs. (7-13) and (7-14) determines the Q point. Knowledge of V_{BE} is again required in Eq. (7-14). Also, the bias curve (Eq. [7-14]) can be plotted by picking

a set of values of I_B and calculating a corresponding set of values of I_C, as shown in Fig. 7-11.

A little reflection should reveal the approach to simple biasing. For transistors, we seek:

1. A relation between I_C and V_{CE}, which is generally found by writing a collector loop equation (dc load line).

2. A relation between I_C and I_B, which is obtained from a base loop equation (bias curve).

Plotting these equations on the characteristics and seeking their intersection automatically assures that Kirchhoff's circuit laws and the physical law of the transistor device are simultaneously satisfied. Actually, a factor of considerable importance has not been taken into account thus far. The current I_C is a fairly sensitive function of temperature, increasing with increasing temperature. Eq. (7-1) contains the term I_{CBO}, which has been neglected in the determination of the Q point. I_{CBO} is proportional to T^3, and even at room temperature the percentage changes in I_{CBO} are appreciable—that is,

$$\frac{\Delta I_{CBO}}{I_{CBO}} = \begin{cases} 11\%/\text{degree K for Ge} \\ 15\%/\text{degree K for Si} \end{cases}$$

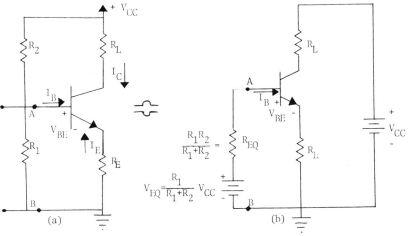

Fig. 7.10 Self-biasing transistor circuit.

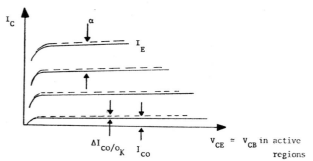

Fig. 7.12 Changes in V-I characteristics and Q point with temperature.

Since I_{CBO} and, consequently, I_C are affected by changes in temperature, the characteristic curves will shift upward or downward with temperature, as indicated in Fig. 7-12, and the quiescent point will change as indicated by Eq. (7-3).

A figure of merit can be defined to measure the percentage change in the quiescent current I_C with respect to changes in I_{CBO}

$$S = \text{stability factor} = \frac{dI_C}{dI_{CBO}} \qquad (7\text{-}15)$$

It follows for a particular transistor circuit that: a small value of S implies good dc stability; a large value of S implies poor dc stability.

Eq. (7-15) is linked to the previous biasing discussion and Eq. (7-3). The bias curve may be substituted into Eq. (7-3) to find I_C as a function of I_{CBO} and the other constants. Next, the dc stability of a circuit can be computed by taking the derivative indicated by Eq. (7-15). The stability for the fixed-bias circuit of Fig. 7-8 is

$$S = \frac{1}{1 - \alpha} \qquad (7\text{-}16)$$

The stability for this circuit is determined solely by the α of the transistor, and dc stability may be poor. On the other hand, the stability for the self-bias circuit of Fig. 7-10 is

$$S = \frac{1}{1 - \alpha + \dfrac{R_E}{R_{EQ}}} \qquad (7\text{-}17)$$

Since R_{EQ} depends upon R_1 and R_2, the stability factor can be reduced over the fixed-bias circuit by adjusting R_E, R_1, and R_2.

Another circuit which achieves good dc stability is shown in Fig. 7-13.

The stability factor for this circuit is

$$S = \frac{1}{1 - \alpha + \dfrac{\alpha R_L}{R_L + R_f}} \qquad (7\text{-}18)$$

The limiting value of S as R_f approaches 0 is 1.

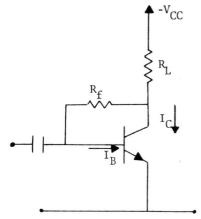

Fig. 7.13 Feedback biasing transistor circuit.

We see that the dc stability has been improved by the addition of the feedback resistor R_f connected from the collector to the base. However, an increase in I_B results in an increase in I_C and a decrease in V_{CE}, which in turn reduces I_B. This is known as a degenerative effect, and reduces the overall gain of the amplifier (see Experiment 13). Some improvement in S is possible if part of the voltage which normally exists across R_f is obtained by the use of a Zener diode, as shown in Fig. 7-14. Since the voltage across a

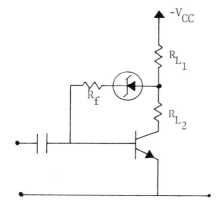

Fig. 7.14 Zener diode feedback biasing transistor circuit.

Zener diode at breakdown is substantially independent of the current through it, R_f can be reduced with an attendant improvement in the dc stability and perhaps only a small loss of ac amplification or degeneration.

The previous discussion has shown that a number of parameters (R_L, α, R_1, R_2, etc.) appear simultaneously in the load line equation and in the expression for the stability factor. Furthermore, if the transistor is to operate in a substantially linear mode, so that undistorted ac components can appear in the output, then the quiescent point must be chosen to allow substantially equal excursions about this point for equal changes in input excitation. For example,

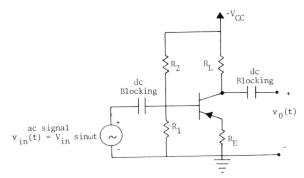

Fig. 7.15 Self-biased common emitter amplifier.

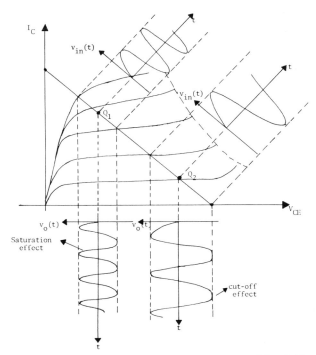

Fig. 7.16 Input and output voltages for the circuit of Fig. 7.15.

we can apply an ac signal to the input of a self-biased transistor circuit, as indicated in Fig. 7-15.

A saturation effect in the output voltage $v_0(t)$ is obtained if Q_1 is the quiescent point and a cutoff effect is observed. in $v_0(t)$ if Q_2 is the quiescent point. For linear operation, Q should be chosen somewhere between Q_1 and Q_2, as shown in Fig. 7-16. That is, the output ac signal is an undistorted replica of the input ac signal provided the Q point is properly selected and the amplitude of the input signal remains small enough to provide an undistorted output.

Stability, linearity, quiescent point, and power limitations are important factors in the design of a transistor amplifier. Consequently, some trade-offs will have to be made in order to achieve an optimum performance. In some circuits, a

simple analysis will reveal the trade-offs which are necessary. In others, such as large-scale integrated circuits, computer-aided design procedures are helping to determine required trade-offs for optimum performance.

Part Two

OBJECTIVE

This experiment will display common-emitter characteristics for some typical *pnp* and *npn* transistors. In particular, the Q point and dc stability factor for some transistor circuits will be studied.

REFERENCES

Alley, C. L., and Atwood, K. W., *Electronic Engineering*. New York: Wiley, 1966, Chapters 4 and 5.

Angelo, E. J., *Electronics: BJTs, FETs, and Microcircuits*. New York: McGraw-Hill, 1969, Chapter 9.

Chirlian, P. M., *Electronic Circuits: Physical Principles, Analysis, and Design*. New York: McGraw-Hill, 1971, Chapters 3 and 5.

Fitchen, F. C., *Transistor Circuit Analysis and Design*. New York: Van Nostrand Reinhold, 1966, Chapters 1, 2, and 3.

Ghausi, M. S., *Electronic Circuits: Devices, Models, Functions, Analysis, and Design*. New York: Van Nostrand Reinhold, 1971, Chapter 3.

Gray, P. E., and Searle, C. L., *Electronic Principles: Physics, Models, and Circuits*. New York: Wiley, 1967, Chapters 7 and 13.

Millman, J., and Halkias, C. C., *Electronic Devices and Circuits*. New York: McGraw-Hill, 1967, Chapters 9 and 10.

Schilling, D. L., and Belove, C., *Electronic Circuits: Discrete and Integrated*. New York: McGraw-Hill, 1968, Chapters 3 and 4.

LABORATORY PREPARATION

1. There are several standard lead configurations for transistors when viewed from the bottom side, as shown in Fig. 7-17.

If your transistors do not fit into the above categories, consult a manufacturer's specifications to find the case designation (for example, TO-1) and then look up the lead configuration for that case designation. Be certain of the lead configurations for your transistors.

Fig. 7.17 Typical lead configurations.

2. A quick method of determining if transistors are defective or not is to use an ohmmeter. By connecting one lead of an ohmmeter to the base and the other lead first to the collector and then to the emitter, you should get two high or two low resistance readings. Now, connect the second ohmmeter lead to the base, and repeat the procedure with the first ohmmeter lead. If the first set of readings were high resistances, the second set should be low resistances (or vice versa). Can you explain how this procedure tests the diode junctions of transistors?

3. In order to determine the type of an unknown transistor, the characteristic between the collector and base terminals may be measured with the emitter open-circuited. Under this condition, the resulting characteristic curve will be that of a simple diode.

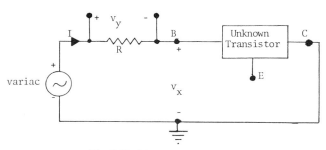

Fig. 7.18 Diode testing circuit.

Fig. 7-18 is similar to the diode testing circuit used in Experiment 6. If the trace on the oscilloscope is as shown in Fig. 7-19, the unknown transistor is an *npn* silicon transistor. What would the trace on the scope look like for a *pnp* germanium transistor?

4. The circuit of Fig. 7-20 can be used to display the common-emitter (output) characteristics of an *npn* transistor.

The only changes in Fig. 7-20 that have to be made for a

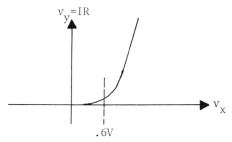

Fig. 7.19 Scope trace for *n–p–n* transistor.

pnp transistor are the reversal of direction of the variable dc supply, the reversal of the leads for the ammeter measuring I_B, and the reversal of the diode direction in the collector circuit. The variable dc supply is used to fix the value of base current during a sweep of the collector circuit. The diode in the collector circuit applies only a forward sweep voltage to the device under test. This is desirable because the maximum voltage levels for transistors are usually different for opposite collector polarities. Note also that only one curve, determined by the value of I_B, will be displayed. The value of I_B must be varied to obtain a parametric family. Can you devise a test circuit which will display a set of values of I_B = constant simultaneously? Explain the purpose of the 1 k resistor in the collector circuit.

5. The circuit of Fig. 7–21 can be used to measure the input curves (I_B versus V_{BE}, with V_{CE} constant) for a common-emitter *pnp* transistor configuration. Describe the use of each element in the circuit. What changes must be made to measure the input characteristics of an *npn* transistor? What will the trace which appears on the CRT look like? What is the maximum rms ac voltage that the variac can be set to in the circuit of Fig. 7-21? Be sure to include the effects of the transformer turns ratio. With this in mind, determine reasonable primary and secondary operating voltages for your transistors.

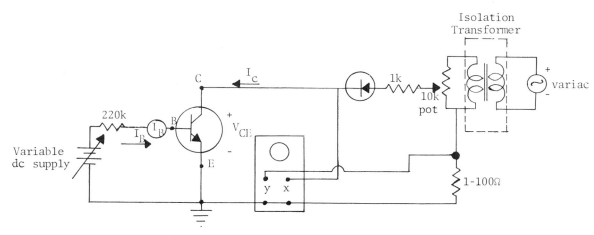

Fig. 7.20 Circuit for transistor output characteristics.

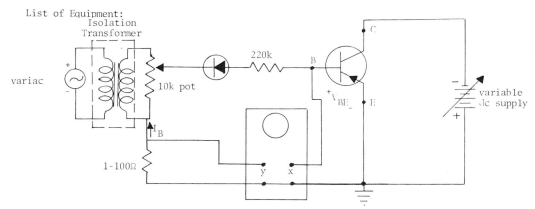

Fig. 7.21 Circuit for transistor input characteristics.

6. Select a transistor such as the 2N526 or 2N697 or a similar transistor and calculate the values of R_B, V_{CC}, and R_L for the circuit of Fig. 7–8 such that the Q point satisfies the following relationships

$$V_{CE} = \tfrac{1}{2} V_{CC} = \tfrac{1}{2} (-20 \text{ volts})$$

$$I_C V_{CE} = \tfrac{1}{2} \text{ Power}_{max} = \tfrac{1}{2} (225 \text{ mW})$$

What is the stability factor for your circuit? What is the maximum excursion of the output voltage for your design? Use the load line and transistor characteristics to determine this excursion.

7. Select a transistor and calculate the values of R_1, R_2, and R_L and R_E such that

$$S = \tfrac{1}{2} \beta = \tfrac{1}{2} \frac{\alpha}{1 - \alpha} \quad \text{and} \quad V_{CE} = \tfrac{1}{2} (\mp V_{CC})$$

for the circuit of Fig. 7–10. Are you free to choose any of the resistors and still meet the design requirements? (Do not exceed the power ratings of your transistor.) What is the maximum output excursion?

8. Design the circuit of Fig. 7–13 with the same requirements as in step 7. Are you free to choose all the resistors in this circuit and still meet the requirements?

9. (optional) Design the circuit of Fig. 7–14 so that the stability factor $S = \tfrac{1}{2} \beta$ and the Q point has the value $V_{CE} = \tfrac{1}{2} V_{CC}$. Select a Zener diode for which you know the characteristics (see Experiment 6).

LABORATORY PROCEDURE

1. Select some transistors such as 2N526 and the 2N697. Test these transistors and determine if they are germanium or silicon and if they are *npn* or *pnp*.

2. Make a quick test to determine if your transistors are "good" or "bad."

3. Select a suitable diode and display the common-emitter output and input curves for your transistors using the circuits of Figs. 7–20 and 7–21. Plot these characteristics on separate graphs. Be sure to cover the same ranges of I_B and V_{CE} that are given by the manufacturers characteristic curves. Compare your results with those of the manufacturer. Discuss any discrepancies which occur. Sweep the variable dc supply up and down quickly and observe the trace on the scope. Be sure not to exceed any of the voltage and power ratings when you do this.

4. Construct the fixed-bias circuit which you have designed and test the Q point. A simple and quick way to test the Q point is to make a few important dc voltage measurements with a dc voltmeter. Connect the ground of the voltmeter to a common ground and connect the high side of the voltmeter to the collector. This voltage measurement is V_{CE}. Does it correspond to your calculated value? If there is a large discrepancy, check with your instructor. Also check the base-to-ground dc voltage. This is V_{BE} for the fixed-bias circuit. Does this correspond to your predicted value? Touch your transistor with your fingertips. Does the Q point change?

5. Construct your self-bias circuit. Check the Q point by making appropriate dc voltage measurements: one from collector to ground, one from emitter to ground, and one from base to ground. *The Q point of all of the circuits in the following experiments which are biased in the normal active region should be checked in this way.* Touch your transistor with your fingertips. Does the Q point change? Vary V_{CC} slightly and measure the change in the Q point.

6. Construct the feedback circuit of Fig. 7–13 which you have designed. Test the Q point and test the stability of the circuit by touching the transistor with your fingertips. Does the Q point change?

7. (optional) Construct your Zener diode feedback-biasing circuit. Test the Q point. Compare your circuit with the circuit with feedback and no Zener diode. Can you design any other circuits which have excellent stability factors?

8. (optional) Learn to use a transistor curve tracer—if one is available in your laboratory—by first reading the manufacturers operation manual. Display the characteristics of your transistors and compare with the characteristics supplied by the manufacturer.

9. (optional) Suppose two black boxes with three terminals each are available: one has a transistor; the other has two diodes connected back to back with the connected cathodes providing the third terminal. How would you identify which is which? Devise a laboratory experiment you could perform to identify each box.

LIST OF EQUIPMENT

1. Cathode-ray oscilloscope
2. General-purpose voltmeter or dc voltmeters and ohmmeters
3. Signal sources: variac, dc power supply
4. Ammeters: dc range 0–50 μA and 0–400 μA
5. Isolation transformer
6. Circuit board
7. Components: transistors, diodes, capacitors, resistors, and 10 k potentiometer.
8. (optional) Transistor curve tracer

Experiment 8/Transistor Parameters and Models

Part One

INTRODUCTION

The design of small-signal current or voltage amplifiers is divided essentially into two parts, which are not completely separate. The first consists of establishing the dc bias. That is, a semigraphical method, as described in Experiment 7, is used to design for a desired Q point. The second part involves gain and impedance calculations dependent upon input frequencies. In this part, small-signal equivalent circuits are used to describe the gain and impedance behavior of transistor circuits. These two parts are not completely separate because output excursions are dependent on the Q point, and thus some of the components in the equivalent circuits depend on the Q point. This experiment will study some small-signal equivalent transistor circuits necessary for the second part of the amplifier design.

THEORY

A transistor which is dc biased in the normal active region can be used as a small-signal amplifier. If the collector swing is small, the transistor is considered to be linear and can be replaced, for purposes of analysis, by a small-signal linear equivalent circuit model. The small-signal model can be specified by either the open-circuit z parameters, the short-circuit y-parameters, the hybrid h-parameters, or any other network parameters. However, the h-parameters are used most often for a transistor because they are easily measurable and provide quick estimates of typical operating conditions.

A transistor is a three-terminal device with one terminal "common," one terminal "input," and the other "output," as shown in Fig. 8-1.

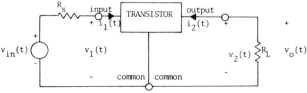

Fig. 8.1 Transistor as a three terminal device.

The biasing circuit has been left out of Fig. 8-1 because we will now concentrate on small-signal behavior about a specific Q point. Assuming then that a specific Q point for a transistor has been established, the four h-parameters can be defined as follows*

$$h_i = \frac{v_1}{i_1}\bigg|_{v_2=0} = h_{11} = \text{Input impedance with ac short-circuited output}$$

$$h_r = \frac{v_1}{v_2}\bigg|_{i_1=0} = h_{12} = \text{Reverse transfer voltage gain with ac open-circuited input}$$

$$h_f = \frac{i_2}{i_1}\bigg|_{v_2=0} = h_{21} = \text{Forward current gain with ac short-circuited output}$$

$$h_o = \frac{i_2}{v_2}\bigg|_{i_1=0} = h_{22} = \text{Output admittance with ac open-circuited input}$$

Subscripts i, r, f, and o stand for input, reverse, forward, and output, respectively. A second subscript (e, b, or c) is added to identify which transistor terminal is common. For example, h_{oe} is the open-circuit output admittance when the emitter is the common terminal. A common-emitter configuration means that the base and collector represent the input and output terminals with the emitter terminal common to both the input and output sides of the transistor but not necessarily connected to ground. The h-parameters are in general different for each configuration, but conversion from one set to another set can be made by using Table 8-1. Numerical values shown are for a typical transistor biased in the normal active region.

Methods for measuring the common-emitter h-parameters are relatively straightforward. The circuit of Fig. 8-2 can be used to measure h_{ie} and h_{fe}; the circuit of Fig. 8-3 can be used to measure h_{re} and h_{oe}. The desired quiescent

---

*Lower-case letters are used for current and voltage to emphasize small time-varying signals about a dc or quiescent point.

TABLE 8.1

Parameter	Common-emitter	Common-base	Common-collector
h_{ie}	1000 Ω	$\dfrac{h_{ib}}{1+h_{fb}}$	h_{ic}
h_{re}	2.5×10^{-4}	$\dfrac{h_{ob}h_{ib}}{1+h_{fb}} - h_{rb}$	$1 - h_{rc}$
h_{fe}	50	$\dfrac{-h_{fb}}{1+h_{fb}}$	$-(1+h_{fc})$
h_{oe}	25 μA/V	$\dfrac{h_{ob}}{1+h_{fb}}$	h_{oc}
h_{ib}	$\dfrac{h_{ie}}{1+h_{fe}}$	22 Ω	$\dfrac{-h_{ic}}{h_{fc}}$
h_{rb}	$\dfrac{h_{ie}h_{oe}}{1+h_{fe}} - h_{re}$	30×10^{-4}	$h_{rc} - 1 - \dfrac{h_{ic}h_{oc}}{h_{fc}}$
h_{fb}	$\dfrac{-h_{fe}}{1+h_{fe}}$	$-.98$	$\dfrac{-(1+h_{fc})}{h_{fc}}$
h_{ob}	$\dfrac{h_{oe}}{1+h_{fe}}$	.49 μA/V	$\dfrac{-h_{oc}}{h_{fc}}$
h_{ic}	h_{ie}	$\dfrac{h_{ib}}{1+h_{fb}}$	1000 Ω
h_{rc}	$1 - h_{re}$	1	1
h_{fc}	$-(1+h_{fe})$	$\dfrac{-1}{1+h_{fb}}$	-51
h_{oc}	h_{oe}	$\dfrac{h_{ob}}{1+h_{fb}}$	25 μA/V
α	$\dfrac{h_{fe}}{1+h_{fe}}$	$-h_{fb}$	$\dfrac{1+h_{fc}}{h_{fc}}$
r_c	$\dfrac{1+h_{fe}}{h_{oe}}$	$\dfrac{1}{h_{ob}}$	$\dfrac{-h_{fc}}{h_{oc}}$
r_e	$\dfrac{h_{re}}{h_{oe}}$	$h_{ib} - \dfrac{h_{rb}}{h_{ob}}(1+h_{fb})$	$\dfrac{1-h_{rc}}{h_{oc}}$
r_b	$h_{ie} - \dfrac{h_{re}}{h_{oe}}(1+h_{fe})$	$\dfrac{h_{rb}}{h_{ob}}$	$h_{ic} + \dfrac{h_{fc}}{h_{oc}}(1-h_{rc})$

points are obtained by adjusting V_{CC}, V_{EE}, and R_B. A large resistor R_B is included to properly bias the transistor.

The hybrid resonant circuit (tank circuit) on the base side of the transistor should have an ac impedance of approximately 500 k at 1 kHz, which is large in comparison with the input impedance of the transistor. The capacitors (C) should approximate ac short circuits to a 1 kHz signal ($C > 10 \mu f$), and R_L in Fig. 8-2 is a small resistance so that the amplitude V_o of the output signal is approximately zero. The value of h_{ie} is measured in Fig. 8-2 as

$$h_{ie} = \frac{v_1}{i_1}\bigg|_{v_0=0} = \frac{V_1 R_s}{V_{in}} \tag{8-1}$$

where V_1 and V_{in} are the amplitudes or the rms values of sinusoidal voltages. h_{ie} can also be shown to be equal to

$$\frac{V_T}{I_B} \cong h_{FE}\left(\frac{V_T}{I_E}\right) = \frac{.025 h_{FE}}{I_E} \tag{8-2}$$

from the Ebers-Moll equations. The parameter h_{fe} can be measured from Fig. 8-2 as

$$h_{fe} = \frac{i_2}{i_1}\bigg|_{v_0=0} = \frac{V_o/R_L}{V_{in}/R_s} = \frac{V_o R_s}{V_{in} R_L} \tag{8-3}$$

with V_o and V_{in} amplitudes of sinusoidal voltages. Note the values of R_s and R_L are required for h_{fe} and should be precision resistors or accurately measured with an impedance bridge.

The value of h_{re} can be measured using the circuit of Fig. 8-3. The base circuit is effectively ac open-circuited because the impedance of the hybrid resonant circuit is large (> 500 k ohms) compared with the input impedance of the transistor. Consequently, h_{re} is measured as

$$h_{re} = \frac{v_1}{v_2}\bigg|_{i_1=0} = \frac{V_1}{V_2} \tag{8-4}$$

and h_{oe} is measured in Fig. 8-3 as

$$h_{oe} = \frac{i_2}{v_2}\bigg|_{i_1=0} = \frac{V_o/R_L}{V_2} = \frac{V_o}{R_L V_2} \tag{8-5}$$

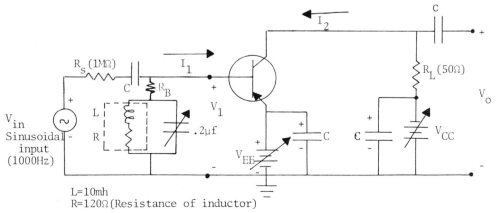

L=10mh
R=120Ω (Resistance of inductor)

Fig. 8.2 Circuit for measuring h_{ie} and h_{fe}.

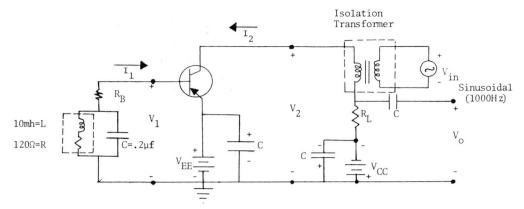

Fig. 8.3 Circuit for measuring h_{re} and h_{oe}.

Often a manufacturer will give sets of h-parameters for the convenience of the designer, so that the above measurements do not have to be made. However, the h-parameters are given at dc emitter-current values or dc collector-emitter voltages, which may be different from the designer's required quiescent values. Typical h-parameter curves are shown in Figs. 8–4 and 8–5.

Suppose that a typical value of h_{fe} is 64 at $I_E = -1$ mA and $V_{CE} = -5$ V and it is desired to obtain h_{fe} at $I_E = -6$ mA and $V_{CE} = -15$ V. We observe from Fig. 8-4 that the normalized value of h_{fe} at $I_E = -1.0$ mA and $V_{CE} = -15$ volts is 1.3. Similarly from Fig. 8-5, h_{fe} is 1.3 at $V_{CE} = -5$ V and $I_E = -6$ mA. Therefore, $h_{fe} = (1.3)(1.3) \cdot (64) = 108$. Of course, this represents only a typical value of h_{fe}. Usually a minimum and a maximum value are specified for the h-parameters. For this example, h_{fe} has a minimum value of 44 and a maximum value of 88, which means that, at the designer's required quiescent point, h_{fe} can vary between 74 and 148, with 108 as a typical value.

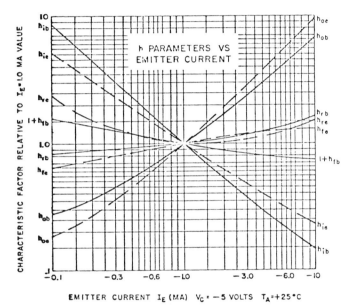

Fig. 8.5 h Parameters vs. emitter current.

Suppose we wanted h_{ie} at this same Q point. We know that $h_{ie} = \dfrac{h_{ib}}{1 + h_{fb}}$ and $h_{fb} = \dfrac{-h_{fe}}{1 + h_{fe}}$ from Table 8-1. The parameter h_{ib} at the desired Q point is $h_{ib} = (1)(.2)(28) = 5.6$ and $h_{fb} = \dfrac{-108}{109}$, with $h_{ie} = \dfrac{5.6}{.01} = 560 \ \Omega$. The common-emitter h-parameter circuit is shown in Fig. 8-6 a, b, c for various approximations.

There are a few important observations to make for the circuit of Fig. 8-6a. First, h_{re} and h_{oe} are very close to zero for most transistors, and Fig. 8-6c represents a good approximation to actual transistor behavior. Second, h_{re} approximately zero means there is no signal transmitted to the input circuit of a common-emitter configuration because of a signal present at the output circuit. On the other hand, a small signal in the input circuit is transmitted to the output circuit because of the dependent current source $h_{fe}i_b$. This is known as a unilateral circuit. Third, there are

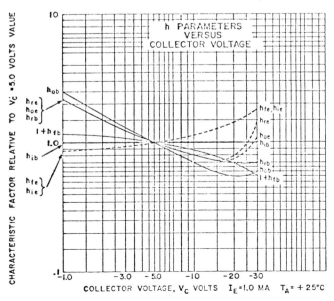

Fig. 8.4 h Parameters vs. collector voltage.

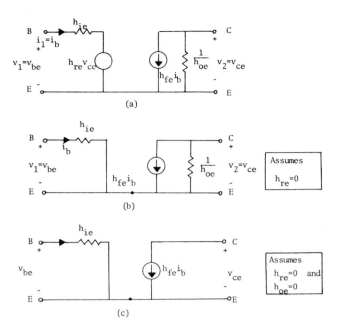

Fig. 8.6 Common emitter h parameter circuits.

no capacitive elements in this equivalent circuit; it is called the low-frequency unilateral model for a transistor.

The common-base h-parameter circuit is shown in Fig. 8-7a, b.

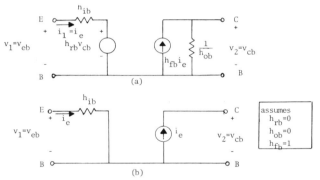

Fig. 8.7 Common base h parameter circuits.

It is easily seen that the base and emitter leads can be interchanged in Fig. 8-6c to obtain another representation of the common-base circuit shown in Fig. 8-7b. That is,

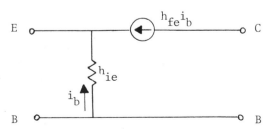

Fig. 8.8 Another common base h parameter circuit.

The common-collector (emitter-follower) h-parameter circuit is shown in Fig. 8-9a and b.

The above models are useful for low-frequency behavior of small-signal amplifiers, and will be used in Experiment 10 to calculate gain and impedance for each configuration.

As the frequency of the input signal is increased, the upper limit of the high-frequency response of the transistor is limited by internal capacitance. Consequently, a high-frequency model of a transistor should include these capacitance effects.

Referring to Experiment 7, we recall that the collector-base junction of a transistor is effectively a reverse-biased junction. The reverse-biased junction behaves like a capacitor whose value varies inversely with the dc voltage $V_{cb'}$. This capacitance $C_{b'c}$ is called the transition capacitance, and is in the range from 1 to 30 pf for most transistors. Some manufacturers label this capacitance C_{ob}.

The base-emitter junction is forward-biased and has a capacitance associated with it, called the diffusion capacitance. A diffusion capacitance $C_{b'e}$ is the result of a time delay that occurs when a hole moves from emitter to collector by diffusing across the base. $C_{b'e}$ is usually much larger than $C_{b'c}$, and is of the order of 100 to 10,000 pf.

The most useful high-frequency model for the common-emitter transistor is called the hybrid pi (CE) model, and is shown in Fig. 8-10. Analysis of circuits using this model is not difficult and gives results which are in excellent agreement with experimental results. (see Experiment 12).

If we consider the low-frequency common-base equivalent circuit shown in Fig. 8-7b and then include the base-emitter and collector-base capacitance, a high-frequency common-base model is obtained as shown in Fig. 8-11.

The short-circuit current gain for the circuit of Fig. 8-11 in terms of Laplace transforms is

$$\frac{I_c(s)}{I_e(s)} = \frac{-h_{fb}\left(\dfrac{h_{fe}}{r_{b'e}C_{b'e}}\right)}{s + \dfrac{h_{fe}}{r_{b'e}C_{b'e}}} \qquad (8\text{-}6)$$

and the value for the upper 3 db frequency of the common-base circuit is $h_{fe}\omega_\beta$.

We should note the similarity between Figs. 8–10 and 8–6b. In Fig. 8–6b, we have the quantity h_{ie}, which is equal to $r_{bb'} + r_{b'e}$. $r_{bb'}$ is the base-spreading resistance, and $r_{b'e}$ is the base-emitter junction resistance and is approximated by $\dfrac{.025 \, h_{fe}}{|I_E|}$ at $T = 300°$. Therefore, $h_{ie} \cong r_{bb'} + \dfrac{.025 \, h_{fe}}{|I_E|}$, with I_E the dc quiescent emitter current. In addition, the dependent current source $h_{fe}i_{b'}$ can be converted into a dependent voltage source if we note that

$$h_{fe}i_{b'} = h_{fe}\left(\frac{v_{b'e}}{r_{b'e}}\right) = g_m v_{b'e} \qquad (8\text{-}7)$$

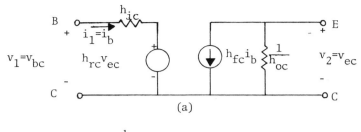

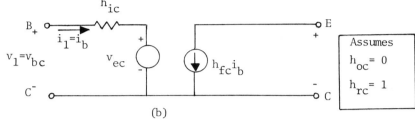

Fig. 8.9 Common collector h parameter circuits.

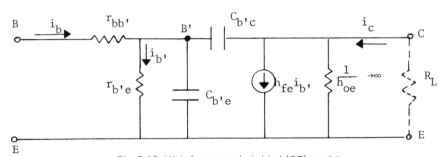

Fig. 8.10 High frequency hybrid pi (CE) model.

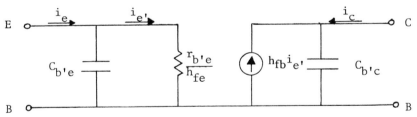

Fig. 8.11 High frequency common base model.

with

$$g_m = \frac{h_{fe}}{r_{b'e}} = \frac{I_E}{.025} \quad \text{at} \quad T = 300^\circ \text{ K} \quad (8\text{-}8)$$

The capacitance $C_{b'c}$ is the measured common-base output capacitance with the emitter input open ($I_E = 0$), and is usually specified by the manufacturer as C_{ob}. The diffusion capacitance $C_{b'e}$ across the emitter junction is directly proportional to the dc emitter current. $C_{b'e}$ is not usually given by the manufacturer, but can be easily calculated if $h_{fe}, r_{b'e}$, and a frequency f_β are known.

Suppose we ac short-circuit the collector-emitter terminals of Fig. 8-10 and calculate the ratio of the transforms of i_c and i_b, i.e.

$$\frac{I_c(s)}{I_b(s)} = \frac{-h_{fe}\dfrac{1}{r_{b'e}(C_{b'e} + C_{b'c})}}{s + \dfrac{1}{r_{b'e}(C_{b'e} + C_{b'c})}} = \frac{-h_{fe}p}{s + p} \quad (8\text{-}9)$$

The pole $p = \omega_\beta$ represents the upper 3 db frequency of the current gain $\left|\dfrac{I_c(j\omega)}{I_b(j\omega)}\right|$. Since $h_{fe} \gg 1$, we introduce another quantity ω_T, at which the short-circuit common-emitter current gain attains unit magnitude—that is,

$$\omega_T \cong h_{fe}\omega_\beta = \frac{h_{fe}}{r_{b'e}(C_{b'c} + C_{b'e})} \cong \frac{h_{fe}}{r_{b'e}C_{b'e}} \quad (8\text{-}10)$$

and

$$C_{b'e} = \frac{h_{fe}}{r_{b'e}\omega_T} \tag{8-11}$$

Also, ω_α of the common base is approximately equal to ω_T. Manufacturers often specify a quantity f_{hfb}, which is approximately equal to

$$\frac{1}{f_{hfb}} = \frac{1}{f_a} + \frac{2(1+\alpha m)}{f_b} \tag{8-12}$$

where

$$f_a = f_T(1 + \alpha m) \tag{8-13}$$

$$f_b = \frac{1}{2\pi r_{bb'}C_{b'c}} \tag{8-14}$$

and m is an excess phase factor whose value is between .2 for diffusion transistors and 1 for drift transistors. For most applications, $f_{hfb} \cong f_T$ is a good approximation.

Manufacturers usually specify h_{fe}, f_T, h_{ie}, and C_{ob}, from which the components of the common-emitter high-frequency equivalent circuit of Fig. 8-10 can be calculated. For example, if f_T = 3.5 mHz, C_{ob} = 18 pf, h_{fe} = 108 at I_E = -6 mA, and V_{CE} = -15 V, and h_{ie} = 560 Ω, then

$$g_m = \frac{I_E}{.025} = \frac{6}{25} = .24 \text{ mho} \tag{8-15}$$

$$r_{b'e} = \frac{.025h_{fe}}{|I_E|} = \frac{h_{fe}}{g_m} = \frac{108}{.24} = 450\ \Omega \tag{8-16}$$

$$r_{bb'} = h_{ie} - r_{b'e} = 560 - 450 = 110\ \Omega \tag{8-17}$$

$$C_{b'c} = C_{ob} = 18 \text{ pf}$$

$$C_{b'e} = \frac{h_{fe}}{r_{b'e}\omega_T} = \frac{108}{(450)(2\pi3.5 \times 10^6)} \cong 11{,}000 \text{ pf} \tag{8-18}$$

The circuit of Fig. 8-10 can be simplified if we assume a resistive load and write KCL at nodes B' and C. The KCL equations are expressed in terms of Laplace transforms as

$$I_b(s) = \left(\frac{1}{r_{b'e}} + sC_{b'e}\right)V_{b'e}(s) - sC_{b'c}(V_{ce}(s) - V_{b'e}) \tag{8-19}$$

$$0 = (g_m - sC_{b'c})V_{b'e}(s) + \left(\frac{1}{R_L} + sC_{b'c}\right)V_{ce}(s) \tag{8-20}$$

If we now limit the frequency range to

$$\omega \ll \frac{g_m}{C_{b'c}}, \frac{1}{R_L C_{b'c}}$$

then Eq. (8-20) is approximated by

$$\frac{V_{ce}(s)}{V_{b'e}(s)} = -g_m R_L$$

and Eq. (8-19) can be simplified to

$$I_b(s) = \left[\frac{1}{r_{b'e}} + s(C_{b'e} + C_{b'c} + g_m R_L C_{b'c})\right]V_{b'e}(s) \tag{8-21}$$

The term $g_m R_L C_{b'c}$ represents the reflection of the capacitance $C_{b'c}$ into the input of the high-frequency equivalent model. The new capacitance $g_m R_L C_{b'c}$ is called the Miller capacitance, and is shown in Fig. 8-12.

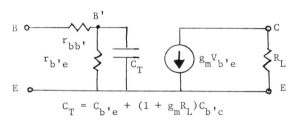

$$C_T = C_{b'e} + (1 + g_m R_L)C_{b'c}$$

Fig. 8.12 High frequency unilateral model.

The high-frequency common-collector (emitter-follower) can be drawn by interchanging the position of a few elements in the common-emitter hybrid pi equivalent circuit shown in Fig. 8-10.

The circuit of Fig. 8-13 cannot be simply reduced to an approximate unilateral model, as was done to the common-emitter circuit.

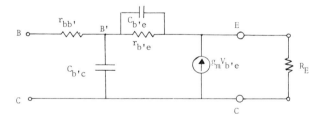

Fig. 8.13 High-frequency hybrid pi (CC) model.

A comparison of various models as well as the gain and impedance of various configurations will be studied in other experiments.

Part Two

OBJECTIVE

In this experiment, data will be obtained from which some low- and high-frequency, small-signal equivalent circuits can be determined for desired quiescent points. Furthermore, some hybrid parameters will be determined from information supplied by transistor manufacturers.

REFERENCES

Alley, C. L., and Atwood, K. W., *Electronic Engineering.* New York: Wiley, 1966, Chapters 4 and 5.
Angelo, E. J., *Electronics: BJTs, FETs, and Microcircuits.* New York: McGraw-Hill, 1969, Chapters 9 and 10.
Chirlian, P. M., *Electronic Circuits: Physical Principles, Analysis, and Design.* New York: McGraw-Hill, 1971, Chapters 6 and 7.
Fitchen, F. C., *Transistor Circuit Analysis and Design.* New York: Van Nostrand Reinhold, 1966, Chapters 4 and 5.
Ghausi, M. S., *Electronic Circuits: Devices, Models, Functions, Analysis, and Design.* New York: Van Nostrand Reinhold, 1971, Chapters 3 and 4.
Gray, P. E., and Searle, C. L., *Electronic Principles: Physics, Models, and Circuits.* New York: Wiley, 1967, Chapters 8, 11, and 12.
Millman, J., and Halkias, C. C., *Electronic Devices and Circuits.* New York: McGraw-Hill, 1967, Chapters 7, 11, and 13.
Schilling, D. L., and Belove, C., *Electronic Circuits: Discrete and Integrated.* New York: McGraw-Hill, 1968, Chapters 6 and 13.

LABORATORY PREPARATION

1. Select some *pnp* and *npn* transistors such as the 2N526 and 2N697 and obtain manufacturer's specifications for your transistors.
2. Select Q points in the normal active regions of your transistors. Calculate the values of V_{EE}, V_{CC}, and R_E required to establish the desired Q points of your transistors using the circuits of Figs. 8–2 and 8–3.
3. Use the manufacturer's specifications to calculate h_{ie}, h_{fe}, h_{re}, h_{oe}, and the other low-frequency h-parameters associated with your transistor Q points.
4. Calculate $C_{b'e}$, $r_{bb'}$, $r_{b'e}$, and g_m for your Q points.

Draw the high-frequency unilateral common-emitter equivalent circuits for your transistor Q points.
5. Draw the high-frequency common-collector (emitter-follower) hybrid pi equivalent circuit for your transistors, and place the estimated values of all components in your circuit diagrams.

LABORATORY PROCEDURE

1. The first step in determining the hybrid parameters is to measure the values of those components which determine the accuracy of the measurements. The measurements can be performed with an impedance bridge (RX meter), or 1% precision components can be used if available. Careful wiring and the use of short leads, is essential for reliable results. Each hybrid parameter should be calculated from the data before the circuit is altered. The Q point should be measured accurately for each transistor circuit that is constructed.
2. Construct the circuit in Fig. 8–2 and measure h_{ie} and h_{fe} for your transistors at your desired Q points. Monitor the Q points by using a dc voltmeter to measure V_{BE}, V_{CE}, and V_{CB}. Apply a small ac input signal and measure all necessary ac signals with an accurate ac voltmeter. Adjust the input frequency until V_o is at its maximum amplitude. Compare your calculated values of h_{ie} and h_{fe} at 1000 Hz with those calculated from the manufacturer's data. Discuss any discrepancies which occur. What range of values do you expect for h_{fe} for a collection of similar transistors at the same Q point?
3. Construct the circuit of Fig. 8–3 and measure h_{re} and h_{oe} for your transistors and your Q points. Monitor the Q points with a dc voltmeter. Compare your measured values with those which you obtained from the manufacturer's data.
4. Use the circuit of Fig. 8–14 to measure C_{ob} of your transistors.

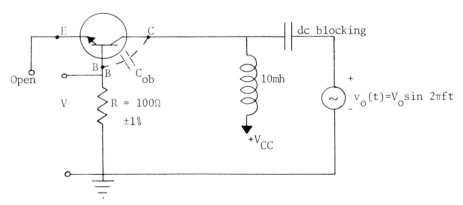

Fig. 8.14 Circuit for measuring C_{ob}.

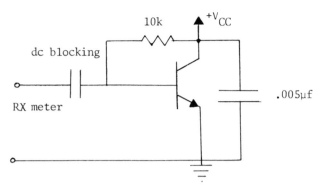

Fig. 8.15 Circuit for measuring $r_{bb'}$.

5. (optional) If your laboratory has an impedance bridge (RX meter), then the circuit of Fig. 8–15 can be used to measure $r_{bb'}$.

If your laboratory has equipment which generates and measures sinusoidal frequencies up to a few hundred megahertz, then the circuit of Fig. 8–16 can be used to measure the cutoff frequency of high-frequency transistors with f_T of higher than 100 MHz. Keep all leads as short as possible.

LIST OF EQUIPMENT

1. Cathode-ray oscilloscope
2. General-purpose voltmeters or ac and dc voltmeters and ohmmeters

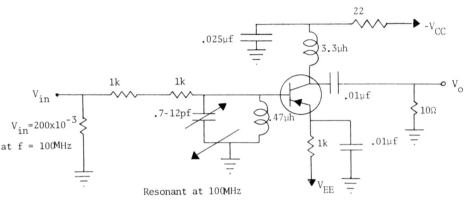

Fig. 8.16 Circuit for measuring f_T.

The frequency of the source should be 100 kHz or higher ($\approx$ 500 kHz). The reactance of C_{ob} is $\dfrac{1}{2\pi f C_{ob}} = X_c$, and

$$\frac{V}{V_o} = \frac{R}{R + X_c} \approx \frac{R}{X_c} \text{ if } X_c \gg R$$

Use an accurate ac voltmeter to measure V and V_o. Compare the measured values of C_{ob} with those given by the manufacturer.

3. Signal Sources: Function generator or sine-wave oscillator, dc power supplies, and a 60 Hz variac
4. Circuit board
5. Isolation transformer
6. Components: Resistors, capacitors, inductors, diodes, and transistors
7. (optional) High-frequency signal source (500 MHz)
8. (optional) High-frequency ac voltmeters
9. (optional) Impedance bridge (RX meter)

Experiment 9/Field-Effect Transistors (JFET and MOS) and Applications

Part One

INTRODUCTION

In a bipolar transistor, the transport of minority carriers across the base region is controlled by the bias of the base region with respect to the emitter. In a field-effect transistor (FET) the conductance of a thin channel is controlled by an electric field. The conductance is changed through variations of either the dimensions or the carrier concentration of the conductive region. In a junction device (junction field-effect transistor–JFET), the width of a conductive channel is controlled by the depletion region of a reverse-biased junction, while in the surface device (metal oxide semiconductor–MOS), the carrier concentration of a surface layer is controlled by an electric field acting through an insulating oxide layer. The MOS device is becoming very popular as an integrated circuit active element because of its simple fabrication and relatively small surface area requirements.

Both types of field effect devices have similar small-signal properties and have the same equivalent circuit elements. This experiment will study biasing, small-signal equivalent circuits, and some applications of field-effect transistors.

THEORY

The three terminals of an FET are designated "source," "drain," and "gate." The analogy between FET's and vacuum tubes has the following form: gate similar to grid, source similar to cathode, and drain similar to the plate. This analogy is valid only to the extent of visualizing how voltages and currents are applied to the device and how the application of these voltages and currents affects the output performance of the device but by no means implies that the magnitudes of these voltages or currents or the physical operation of these devices are the same. Indeed, they are quite different.

A general model for a field-effect device is shown in cross section in Fig. 9-1. In general, there are two control gates (very often connected together), which may be at different potentials. They are separated from the conductive chan-

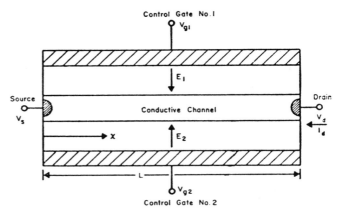

Fig. 9.1 General model of field-effect device.

nels by regions through which the channel controlling electric fields E_1 and E_2 act and which are free from conductance electrons or holes. For the JFET, the regions separating the control gates and the conductive channel are junction depletion regions. For the MOS device, one of these regions is an SiO_2 layer and the other is a depletion region between the surface inversion layer and the bulk substrate on which the device is formed. There are two basic modes of operation of MOS devices—depletion and enhancement. Depletion mode refers to the decrease of carriers in the channel due to variation in gate voltage. En-, hancement mode refers to increase of carriers in the channel due to application of the gate voltage.

Fig. 9-2 shows the symbols used for an n-channel and p-channel FET.

Figs. 9-3 and 9-4 show the V-I characteristics of typical n-channel JFET and MOS devices, respectively.

Junction Field-Effect Devices

An ideal JFET characteristic is shown in Fig. 9-5 for the case where the gate-to-source voltage v_{GS} is zero.

Note that the drain current i_D increases rapidly as the drain-to-source voltage increases until v_{DS} reaches the

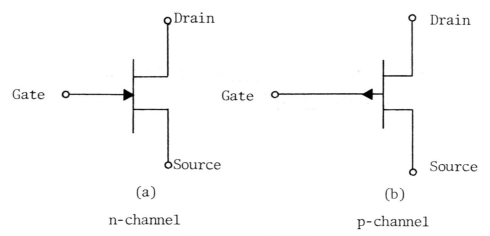

Fig. 9.2 Symbols for FET'S.

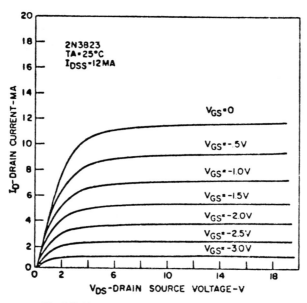

Fig. 9.3 V-I characteristics for *N*-channel JFET.

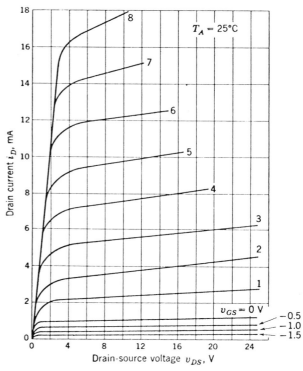

Fig. 9.4 V-I characteristics for *N*-channel MOS.

pinch-off voltage V_{po}. The drain current remains constant at the value I_{DSS} until v_{DS} equals the breakdown voltage BV_{DSS} and avalanche breakdown occurs (see Experiment 6) and the drain current again rises rapidly.

At drain-to-source potentials between pinch-off and breakdown, called the saturation region, the drain current in a JFET is almost constant and can be approximated by

$$i_D = I_{DSS}\left[1 + \frac{3v_{GS}}{V_{po}} + 2\left(-\frac{v_{GS}}{V_{po}}\right)^{\frac{3}{2}}\right] \quad v_{GS} < 0 \quad (9\text{-}1)$$

If $v_{GS} = -V_{po}$, i_D is zero from Eq. (9-1). In a physical device, some current i_D (off) still flows for $|v_{GS}| \geq |V_{po}|$. Note also that the drain current is proportional to v_{GS} and

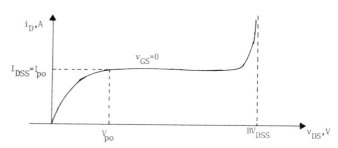

Fig. 9.5 Ideal V-I characteristic for JFET.

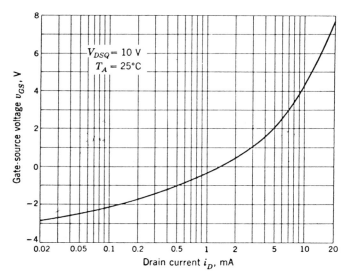

Fig. 9.6 Self-biased common source JFET amplifier.

the $\frac{3}{2}$ power of v_{GS}, and that the JFET is usually operated in the saturation region for linear amplifier application.

The circuit of Fig. 9–6 represents a typical self-biased common-source JFET amplifier.

The semigraphical analysis that is employed to determine the Q point of the JFET is identical to the approach used for bipolar transistors. The dc load line equation is obtained from the drain source loop

$$V_{DD} = (R_d i_D - R_S i_S + v_{DS}) \quad \text{(load line)} \quad (9\text{-}2)$$

The bias equation is

$$i_G R_g + v_{GS} - i_S R_S = 0 \quad \text{(bias curve)} \quad (9\text{-}3)$$

However, since the gate current in a properly biased JFET is less than .01 μA, we can assume that $i_G \cong 0$; and because $i_G + i_D + i_S = 0$, we know that the bias curve is

$$i_D = -\frac{1}{R_S} v_{GS} \quad (9\text{-}4)$$

Eqs. (9–2) and (9–4) can now be used with the V-I characteristics to determine the Q point.

Insulated-Gate MOS Devices

The V-I drain characteristics of an n-channel MOS is given in Fig. 9–4; its transfer curve (i_D vs v_{GS}) for $V_{DS} = 10$V is given in Fig. 9–7.

An approximate expression for the drain current above pinch-off is given by

$$i_D = I_{DSS} \left(1 + \frac{v_{GS}}{V_{po}}\right)^2 \quad (9\text{-}5)$$

Note that the drain current in an MOS is proportional to the square of the gate-to-source voltage and that the MOS is essentially a square law device.

The self-biasing of a common-source MOS amplifier is similar to that of a common-emitter transistor amplifier, and is shown in Fig. 9–8.

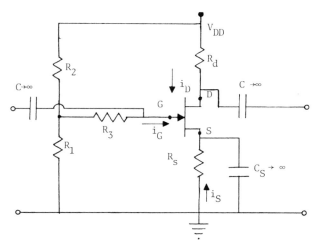

Fig. 9.7 Transfer curve for MOS.

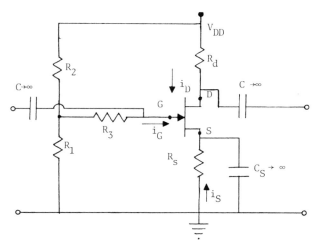

Fig. 9.8 Self-biased common source MOS amplifier.

The dc load line equation for the circuit of Fig. 9–8 is given by

$$V_{DD} = (R_d + R_s)\,i_D + v_{DS} \quad \text{(load line)} \quad (9\text{-}6)$$

Kirchhoff's voltage law around the gate-source circuit can be written if we use a Thevenin equivalent circuit between the gate connection and ground

$$-\frac{R_1}{R_1 + R_2} V_{DD} + \left(\frac{R_1 R_2}{R_1 + R_2} + R_3\right) i_G + v_{GS} - R_s i_S = 0 \quad (9\text{-}7)$$

Again assuming that $i_G \cong 0$, the bias curve is

$$i_D = \frac{1}{R_s} \left(\frac{R_1}{R_1 + R_2} V_{DD} - v_{GS}\right) \quad \text{(bias curve)} \quad (9\text{-}8)$$

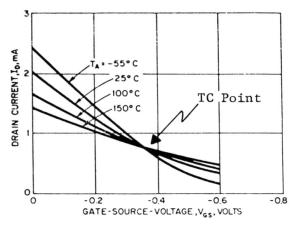

Fig. 9.9 Transfer characteristics vs temperature for a 2N3821 with a V_{DS} of 10 V.

Once again, Eqs. (9-6) and (9-8) and the V-I characteristics can be used to determine the Q point. R_3 serves simply to provide a large ac input impedance, and is usually of the order of a 1 Megohm or more.

A suitable choice of bias network for either the JFET or MOS device will allow the device to operate at either a constant I_D or y_{fs} (see Eq. [9-12]) level over a wide temperature range. It is, in fact, possible to bias a field-effect transistor for zero drain-current drift. As the operating temperature is varied, the +25°C transfer curve (I_D vs V_{GS}) for many devices exhibits a change in transfer characteristics and a change in y_{fs}, as shown in Figs. 9-9 and 9-10.

The curves for various levels of operating temperature pivot around a common point. If the device is biased to this zero temperature coefficient (*TC*) point, there will be no change in quiescent drain current or transconductance as temperature is varied. However, biasing to a zero *TC* point is often achieved at the expense of a smaller value of g_m and voltage gain.

Small-Signal Analysis

While the details of carrier motion and control are different for different types of field effect devices, the basic equations (such as Eqs. [9-1] and [9-5]) describing all types of FET devices have a similar mathematical form and can be treated using a unified approach. The purpose here is to present and discuss a generalized model of field-effect devices and obtain a general equivalent circuit which is identical for both junction and MOS field-effect devices. Only the magnitudes of the small-signal equivalent circuit elements and their dependence upon the dc terminal voltages differ because of the differences in carrier motion and carrier control in the conductive channel.

The drain current i_D can be expressed as a function of drain voltage v_{DS}, and the gate voltage v_{GS} by

$$i_D = f(v_{DS}, v_{GS}) \qquad (9-9)$$

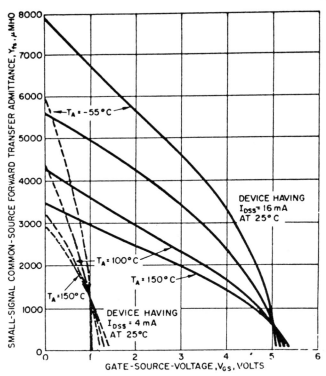

Fig. 9.10 Common-source forward transfer admittance versus gate-to-source voltage at various temperatures for two 2N3823 FET's. Measured at $V_{DS} = 15V$, $f = 1k$ Hz.

A small change in the drain current can be approximated by the first two terms in a Taylor's series expansion about the Q point

$$\Delta i_D = \frac{\partial i_D}{\partial v_{DS}}\bigg|_{Q\text{ point}} \Delta v_{DS} + \frac{\partial i_D}{\partial v_{GS}}\bigg|_{Q\text{ point}} \Delta v_{GS} \qquad (9-10)$$

The output admittance y_{os} or drain-to-source output resistance r_{ds} is defined as

$$r_{ds} = \frac{1}{y_{os}} \triangleq \frac{\partial v_{DS}}{\partial i_D}\bigg|_{Q\text{ point}} \qquad (9-11)$$

y_{os} typically ranges from $2\,\mu$ to $50\,\mu$mhos.

The transconductance y_{fs} is often replaced by the symbol g_m and defined as

$$y_{fs} = g_m \triangleq \frac{\partial i_D}{\partial v_{GS}}\bigg|_{Q\text{ point}} \qquad (9-12)$$

If we use Eq. (9-1) to approximately describe the drain current above pinch-off for a JFET device, then Eq. (9-12) becomes

$$g_m = \frac{3I_{DSS}}{V_{po}}\left[1 - \left(\frac{v_{GS}}{V_{po}}\right)^{1/2}\right] = g_{mo}\left[1 - \left(\frac{v_{GS}}{V_{po}}\right)^{1/2}\right] \qquad (9-13)$$

with $g_{mo} = \dfrac{3I_{DSS}}{V_{po}}$ and if we use Eq. (9-5) for an MOS device

$$g_m = \frac{2I_{DSS}}{V_{po}}\left[1 + \frac{v_{GS}}{V_{po}}\right] = g_{mo}\left[1 + \frac{v_{GS}}{V_{po}}\right] \quad (9\text{-}14)$$

with $g_{mo} = \dfrac{2I_{DSS}}{V_{po}}$ and both gates connected together.

Often a four-terminal JFET is used in a separate bias mode under saturation conditions. The bias voltages and small signals are applied independently to the two gates. The transconductances for this case are approximately

$$g_{m1} = \frac{g_{mo}}{2}\left[1 - \left(\frac{v_{GS1}}{V_{po}}\right)^{1/2} + \left(\frac{v_{GS1} - v_{GS2}}{4V_{po}}\right)\right] \quad (9\text{-}15)$$

$$g_{m2} = \frac{g_{mo}}{2}\left[1 - \left(\frac{v_{GS2}}{V_{po}}\right)^{1/2} + \left(\frac{v_{GS2} - v_{GS1}}{4V_{po}}\right)\right] \quad (9\text{-}16)$$

where

$$v_{GS1} = V_{GS1} + v_{gs1} \quad \text{and} \quad v_{GS2} = V_{GS2} + v_{gs2}$$

The small-signal drain current is

$$i_D = g_{m1}v_{gs1} + g_{m2}v_{gs2}$$

Typical values of g_m's range from 1 to 5 millimhos. The amplification factor μ is often defined as

$$\mu \triangleq \left.\frac{\partial v_{DS}}{\partial v_{GS}}\right|_{Q\text{ point}} = \left.\frac{\partial v_{DS}}{\partial i_D}\right|_{Q\text{ point}} \cdot \left.\frac{\partial i_D}{\partial v_{GS}}\right|_{Q\text{ point}} \quad (9\text{-}17)$$

Therefore, by substitution of Eqs. (9-11) and (9-12) into Eq. (9-17), we obtain

$$\mu = r_{ds}g_m \quad (9\text{-}18)$$

A gate-to-source input admittance y_{is} is sometimes replaced by the gate-to-source resistance r_{gs}, and can be determined by

$$r_{gs} = \frac{1}{y_{is}} = \left.\frac{\partial v_{GS}}{\partial i_G}\right|_{Q\text{ point}} \to \infty \quad (9\text{-}19)$$

This resistance approaches infinity because negligible gate current flows in an FET device. A low-frequency model of an FET device can now be drawn if we use Eqs. (9-10) and (9-18).

The circuit of Fig. 9-11 does not include the capacitance effect between pairs of nodes of the FET device. For ex-

ample, in a junction FET, the back-biased gate gives rise to capacitances C_{gs} and C_{gd}, which are inversely proportional to the dc gate-bias voltages, i.e.

$$C_{gs} \propto \frac{1}{(-V_{GS})^{1/2}} \quad \text{for } V_{GS} \leqslant 0 \quad (9\text{-}20)$$

and

$$C_{gd} \propto \frac{1}{(-V_{GD})^{1/2}} \quad \text{for } V_{GD} \leqslant 0 \quad (9\text{-}21)$$

On the other hand, C_{gs} and C_{gd} of MOS devices show no appreciable change with dc voltages. In addition, C_{ds} represents the drain-to-source capacitance of the channel. A complete model of an FET device would then be as shown in Fig. 9-12.

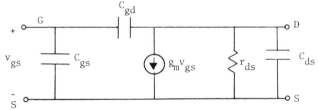

Fig. 9.12 High frequency common source model.

The model of Fig. 9-12 assumes that r_{gs} is very large, and is effectively an open circuit. Typical values of C_{gs} range from 1 to 50 pf, C_{gd} ranges from .1 to 5 pf, and C_{ds} ranges from .1 to 1 pf. In JFET's, r_{ds} can range from .1 M to 1 M ohm, whereas in MOS devices, r_{ds} ranges from 1 k to 100 k ohms. The reverse transfer capacitance C_{rss} is C_{gd}, and C_{oss} is $C_{ds} + C_{gd}$. The common-source circuit input capacitance C_{iss} is $C_{gs} + C_{gd}$, but at high frequencies the reactance of C_{gs} is comparable to $1/r_{gs}$, and the total input admittance y_{is} is specified as a complex number dependent on frequency.

Applications

High Frequency Common-Source Amplifier—The circuit of Fig. 9-6 is known as an FET common-source amplifier. The FET will be replaced by its high-frequency model shown in Fig. 9-12, with the results shown in Fig. 9-13.

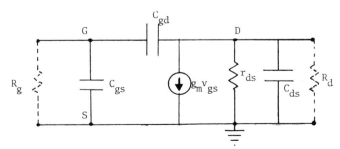

Fig. 9.13 Common source high frequency model.

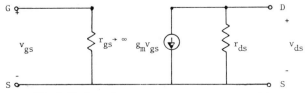

Fig. 9.11 Low frequency common source model.

Note that is is assumed that the reactance of C_s of Fig. 9-6 is approximately 0 for the input frequencies which will be applied. If we use Laplace transforms and write Kirchhoff's current law at the gate and drain nodes in terms of the gate-to-source and drain-to-source node voltages, we have at node G

$$[G_g + s(C_{gs} + C_{gd})] \, V_{gs}(s) - sC_{gd}V_{ds}(s) = 0 \quad (9\text{-}22)$$

and at node D

$$g_m V_{gs}(s) - sC_{gd}V_{gs}(s)$$
$$+ [G_d + g_{ds} + s(C_{ds} + C_{gd})] \, V_{ds}(s) = 0 \quad (9\text{-}23)$$

Now divide Eq. (9-23) by C_{gd}, let $s = j\omega$, and assume that $C_{ds} \approx 0$, with

$$\omega \ll \frac{g_m}{C_{gd}}$$

and

$$\omega \ll \frac{G_d + g_{ds}}{C_{gd}}$$

Then Eq. (9-23) reduces to

$$\frac{g_m}{C_{gd}} V_{gs}(j\omega) + \left[\frac{G_d + g_{ds}}{C_{gd}}\right] V_{ds}(j\omega) = 0 \quad (9\text{-}24)$$

and from Eq. (9-24)

$$V_{ds}(j\omega) = \frac{-g_m}{G_d + g_{ds}} V_{gs}(j\omega) = -g_m \frac{R_d r_{ds}}{R_d + r_{ds}} V_{gs}(j\omega) \quad (9\text{-}25)$$

We now substitute Eq. (9-25) into Eq. (9-22)

$$\left[G_g + j\omega \left(C_{gs} + C_{gd} + \frac{C_{gd}g_m}{G_d + g_{ds}}\right)\right] V_{gs}(j\omega) = 0 \quad (9\text{-}26)$$

The capacitance

$$C_M = C_{gd} \left(1 + \frac{g_m}{G_d + g_{ds}}\right)$$

is the Miller capacitance. A new approximate model can now be used for analysis purposes, and it is shown in Fig. 9-14.

If a voltage source $v_i(t)$ in series with its internal resistance R_i is applied to the input (i.e., between gate and source), the transform of the ratio of output voltage to the input voltage is the voltage gain $A_v(s)$

$$A_v(s) = \frac{V_o(s)}{V_i(s)} = \frac{-g_m(r_{ds}||R_d)/C_T R_i}{s + \frac{1}{C_T(R_g||R_i)}} = \frac{A_v(0)p}{s + p} \quad (9\text{-}27)$$

where $C_T = C_{gs} + C_M$

$$r_{ds}||R_d = \frac{r_{ds}R_d}{r_{ds} + R_d} \quad \text{and} \quad R_g||R_i = \frac{R_g R_i}{R_g + R_i}$$

The dc voltage gain $A_v(s)$ at $s = 0$ is

$$A_v(0) = \frac{-g_m R_d r_{ds} R_g}{(R_g + R_i)(r_{ds} + R_d)} \quad (9\text{-}28)$$

For $r_{ds} \gg R_d$ and $R_g \gg R_i$, Eq. (9-28) reduces to

$$A_v(0) = -g_m R_d \quad (9\text{-}29)$$

and Eq. (9-28) exhibits a pole at

$$p = \frac{1}{C_T(R_g||R_i)} \quad (9\text{-}30)$$

which is the upper 3 db frequency of the amplifier. The pole-zero diagram and Bode asymptotic plot for Eq. (9-27) are shown in Figs. 9-15 and 9-16.

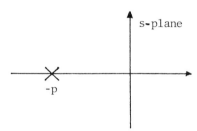

Fig. 9.15 Pole-zero diagram.

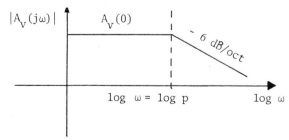

Fig. 9.16 Bode asymptotic plot.

Chopper Amplifiers—A chopper is basically a device that converts a dc voltage (or low-frequency ac) into an ac voltage of the same amplitude. To accomplish this, the device alternately connects and disconnects the source to the load at some periodic frequency. In essence, the chopper should behave as an ideal switch which offers no resistance to the source signal when closed and infinite impedance when

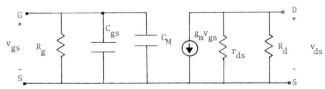

Fig. 9.14 High frequency common source unilateral model.

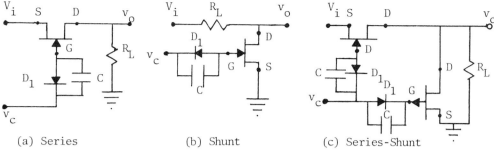

Fig. 9.17 Chopper amplifiers.

open. The FET chopper is a very good approximation to a switch because when the FET is turned fully ON, the path from drain to source is a pure resistance of about 25 to 500 ohms, and when the FET is turned OFF, the resistance approaches infinity and is of the order of 10^{12} ohms.

There are three basic types of FET choppers: series, shunt, and series-shunt, as shown in Fig. 9-17a, b, c. V_i represents the dc input signal, v_c is the ac chopping signal (usually a square-wave), and v_o is the ac output signal whose peak-to-peak amplitude is equal to V_i and whose frequency is equal to the frequency of the chopping signal v_c. The purpose of the diode D_1 is to prevent the flow of gate current under a forward-bias condition. Capacitor C is to remove undesirable charge on the gate terminal of the device.

Fig. 9-17a shows an n-channel FET connected in a common-source configuration. The current I_D has its greatest magnitude for $V_{GS} = 0$, and decreases for increas-

ingly negative values of V_{GS}. Hence, the device is fully turned ON and has its lowest value of drain-source resistance; this resistance is designated r_{ds} (ON). A reduction of I_D occurs when the gate terminal is made negative with respect to the source terminal. The FET is turned OFF when V_{DS} is more negative than the pinch-off voltage; the resistance for this case is designated r_{ds} (OFF). Resistance of the drain-source channel is not affected by the direction of drain-source current flow. Thus r_{ds} (ON) of the FET has the same value for either polarity of drain-source voltage. However, for either polarity of V_{DS}, the gate must be negative with respect to the most negative of the gate and drain terminals.

Fig. 9-17b shows a shunt type switching circuit in which an n-channel FET is used as the switch element. The diode D_1 prevents the gate-drain junction from becoming forward-biased when V_i is negative. A zero-level chopping signal to the diode biases the FET to the I_{DSS} current level,

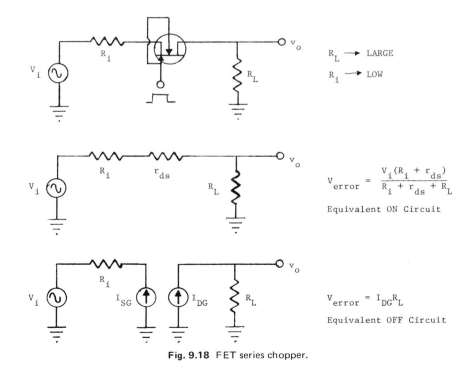

$$R_L \longrightarrow \text{LARGE}$$
$$R_i \longrightarrow \text{LOW}$$

$$V_{error} = \frac{V_i(R_i + r_{ds})}{R_i + r_{ds} + R_L}$$

Equivalent ON Circuit

$$V_{error} = I_{DG}R_L$$

Equivalent OFF Circuit

Fig. 9.18 FET series chopper.

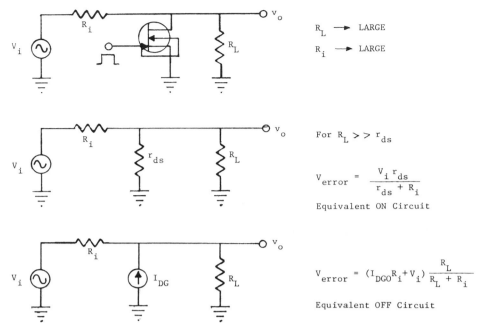

For $R_L \gg r_{ds}$

$$V_{error} = \frac{V_i r_{ds}}{r_{ds} + R_i}$$

Equivalent ON Circuit

$$V_{error} = (I_{DGO}R_i + V_i)\frac{R_L}{R_L + R_i}$$

Equivalent OFF Circuit

Fig. 9.19 FET shunt chopper.

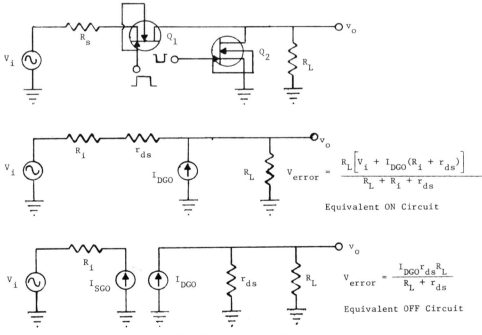

$$V_{error} = \frac{R_L\left[V_i + I_{DGO}(R_i + r_{ds})\right]}{R_L + R_i + r_{ds}}$$

Equivalent ON Circuit

$$V_{error} = \frac{I_{DGO}r_{ds}R_L}{R_L + r_{ds}}$$

Equivalent OFF Circuit

Fig. 9.20 Series-shunt chopper.

and a large negative gate input signal pinches off the FET for either polarity of V_i. The least negative value of the chopping signal which will insure pinch-off is given by

$$|v_c| \geqslant |-V_i| + |V_{po}| + |V_{D_1}| \qquad (9\text{-}31)$$

where V_{D_1} is the forward voltage drop of diode D_1. In the

shunt chopper circuit, the gate terminal is at a negative potential when the chopping signal is at the $-v_c$ level. When the chopping signal rises to 0 volts, the negative charge on the gate terminal of the FET must be removed if the device is to be turned OFF. This charge is removed by the capacitor across the diode.

An additional FET and a diode can be added to the series

chopper, as shown in Fig. 9-17c, in order to improve the turn-off time of the output voltage waveform v_o. When one FET is pinched off, the other is allowed to conduct, and vice versa. The load capacitance of the series chopper is allowed to discharge quickly through the low r_{ds} (ON) of the shunt FET chopper.

Two equivalent circuits can be used for the dc analysis of the series, shunt, and series-shunt choppers. Figs. 9-18, 9-19, and 9-20 show the equivalent dc circuits for the ON and OFF conditions of the FET switches. The voltage error V_e is given by the difference in the steady state value of the voltage v_o and V_i.

Part Two

OBJECTIVE

In this experiment, the terminal characteristics of field-effect transistors and some of their applications will be studied.

REFERENCES

Alley, C. L., and Atwood, K. W., *Electronic Engineering.* New York: Wiley, 1966, Chapter 6.

Angelo, E. J., *Electronics: BJTs, FETs, and Microcircuits.* New York: McGraw-Hill, 1969, Chapters 6 and 7.

Chirlian, P. M., *Electronic Circuits: Physical Principles, Analysis, and Design.* New York: McGraw-Hill, 1971, Chapters 3, 5, 6, and 7.

Fitchen, F. C., *Transistor Circuit Analysis and Design.* New York: Van Nostrand Reinhold, 1966, Chapters 3, 4, and 5.

Ghausi, M. S., *Electronic Circuits: Devices, Models, Functions, Analysis, and Design.* New York: Van Nostrand Reinhold, 1971, Chapters 3 and 4.

Gray, P. E., and Searle, C. L., *Electronic Principles: Physics, Models, and Circuits.* New York: Wiley, 1967, Chapters 9, 10, 12, and 13.

Millman, J., and Halkias, C. C., *Electronic Devices and Circuits.* New York: McGraw-Hill, 1967, Chapter 14.

Schilling, D. L., and Belove, C., *Electronic Circuits: Discrete and Integrated.* New York: McGraw-Hill, 1968, Chapters 10, 12, and 13.

LABORATORY PREPARATION

1. The circuits of Figs. 7-20 and 7-21 can be used to display the V-I characteristics of FET devices. Explain how these circuits should be modified to display the V-I characteristics of some typical JFET and MOS devices such as the 2N3819, 2N3820, 2N3823, and 2N3796.

2. The circuit of Fig. 9-21 can be used to measure the transconductance ($g_m = y_{fs}$) of an *n*-channel JFET such as the 2N3819. Explain how this circuit can be used to measure g_m. Determine the values of V_{GG}, V_{DD}, and R_d for your FET device ($R_G = 100\,k\Omega$).

How should the circuit of Fig. 9-21 be modified to measure the g_m of an *n*-channel MOS field-effect transistor such as the 2N3796 and the g_m of a *p*-channel JFET such as the 2N3820? Obtain manufacturer's specifications for your FET devices.

3. The circuit of Fig. 9-22 can be used to measure the drain-source resistance ($r_{ds} = 1/y_{os}$) of an *n*-channel JFET. Explain the operation of this circuit. How should this cir-

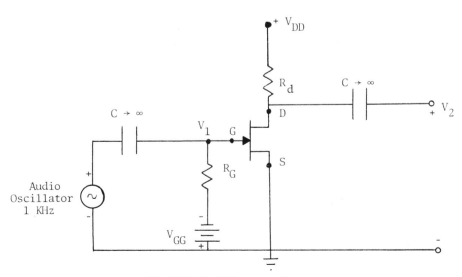

Fig. 9.21 Circuit for measuring g_m.

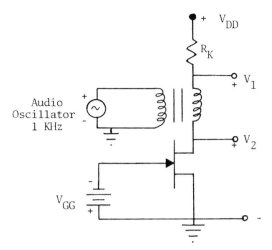

Fig. 9.22 Circuit for measuring r_{ds}.

cuit be modified to measure r_{ds} for an *n*-channel MOS and a *p*-channel JFET?

4. The circuit of Fig. 9–6 will be used as a common-source JFET amplifier. For some desired values of V_{DS} and I_D ($V_{DS} = 9$ V and $I_{DS} = 3.7$ mA for the 2N3819), determine R_D and R_s to be used in your design. Determine the input impedance, output impedance, and voltage gain at midband using estimated values of g_m and r_{ds} obtained from your characteristic curves or from the manufacturer's specifications.

Perform the same calculations for a MOS field-effect transistor such as the 2N3796. (Modify the biasing circuitry for the MOS device as shown in Fig. 9–8.)

5. Determine the high-frequency voltage gain $V_o(s)/V_{in}(s)$ using the equivalent circuit shown in Fig. 9–12. Does this gain have a finite pole and a finite zero? Draw the pole-zero diagram and the Bode asymptotic plot of gain.

6. Use the equivalent circuit shown in Fig. 9–14 and determine the gain $V_o(s)/V_{in}(s)$ and compare with step 5.

7. The circuits of Fig. 9–17*a*, *b*, and *c* are typical series,

shunt, and series-shunt choppers. Explain the operation of these circuits and sketch the approximate output waveforms for a given JFET (e.g., 2N3819) when $v_c(t)$ is a square wave and V_i is first +10 volts and then is –10 volts. Use a diode such as a 1N34A, 1N270, 1N627, or 1N914. The capacitance C should be about 100 pf.

8. (optional) Often it is desirable for the chopping signal $v_c(t)$ to be fed first into a driver circuit before being applied to the FET. The purpose of the driver circuitry is to amplify the chopping signal, to provide a positive and negative swing for the chopping signal, and to improve the rise time of the output signal. A typical driver circuit is shown in Fig. 9–23. Note that three power supplies and two transistors (one *npn* and one *pnp*) are required for this particular driver circuitry. Typically a 2N526 and a 2N542 (or 2N647) can be used. For a 25 volt output swing, $V_{CC1} = 21V$, $V_{CC2} = -12.5$ V, and $V_{CC3} = 12.5$ V, $R_1 = 1$ k, $R_2 = 1.5$ k, $R_3 = 390$, $R_4 = 2$ k, $C_2 = C_4 = 100$ pf. Determine where the Q point is for T_1 and T_2 and what happens to each transistor when $v_c(t)$ is a square wave of 4 V peak to peak.

9. (optional) Design a circuit which could be used to measure the small-signal transconductances of a four-terminal field-effect transistor such as the 3N124.

LABORATORY PROCEDURE

1. Display the characteristics of some FET devices on your oscilloscope. Use the circuits you designed in step 1 of your preparation.

2. Construct the circuit of Fig. 9–21 and measure the transconductance of your field-effect devices. Be careful with power supply polarities for the *n*-channel and *p*-channel devices. Do not exceed the absolute maximum ratings given by the manufacturer. Compare your measured values with the manufacturer's specifications.

3. Construct the circuit of Fig. 9–22 and measure r_{ds} for your field-effect devices. Compare your measured values with the manufacturer's specifications. Are you operating

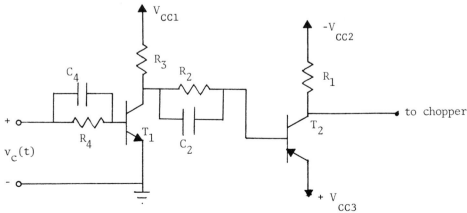

Fig. 9.23 Driver circuit.

at the quiescent point for which the manufacturer's values are valid? If not, either modify your Q point to correspond to the manufacturer's or convert the manufacturer's values of g_m and r_{ds} to correspond to the Q point at which you are measuring r_{ds} and g_m. Calculate the value of the gain μ for your devices.

4. Measure the input impedance, output impedance, and voltage gain at midband frequencies of the common-source FET amplifiers shown in Fig. 9-6. Be sure that you first measure the Q point of your amplifier. The methods you employ to measure input and output impedances for the field-effect transistor will also apply to the bipolar transistors in Experiment 10. The circuit for measuring input impedance is shown in Fig. 9-24.

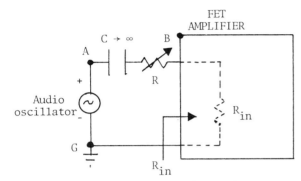

Fig. 9.24 Circuit for measuring input resistance.

Vary R until the ac voltage between B and G is one half the voltage between A and G. Use a sensitive ac voltmeter to measure the amplitude of v_{BG} and v_{AG}. For these values of voltage, $R_{in} = R$. That is,

$$v_{BG} = \frac{R}{R + R_{in}} \cdot v_{AG} = \frac{1}{2} v_{AG} \qquad (9\text{-}32)$$

and

$$\frac{R}{R + R_{in}} = \frac{1}{2} \quad \text{implies} \quad R = R_{in}$$

Similarly, the output impedance can be measured using the circuit of Fig. 9-25. Measure the amplitude of the ac signal v_{AG} with the switch S open. Now close the switch and adjust R until v_{BG} is one half the measured value of v_{AG}. Once again

$$\frac{R}{R + R_o} = \frac{1}{2} \quad \text{and} \quad R = R_o \qquad (9\text{-}33)$$

5. Take enough data to make a rough plot of the voltage gain of the amplifier shown in Fig. 9-6 as the input frequency is varied. Measure the upper 3 db frequency and compare with your calculated value.

6. Measure the phase difference between input and output of your amplifier as the frequency is varied. The method described in Experiment 1 for measuring phase differences can be used.

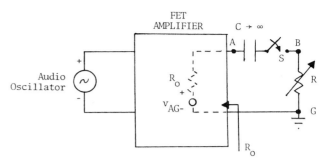

Fig. 9.25 Circuit for measuring output resistance.

7. Construct the circuit of Fig. 9-17a, but reverse the drain and source leads. Apply a 25 V peak-to-peak chopping square wave of 50 kHz to the gate. The dc input voltage is now applied to the drain. The input voltage V_i should be set to +10 volts and then to –10 volts. The resistance R_L should vary between 5 and 80 k. Place a capacitor of about 16 pf across R_L. Now measure the rise time of the output voltage as R_L varies. Plot the output waveform and explain any difference between the output waveform and a perfect square-wave. You have now converted a dc input voltage V_i into an ac voltage of approximately the same amplitude. Vary the input frequency above 100 kHz and observe the effects.

8. Construct the circuit of Fig. 9-17b, but use a p-channel FET such as the 2N3820. Perform the same measurements as in step 7. There is no need to put a capacitor across the load resistor in this circuit. Why?

9. Construct the series-shunt chopper circuit shown in Fig. 9-17c with a capacitor of 16 pf across the load resistor R_L. Perform the same measurements in step 7 and compare steps 7, 8, and 9.

10. (optional) Construct the driver circuitry you have designed and connect it first to the series chopper, then to the shunt chopper, and finally to the series-shunt chopper. Measure, in turn, the rise time of $v_o(t)$ for each chopper as R_L is varied between 5 and 80 k. Plot the rise time in microseconds versus R_L for each of your driven choppers. Compare with steps 7, 8, and 9. Discuss any distortions in the output voltage $v_o(t)$ which occur.

11. (optional) Measure the small-signal transconductances of a four-terminal field-effect transistor.

LIST OF EQUIPMENT

1. Cathode-ray oscilloscope
2. General-purpose voltmeters or ac and dc voltmeters and ohmmeters
3. Signal sources: Function generator or sine-wave and square-wave oscillator, dc power supplies
4. Circuit board
5. Isolation transformer
6. Components: Resistors, capacitors, diodes, bipolar transistors, and field-effect transistors

Experiment 10/Midband Frequency Calculations in Transistor Amplifiers

Part One

INTRODUCTION

A transistor amplifier is called a midband or low-frequency stage when its frequency response at relatively low frequencies is constant. In addition, a transistor stage is called a low-power or small-signal stage when the input power stays well below the permissible power dissipation of its transistor. Therefore, a small-signal midband stage is one for which the collector swing is small enough for the transistor to be considered as a linear device and replaceable, for purposes of analysis, by a small-signal equivalent-circuit model which is independent of the input signal frequency.

It is assumed, then: that a suitable Q point has been established by the use of dc biasing circuits, that the input signal power stays below the dissipation limitations of the transistor, that the "small" collector swing allows the transistor to be replaced by a linear circuit model, and that restriction of the frequency range allows models not containing frequency-dependent elements to be valid. Under these assumptions, the analysis and design of various transistor amplifier configurations will mainly involve the determination of their small signal gains and impedances employing the small-signal equivalent circuits derived in Experiments 8 and 9. The next experiment will consider the case where the input frequency is not restricted but the input signal amplitude is still restricted so that the small-signal frequency-dependent models of Experiment 8 are applicable.

THEORY

There are three basic configurations for transistor amplifiers. These are the common-emitter, common-base, and common-collector configurations. As was pointed out in Experiment 8, these designations do not necessarily imply that the emitter, base, or collector terminals of these amplifier configurations are grounded. For example, a resistor could be placed between emitter and ground, and the configuration could still be called a common-emitter configuration. The designation "common-emitter" refers to an input signal applied at the base and an output signal available at the collector.

Four important quantities will be derived for each of the configurations mentioned. The current gain, voltage gain, input impedance, and output impedance will be specified in terms of the h-parameters. The simplest equivalent circuits will be derived which are valid for most analysis and design requirements. Simplifying assumptions will be made based upon the fact that the theoretical results obtained with these assumptions are in close agreement with experimental evidence. By performing this experiment, you should obtain the evidence to substantiate or refute the assumptions made in the analysis. In addition, you should be able to convert transistors into different configurations, understand the purpose of each configuration, and compare the advantages and disadvantages of one configuration with another. This experiment will deal mainly with bipolar transistors. The calculations and analysis methods employed with the bipolar transistors in this experiment are also applicable to FET transistors, and, hence, only a summary of important quantities for FET transistors is given in Table 10-1.

Common-Emitter Configuration

In this section we will use the small-signal equivalent model given in Fig. 8-6c. The circuit for the common-emitter amplifier and its equivalent model are shown in Fig. 10-1a and b.

The small-signal model within the dashed line of Fig. 10-1b is the linear model obtained by biasing the transistor in the normal active region. The transistor R_1, R_2, R_L, R_E, and V_{CC} determine the Q point. R_B is the parallel combination of R_1 and R_2, and note that C_1, C_2 and C_E are short circuits (very small reactances) to the input frequencies which will be applied. When C_E is very large, we say that the emitter resistor R_E is bypassed. The values of h_{ie} and h_{fe} can be determined by the methods described in Experiment 8. The current gain, voltage gain, input imped-

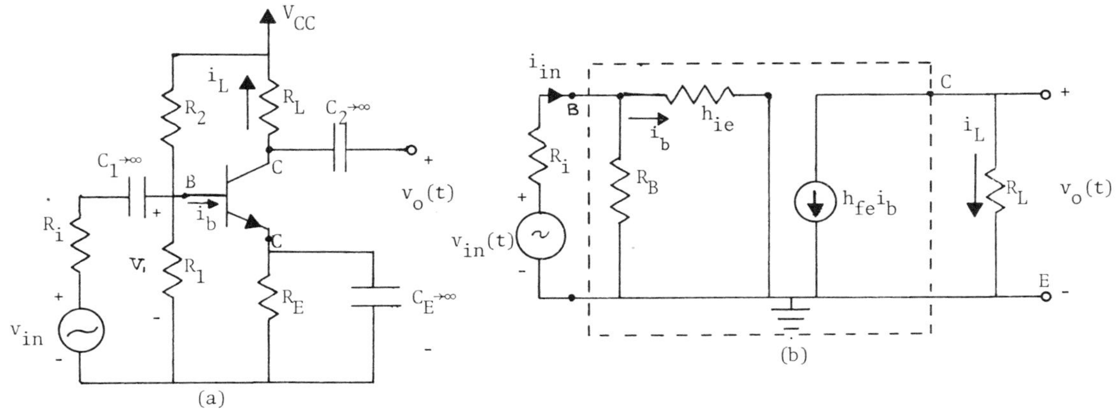

Fig. 10.1 Common-emitter amplifier and model.

ance, and output impedance can be calculated directly from Fig. 10-1b.

For the current gain

$$i_b = \frac{R_B}{R_B + h_{ie}} i_{in} \qquad (10\text{-}1)$$

and

$$i_L = -h_{fe}i_b = -h_{fe} \frac{R_B}{R_B + h_{ie}} i_{in} \qquad (10\text{-}2)$$

Therefore

$$A_i = \frac{i_L}{i_{in}} = \frac{-h_{fe}R_B}{R_B + h_{ie}} \qquad (10\text{-}3)$$

If R_B is much larger than h_{ie}, then Eq. (10-3) reduces to

$$A_i = -h_{fe} \qquad (10\text{-}4)$$

For the voltage gain

$$i_b = \frac{\dfrac{R_B}{R_B + h_{ie}}}{R_i + \dfrac{R_B h_{ie}}{R_B + h_{ie}}} v_{in} \qquad (10\text{-}5)$$

$$v_o(t) = R_L i_L = -R_L h_{fe} i_b \qquad (10\text{-}6)$$

Therefore

$$A_v = \frac{v_o}{v_{in}} = \frac{\dfrac{-R_L h_{fe} R_B}{R_B + h_{ie}}}{R_i + \dfrac{R_B h_{ie}}{R_B + h_{ie}}} \qquad (10\text{-}7)$$

If $R_i \ll \dfrac{R_B h_{ie}}{R_B + h_{ie}}$ or if the input voltage is measured from base to ground, then

$$A_v = \frac{-R_L h_{fe}}{h_{ie}} \qquad (10\text{-}8)$$

The input impedance is defined as

$$\frac{v_{in}}{i_{in}} = Z_i = R_i + \frac{R_B h_{ie}}{R_B + h_{ie}} \qquad (10\text{-}9)$$

Assuming once again that $R_B \gg h_{ie}$, then

$$Z_i = R_i + h_{ie} \qquad (10\text{-}10)$$

Very often R_i is much smaller than $\dfrac{R_B h_{ie}}{R_B + h_{ie}}$ or if the input voltage is measured from base to ground, then

$$Z_i \approx h_{ie} \qquad (10\text{-}11)$$

The calculation of the output impedance (with R_L considered external to the amplifier) is even simpler. If h_{oe} is taken into account, then

$$Z_o = \left.\frac{v_{ce}}{i_c}\right|_{i_{in} = 0} = \frac{1}{h_{oe}} \qquad (10\text{-}12)$$

If we neglect h_{oe} as indicated in Fig. 10-1b, then

$$Z_o = \infty \qquad (10\text{-}13)$$

The parameters h_{re} and h_{oe} are almost never specified by the manufacturer, and are usually neglected in calculations.

Suppose we now consider the case when R_E is not bypassed.

The model of Fig. 10-2 can be simplified by splitting the

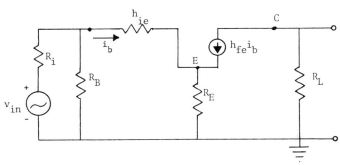

Fig. 10.2 Common-emitter amplifier model with emitter resistor.

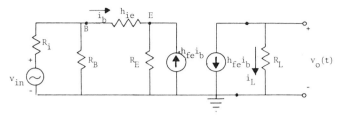

Fig. 10.3 Simplified model.

current source $h_{fe}i_b$ into two sources of equal magnitude, with one current source entering node E and another leaving node C as shown in Fig. 10-3. Now we observe that currents i_b and $h_{fe}i_b$ are passing through resistor R_E. Therefore, resistor R_E can be replaced by a resistance whose value is $R_E(1 + h_{fe})$ which has current i_b passing through it as shown in Fig. 10-4.

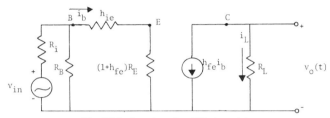

Fig. 10.4 Another simplified model.

The current gain is now expressed as

$$A_i = \frac{-h_{fe}R_B}{R_B + h_{ie} + (1 + h_{fe})R_E} \qquad (10\text{-}14)$$

and the voltage gain for

$$R_i \ll \frac{R_B[h_{ie} + (1 + h_{fe})R_E]}{R_B + h_{ie} + (1 + h_{fe})R_B} \qquad (10\text{-}15)$$

is

$$A_v = \frac{-R_L h_{fe}}{h_{ie} + (1 + h_{fe})R_E} \qquad (10\text{-}16)$$

Very often $(1 + h_{fe})R_E \gg h_{ie}$ and $h_{fe} \gg 1$; then Eq. (10-16) simplified to

$$A_v = -\frac{R_L}{R_E}$$

The input impedance, if inequality Eq. (10-15) holds, is

$$Z_i \approx \frac{R_B[h_{ie} + (1 + h_{fe})R_E]}{R_B + h_{ie} + (1 + h_{fe})R_E} \qquad (10\text{-}17)$$

If $R_B \gg h_{ie} + (1 + h_{fe})R_E$, then the input impedance is approximated by

$$Z_i \approx h_{ie} + (1 + h_{fe})R_E \qquad (10\text{-}18)$$

The output impedance is still

$$Z_o = \frac{1}{h_{oe}} \qquad (10\text{-}19)$$

Very often the power gain of a common-emitter amplifier is required. The power gain A_p is defined as the ratio of the output power to the input power

$$A_p = \frac{P_L}{P_i} = \frac{\frac{1}{2}R_L i_L^2}{\frac{1}{2}Z_i i_{in}^2} = \frac{R_L}{Z_i}A_i^2 \qquad (10\text{-}20)$$

with A_i and Z_i given by Eqs. (10-14) and (10-17), respectively.

Common-Collector (Emitter-Follower) Configuration

The common-collector configuration is shown in Fig. 10-5a, and its model in Fig. 10-5b. From Fig. 10-5b,

$$i_{in} = i_b + \frac{1}{R_B}(h_{ic}i_b + v_{ec}) \qquad (10\text{-}21)$$

and

$$v_{ec} = -R_E h_{fc}i_b = R_E i_e \qquad (10\text{-}22)$$

The current gain can be calculated from Eqs. (10-21) and (10-22).

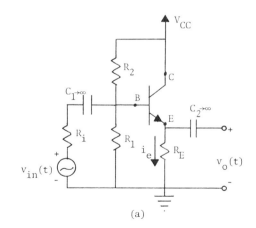

(a)

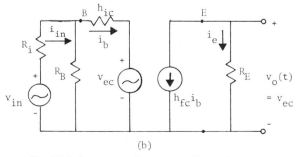

(b)

Fig. 10.5 Common-collector amplifier and model.

$$A_i = \frac{i_e}{i_{in}} = \frac{-h_{fc}}{1 + \dfrac{h_{ic}}{R_B} - \dfrac{R_E h_{fc}}{R_B}} \qquad (10\text{-}23)$$

Assuming $\dfrac{h_{ic}}{R_B} - \dfrac{R_E h_{fc}}{R_B} \ll 1$ yields

$$A_i \approx -h_{fc} \qquad (10\text{-}24)$$

and using Table 8-1

$$A_i \approx -(1 + h_{fe}) \qquad (10\text{-}25)$$

The voltage gain is

$$A_v = \frac{v_{ec}}{v_{in}} = \frac{1}{\left(\dfrac{R_i + R_B}{R_B}\right)\left(1 - \dfrac{h_{ic}}{R_E h_{fc}}\right) - \dfrac{R_i}{R_E h_{fc}}} \qquad (10\text{-}26)$$

If we let $R_i \rightarrow 0$ and use Table 8-1, we obtain

$$A_v = \frac{1}{1 + \dfrac{h_{ie}}{R_E(1 + h_{fe})}} \qquad (10\text{-}27)$$

Eq. (10-27) is very close to 1 if $R_E(1 + h_{fe}) \gg h_{ie}$. The input impedance

$$Z_i = \frac{v_{in}}{i_{in}} = R_i + \frac{R_B(h_{ic} - h_{fc}R_E)}{R_B + h_{ic} - h_{fc}R_E} \qquad (10\text{-}28)$$

and using Table 8-1 and assuming that

$$R_B \gg h_{ie} + (1 + h_{fe})R_E$$

then

$$Z_i = R_i + h_{ie} + (1 + h_{fe})R_E \qquad (10\text{-}29)$$

and to the right of terminals BC, the impedance is $h_{ie} + (1 + h_{fe})R_E$.

The output impedance to the left of terminals EC is

$$Z_o = -\frac{v_{ec}}{i_e} = +\frac{v_{ec}}{h_{fc}i_b} \qquad (10\text{-}30)$$

with

$$v_{ec} = -\left(h_{ic} + \frac{R_B R_i}{R_B + R_i}\right)i_b + \frac{R_B}{R_i + R_B}v_{in} \qquad (10\text{-}31)$$

If we assume $v_{in} = 0$, then

$$Z_o = -\frac{\left(h_{ic} + \dfrac{R_B R_i}{R_B + R_i}\right)}{h_{fc}} \qquad (10\text{-}32)$$

Again, using Table 8-1 yields

$$Z_o = \frac{h_{ie} + \dfrac{R_B R_i}{R_B + R_i}}{1 + h_{fe}} = h_{ib} + \frac{R_B||R_i}{1 + h_{fe}} \qquad (10\text{-}33)$$

Of course, the output impedance including the resistor R_E is simply $R_E||Z_o$.

Common-Base Configuration

We first note that the base of the transistor in the circuit of Fig. 10-6a is ac connected to ground by the resistor C_1. This means that resistor R_1 is used to bias the transistor but is effectively ac short-circuited by capacitor C_1.

The current gain for the model shown in Fig. 10-6b is simply

$$A_i = \frac{i_L}{i_{in}} = +1 \qquad (10\text{-}34)$$

because the amplification factor h_{fb} is assumed to be 1 and $h_{ob} = 0$. If, instead, the model in Fig. 8-7a is used, we

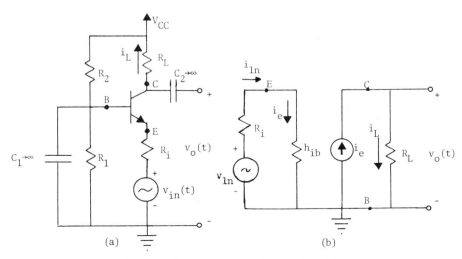

Fig. 10.6 Common-base amplifier and model.

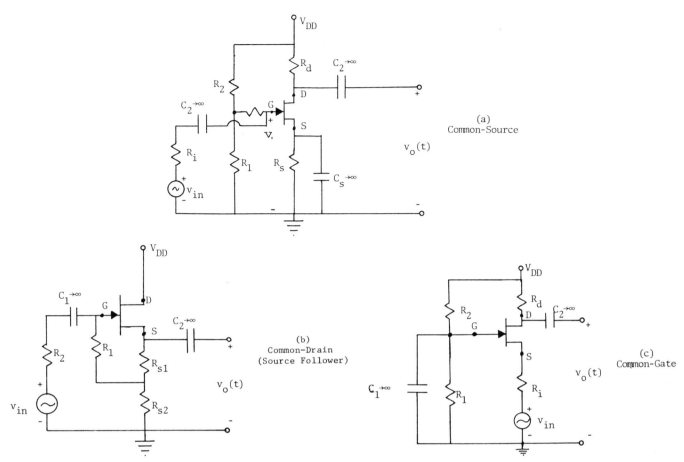

Fig. 10.7 FET amplifier configurations.

TABLE 10-1 APPROXIMATE PARAMETERS.

	Current Gain A_i	Voltage Gain A_v	Input Impedance $Z_i(R_i = 0)$	Output Impedance Z_o
Common-emitter	$-h_{fe}$	$\dfrac{-R_L h_{fe}}{h_{ie}}$	h_{ie}	$\dfrac{1}{h_{oe}}$
Common-collector (Emitter-follower)	$-h_{fc} = -(1 + h_{fe})$	$\dfrac{1}{1 + \dfrac{h_{ie}}{R_E(1 + h_{fe})}}$	$h_{ie} + (1 + h_{fe})R_E$	$h_{ib} + \dfrac{R_B \Vert R_i}{1 + h_{fe}}$
Common-base	$h_{fb} = -\dfrac{h_{fe}}{1 + h_{fe}}$	$\dfrac{R_L}{R_i + h_{ib}}$	h_{ib}	$\dfrac{1}{h_{ob}}$
Common-source	$-\dfrac{g_m r_{ds} r_{gs}}{r_{ds} + R_d}$	$-\dfrac{g_m r_{ds} R_d}{r_{ds} + R_d}$ $(R_i = 0)$	r_{gs}	r_{ds}
Common-drain (Source-follower)	0 $(R_s \rightarrow \infty)$	$\dfrac{g_m r_{ds}}{1 + g_m r_{ds}} = \dfrac{\mu}{1 + \mu}$ $(R_s \rightarrow \infty)$	$(1 + \mu)R_1$ $(R_{s_2} \gg R_{s_1})$	$\dfrac{r_{ds}}{1 + g_m r_{ds}} = \dfrac{r_{ds}}{1 + \mu}$
Common-gate	1	$\dfrac{(1 + \mu)R_d}{R_i(1 + \mu) + r_{ds} + R_d}$	$\dfrac{r_{ds} + R_d}{1 + \mu}$	$r_{ds} + (1 + \mu)R_s$

obtain

$$A_i = \frac{i_L}{i_{in}} = \frac{\dfrac{h_{fb}}{h_{ob}}}{R_L + \dfrac{1}{h_{ob}}} \qquad (10\text{-}35)$$

Assuming that $R_L \ll 1/h_{ob}$ yields

$$A_i = h_{fb} = -\frac{h_{fe}}{1 + h_{fe}} \qquad (10\text{-}36)$$

The voltage gain from Fig. 10-6b is

$$A_v = \frac{v_o}{v_{in}} = \frac{R_L}{R_i + h_{ib}} \qquad (10\text{-}37)$$

The input and output impedances by inspection are

$$Z_i = R_i + h_{ib}$$

and

$$Z_o = \infty \; (h_{ob} \to 0) \qquad (10\text{-}38)$$

If we assume that h_{ob} does not approach 0 and we use the model of Fig. 8-7a, then the output impedance to the left of terminals CB with $v_{in}(t) = 0$ is

$$Z_o = \frac{\dfrac{1}{h_{ob}}}{1 + \dfrac{h_{rb}h_{fb}}{h_{ob}(R_i + h_{ib})}} \qquad (10\text{-}39)$$

Eq. (10-39) reduces to $1/h_{ob}$ when

$$\frac{h_{rb}h_{fb}}{h_{ob}(R_i + h_{ib})} \ll 1$$

Table 10-1 shows the approximate gains and impedances for the various configurations of bipolar transistors. In addition, the parameters for the common configurations of FET amplifiers are also given for the purposes of comparison, and the JFET circuits are shown in Fig. 10-7a, b, c.

Part Two

OBJECTIVE

This experiment was designed to be a study of the transistor as a circuit element. The voltage and current gains and the input and output impedances of the three common configurations will be calculated using small-signal analysis and compared with their experimental values measured in the laboratory.

REFERENCES

Alley, C. L., and Atwood, K. W., *Electronic Engineering.* New York: Wiley, 1966, Chapters 4 and 5.

Angelo, E. J., *Electronics: BJTs, FETs, and Microcircuits.* New York: McGraw-Hill, 1969, Chapters 10 and 12.

Chirlian, P. M., *Electronic Circuits: Physical Principles, Analysis, and Design.* New York: McGraw-Hill, 1971, Chapters 3 and 6.

Fitchen, F. C., *Transistor Circuit Analysis and Design.* New York: Van Nostrand Reinhold, 1966, Chapters 5 and 6.

Ghausi, M. S., *Electronic Circuits: Devices, Models, Functions, Analysis, and Design.* New York: Van Nostrand Reinhold, 1971, Chapters 3 and 4.

Gray, P. E., and Searle, C. L., *Electronic Principles: Physics, Models, and Circuits.* New York: Wiley, 1967, Chapter 11.

Millman, J., and Halkias, C. C., *Electronic Devices and Circuits.* New York: McGraw-Hill, 1967, Chapters 11 and 12.

Schilling, D. L., and Belove, C., *Electronic Circuits: Discrete and Integrated.* New York: McGraw-Hill, 1968, Chapter 6.

LABORATORY PREPARATION

Common-Emitter Configuration

1. Select a low-power audio amplifier type transistor such as the 2N526 or 2N647. Design the circuit of Fig. 10-1a for a Q point which will provide for linear operation. The first step is to select the quiescent operating point, a process which begins by drawing the load line on the output characteristics. The bias curve is drawn next, and its intersection with the load line determines the operating point. The stability factor should also be chosen to be less than one half of the h_{fe} of your transistor. What are your values of $R_1, R_2, R_L, R_E,$ and V_{CC}? (See Experiments 7 and 8.) These specifications are not intended to be sufficiently detailed to produce a unique design.

2. Determine the rms value of the maximum sinusoidal output voltage from the characteristics.

3. Assume operation in the midband frequency range where C_1 is effectively a short circuit and C_E bypasses resistor R_E. Calculate the voltage gain, current gain, power gain, and input and output impedances using the approximate formulas given in this experiment and your values of $R_1, R_2, R_L, h_{fe},$ and h_{ie}. The ac output and input voltages should be defined across terminals where these voltages are directly measurable. Remove the bypass capacitor C_E, and

once again calculate A_i, A_v, A_p, Z_i, and Z_o. Which of these parameters change when C_E changes?

4. (optional) Design a common-source FET amplifier using both a JFET and an MOSFET. This design should proceed as described in experiment 9. Calculate according to the formulas given in Table 10–1 (verify these formulas) the voltage gain, current gain, input and output impedance, using your values of μ, r_{gs}, r_{ds}, etc. Compare the values of the midband gains and impedances of these amplifiers with the bipolar common-emitter transistor amplifier which you have designed.

Common-Collector Configuration

5. Design the circuit of Fig. 10–5a according to the specifications given in step 1 when R_E is not bypassed. Design for the same Q point that was used in step 1.

6. Repeat steps 2 and 3 for the common-collector (emitter-follower) configuration.

7. What are the essential differences in gains and impedances between the common-collector and the common-emitter amplifiers?

8. Place a resistor R_L between the collector and the power supply V_{CC} of Fig. 10–5a. Now select R_L so that the sum of $R_L + R_E$ is identical to the value of R_E selected in step 5. Now repeat steps 6 and 7.

9. (optional) Design a common-drain FET amplifier using both a JFET and MOSFET. Repeat step 4 of the preparation.

Common-Base Configuration

10. Repeat steps 1, 2, and 3 where applicable for the circuit of Fig. 10-6a.

11. Compare all three configurations with respect to voltage gain, current gain, input impedance, and output impedance. This comparison should include the effects of R_1, R_2, R_L, and R_E when they are different for each configuration.

12. (optional) Design a common-gate FET amplifier using both a JFET and an MOSFET. Repeat step 4 of the preparation. Compare all three common FET configurations with respect to voltage gain and input and output impedances.

LABORATORY PROCEDURE

Common-Emitter Configuration

1. Assemble the circuit of Fig. 10-1a. Measure all the voltages necessary to completely specify the Q point. Does this agree with your calculated Q point? If it does not, do not go on until you have determined where the error has occurred. If you are having difficulties, check with your instructor at this time.

2. Apply a sinusoidal input signal frequency of about 1 kHz. Remember that all transistor capacitances and parameter variations with frequency have been neglected. All measurements should be made without violating the assumptions of the small-signal theory, and an oscilloscope should be used to check the wave shape of the voltages.

3. The voltage and current gains are simply obtained by measuring appropriate input and output voltages. The appropriate input voltage is set to some convenient value such as .01 or .1 volt. The currents are obtained by dividing measured voltages by known resistances.

4. The above measurements should be repeated for the case with R_E unbypassed and compared with the calculated values.

5. The input impedance is measured by placing a variable resistance R in series with the ac input signal and between the ac input signal and the base of the transistor. Now determine the value of R required to reduce v_o to one half of the value it had for $R = 0$. Determine a suitable value of this resistance. Will changing R change the output impedance? Will changing R change A_v? With the emitter bypass capacitor present, the output voltage wave shape is influenced by the value of R. This can be observed by adjusting the amplitude of the sine-wave oscillator ($v_{in}(t)$) to keep the amplitude of $v_o(t)$ approximately constant as R is varied. Observe that, unless R is relatively large, even output voltages of moderate magnitude are distorted. This is due to the fact that the transistor is a linear amplifier but its input resistance is nonlinear. The need for a large source resistance, in order to avoid substantial distortion, is often a disadvantage of the common-emitter amplifier since it reduces the useful voltage amplification.

6. The output impedance is measured by placing a resistor R across v_o (from collector to ground). Now determine the value of R required to reduce v_o to one half of the value it had for $R = \infty$ (open circuit). Perform the same measurement with R_E unbypassed.

7. (optional) Measure the Q point, current gain, voltage gain, input impedance, and output impedance for the common-source FET amplifiers you designed in step 4 of the preparation. Compare measured and calculated values. Compare the gains and impedances of these amplifiers with those for your bipolar common-emitter transistor amplifier.

Common-Collector Configuration

8. Repeat steps 1 through 6 for the circuit of Fig. 10-5a. Use the values of R_1, R_L, etc. which you calculated in step 5 of the preparation. Compare all calculated and measured values as well as with the common-emitter amplifier gains and impedances. Making a table such as Table 10–1 containing your measured values should be helpful.

9. (optional) Repeat step 7 for the common-drain FET amplifiers you designed in step 9 of the preparation.

Common-Base Configuration

10. Repeat steps 1 through 6 for the circuit of Fig. 10-6a. Use the values of R_1, R_L, etc. which you calculated in step 10 of the preparation. Complete the table suggested in step 8.

11. (optional) Repeat step 7 for the common-gate FET amplifiers you designed in step 12 of the preparation.

LIST OF EQUIPMENT

1. Cathode-ray oscilloscope
2. General-purpose voltmeter or ac and dc voltmeter and ohmmeters
3. Signal sources: Function generator or sine-wave oscillator, dc power supply
4. Circuit board
5. Components: Resistors, capacitors, transistors (bipolar and FET's)

Experiment 11/Low- and High-Frequency Response of RC-Coupled Transistor Amplifiers (Bipolar and FET's)

Part One

INTRODUCTION

Small-signal transistor stages can be coupled by the use of resistive-capacitive (RC) type networks. Both the low-frequency effects, due mainly to RC coupling and external elements, and the high-frequency effects, due to the transistors, will be included in the analysis and design of RC-coupled amplifiers. The input signal to these amplifiers will be either sinusoidal or square waveforms. However, the linear analysis will employ Laplace transforms, which are applicable to a rather large class of inputs. The steady-state sinusoidal response will also be studied.

THEORY

A typical response of current or voltage gain with frequency is illustrated in Fig. 11-1.

The maximum value A_m of the gain $|A(j\omega)|$ occurs over a frequency range where all capacitors can be neglected. The analysis and design of the amplifiers presented in this experiment were valid for this range of frequencies.

The fall-off of the gain at low frequencies is caused by the use of coupling and bypass capacitors. Amplifiers not employing coupling and bypass capacitors such as integrated circuits and dc amplifiers are capable of amplifying very low-frequency signals. The fall-off at high frequencies is due to the internal capacitance of the transistors (see Experiment 8) and external stray capacitances.

The boundaries separating the three ranges are not always easily discernible. However, throughout this experiment we assume that these bands are distinguishable and that a different simplified equivalent circuit model can be used to calculate the responses in each band. In the low-frequency range, the coupling and bypass capacitors determine the response, while stray and transistor capacitances are effectively open circuits. In the midband-frequency range, the coupling and bypass capacitors are short circuits, and the stray and transistor capacitances are open circuits. Therefore, no capacitances appear in the midband-equivalent circuit. In the high-frequency band, the coupling and bypass capacitors are short circuits, and the stray and transistor capacitances determine the response.

The lower 3 db frequency f_1 usually determines the upper bound of the low-frequency range and the lower bound of the midband range. The upper 3 db frequency f_2 usually fixes the upper bound of the midband range and the lower bound of the high-frequency range. The upper and lower 3 db frequencies (f_2 and f_1) are defined as those frequencies for which the transfer function has fallen 3 db below A_m, as shown in Figure 11-1. The total midband-frequency range is called the bandwidth BW, and is defined as

$$BW = f_2 - f_1$$

(Note that if $f_2 \gg f_1$, then $BW \approx f_2$. See Experiments 4 and 5.)

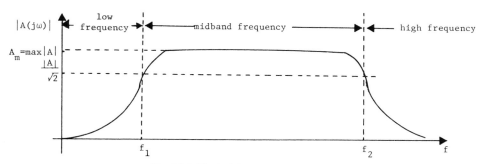

Fig. 11.1 Typical frequency response.

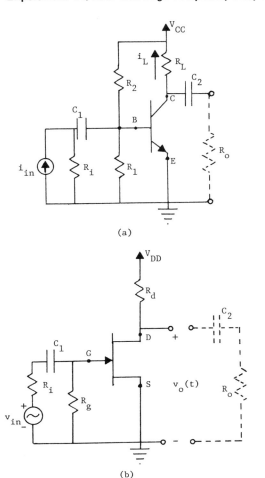

(a)

(b)

Fig. 11.2 Common emitter and common source amplifiers.

Low-Frequency Response

The low-frequency response of a common-emitter or common-source amplifier is determined by the coupling capacitors and the bypass capacitors. We will consider the effects of each type of capacitor separately and then the combined effect. The capacitor C_1 in Fig. 11-2a and b is used to couple the ac signal source to the active device and also to block dc signals so as not to upset the bias conditions.

The low-frequency, small-signal models for the transistors are used in the equivalent circuits of Fig. 11-3a and b.

They correspond, respectively, to the circuits of Fig. 11-2a and b.

The current gain for the bipolar transistor circuit with input coupling can be obtained by first solving for the transform of the current i_b using Kirchhoff's laws

$$I_b(s) = \frac{\left(\dfrac{R_i}{h_{ie}}\right)(R_B \| h_{ie}) I_{in}(s)}{R_i + \dfrac{1}{sC_1} + R_B \| h_{ie}} \qquad (11\text{-}1)$$

The output current $I_L(s)$ is simply equal to $-h_{fe}I_b(s)$, and, consequently, the current gain is

$$A_i(s) = \frac{I_L(s)}{I_{in}(s)} = \frac{-h_{fe}R_i R_B s/(R_i(R_B + h_{ie}) + R_B h_{ie})}{s + \dfrac{1}{C_1[R_i + R_B \| h_{ie}]}} \qquad (11\text{-}2)$$

This transfer function has the following pole-zero form

$$A_i(s) = \frac{+A_i(\infty)s}{s + p_1} \qquad (11\text{-}3)$$

where

$$A_i(\infty) = \frac{-h_{fe}R_i R_B}{R_i(R_B + h_{ie}) + R_B h_{ie}} \qquad (11\text{-}4)$$

and

$$p_1 = \frac{1}{C_1[R_i + R_B \| h_{ie}]} \qquad (11\text{-}5)$$

A similar form is obtained for the FET voltage gain, which is

$$A_v(s) = \frac{V_0(s)}{V_{in}(s)} = \frac{-g_m R_g R_d s/(R_i + R_g)}{s + \dfrac{1}{C_1[R_i + R_g]}} \qquad (11\text{-}6)$$

where

$$A_v(s) = \frac{+A_v(\infty)s}{s + p_1'} \qquad (11\text{-}7)$$

with

$$A_v(\infty) = \frac{-g_m R_g R_d}{R_i + R_g} \qquad (11\text{-}8)$$

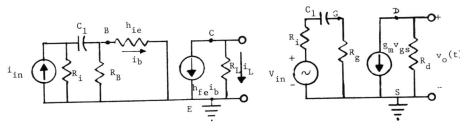

Fig. 11.3 Models for common emitter and common source amplifiers.

and

$$p_1' = \frac{1}{C_1 [R_i + R_g]} \qquad (11\text{-}9)$$

The pole-zero diagram and asymptotic plot of gain are shown in Fig. 11-4a and b. An asymptotic plot of phase can also be drawn. It is important to note that there is a finite zero and a pole in each of the transfer functions

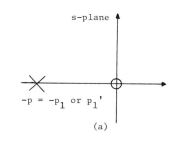

(a)

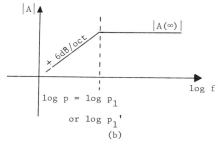

(b)

Fig. 11.4 Pole-zero diagram and Bode asymptotic plot of gain.

(Eqs. [11-2] and [11-6]) and that the break frequency is due to C_1 (both p_1 and p_1' depend upon C_1). Therefore, there is a low-frequency fall-off in the transfer function due to the presence of the input coupling circuit. The lower 3 db frequency is obtained by solving for the frequency at which the gain is .707 of the midband gain $|A(\infty)|$ (down 3 db). That is,

$$|A(j\omega)| = \frac{|A(\infty)| \omega}{[\omega^2 + p^2]^{1/2}} = \frac{|A(\infty)|}{\sqrt{2}} \qquad (11\text{-}10)$$

Solving for ω^2, we obtain

$$\omega_2 = p^2 \Rightarrow \omega = \pm p$$

We accept the real positive frequency as ω_1 and

$$\omega_1 = p \qquad (11\text{-}11)$$

This demonstrates that the lower 3 db frequency is determined by the pole location which is dependent on C_1 and input resistances. A similar transfer function and frequency response is obtained when the output coupling circuit is considered containing capacitor C_2 and a resistance due to a load or input of a second stage (R_0).

The effect of adding an emitter resistance R_E or source resistance R_s with bypass capacitor C_E or C_s (both of which have finite values, $C_E, C_s \neq \infty$) produces essentially the same effect as the input and output coupling capacitors.

Suppose that we consider the common-emitter transistor amplifier and its model as shown in Fig. 11-5a and b.

Consider the emitter resistance and bypass capacitor as in impedance $Z_E(s)$; then

$$(1 + h_{fe}) Z_E(s) = \frac{(1 + h_{fe}) R_E \left(\frac{1}{sC_E}\right)}{R_E + \frac{1}{sC_E}} = \frac{(1 + h_{fe}) \frac{1}{C_E}}{s + \frac{1}{R_E C_E}}$$

$$= \frac{(1 + h_{fe}) \frac{1}{C_E}}{s + p_E} \qquad (11\text{-}12)$$

with

$$p_E = \frac{1}{R_E C_E}$$

The transform of the current in the base is

$$I_b(s) = \frac{R_B I_{in}(s)}{R_B + h_{ie} + (1 + h_{fe}) Z_E(s)} \qquad (11\text{-}13)$$

and the load current is

$$I_L(s) = -h_{fe} I_b(s) = \frac{-h_{fe} R_B I_{in}(s)}{R_B + h_{ie} + (1 + h_{fe}) Z_E(s)}$$

$$(11\text{-}14)$$

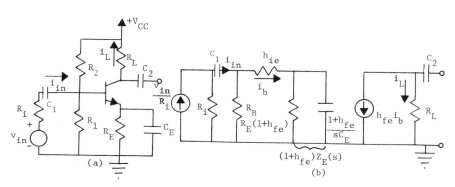

Fig. 11.5 Common-emitter amplifier and model.

The current gain can be simplified to

$$A_i(s) = \frac{I_L(s)}{I_{in}(s)} = \frac{\dfrac{-h_{fe}R_B}{R_B + h_{ie}}(s + p_E)}{s + p_E + \dfrac{1 + h_{fe}}{C_E(R_B + h_{ie})}}$$

$$= \frac{K(s + p_E)}{s + p_E + \dfrac{1 + h_{fe}}{C_E(R_B + h_{ie})}} \quad (11-15)$$

with

$$K = \frac{-h_{fe}R_B}{R_B + h_{ie}}; \quad A(0) = \frac{-h_{fe}R_B}{R_B + h_{ie} + R_E(1 + h_{fe})} \quad (11-16)$$

and

$$A(\infty) = \frac{-h_{fe}R_B}{R_B + h_{ie}} \quad (11-17)$$

$A(\infty)$ is the midband gain. The current gain has a finite pole and zero (dipole pair), which is shown with the asymptotic plot of gain in Fig. 11-6a and b.

In most applications, both C_E and C_1 are present, and the analysis is more complicated. A transfer function can be derived considering both C_1 and C_E. However, the emitter bypass capacitor usually determines the low-frequency response, and this requires that the pole in the transfer function due to C_1 be far to the left of $-\dfrac{1}{R_E C_E}$. This implies that

$$\frac{1}{C_1(R_i + R_B \| h_{ie})} \gg \frac{1}{R_E C_E} \quad (11-18)$$

If $R_i + R_B \| h_{ie}$ is of the same order of magnitude as R_E, then $C_E \gg C_1$.

FET common-source amplifiers with bypass capacitors have voltage gain expressions similar to Eq. (11-15) and, hence, frequency responses similar to bipolar transistors.

Each of the low-frequency responses calculated thus far have been for a single stage. Suppose that we now couple two or more identical stages and that the low-frequency

gain function is given by

$$A(s) = \frac{A(\infty)s^n}{(s + p)^n} \quad (11-19)$$

The low-frequency cutoff ω_1 is determined from

$$\frac{|A(\infty)(j\omega_1)^n|}{|(j\omega_1 + p)^n|} = \frac{A(\infty)}{\sqrt{2}} \quad (11-20)$$

and the low-frequency cutoff is given by

$$\omega_1 = \frac{p}{\sqrt{2^{1/n} - 1}} \quad (11-21)$$

Eq. (11-21) shows that the lower 3 db cutoff frequency increases as n increases. This means that more and more lower frequencies are attenuated as the number of stages increases. Even if the stages are not identical, the lower 3 db cutoff frequency still increases as n increases.

Now we consider the case where the input is a unit step function. This means that

$$I_{in}(s) = \frac{1}{s} \quad (11-22)$$

and that the load current for the circuit of Fig. 11-2a is

$$I_L(s) = \frac{+A(\infty)s}{s(s + p_1)} \quad (11-23)$$

The inverse transform (time function) of the load current is the output time response

$$i_L(t) = +A(\infty)e^{-p_1 t}u(t) = A(\infty)e^{-(t/T_1)}u(t); \quad p_1 = \frac{1}{T_1} \quad (11-24)$$

Eq. (11-24) is a decaying exponential, and is shown in Fig. 11-7.

Suppose that we now have a square wave input which has a period T and alternating $+1$ and -1 amplitudes. This square wave can be represented by a sum of delayed unit step functions

$$i_{in}(t) = u(t) - 2u\left(t - \frac{T}{2}\right) + 2u(t - T) - 2u\left(t - \frac{3T}{2}\right)\cdots \quad (11-25)$$

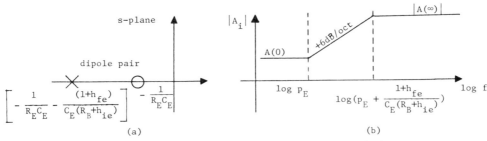

Fig. 11.6 Pole-zero diagram and Bode asymptotic plot of gain.

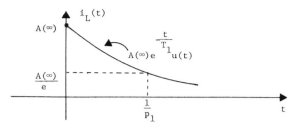

Fig. 11.7 Graph of equation 11-24.

The square-wave input is simply a series of rectangular pulses, as shown in Fig. 11-8.

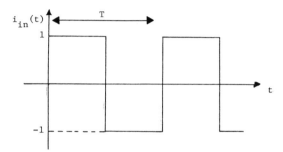

Fig. 11.8 Square wave input.

The Laplace transform of the input is

$$I_{in}(s) = \frac{1}{s} - \frac{2e^{-(Ts/2)}}{s} + \frac{2e^{-Ts}}{s} - \cdots \quad (11\text{-}26)$$

The load current for Fig. 11-2a is

$$I_L(s) = A(\infty)\left[\frac{1}{s+p_1} - \frac{2e^{-(T/2)s}}{s+p_1} + \frac{2e^{-Ts}}{s+p_1} \cdots\right]$$

$$(11\text{-}27)$$

The zero state or time response is

$$i_L(t) = A(\infty)\left[e^{-p_1 t}u(t) - 2e^{-p_1(t-(T/2))}u\left(t-\frac{T}{2}\right)\right.$$

$$\left. + 2e^{-p_1(t-T)}u(t-T) + \cdots\right] \quad (11\text{-}28)$$

We can conclude that the current through the load resistor is a sum of decaying exponentials, as shown in Fig. 11-9.

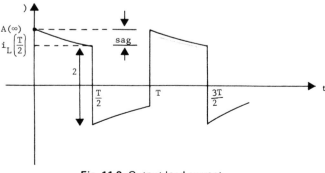

Fig. 11.9 Output load current.

The flat-top response shown in Fig. 11-9 is characterized by a sag or tilt. The fractional sag δ is defined as

$$\delta \triangleq \frac{sag}{A(\infty)} = [1 - e^{-p_1(T/2)}]$$

where the sag is

$$sag = i_L\left(\frac{T}{2}\right) - i_L(0^+)$$

If the input square-wave period is small compared with $\frac{1}{p_1}$ (i.e. $T \ll \frac{1.0}{p_1}$), the sag/sec. is specified approximately by the slope of the output load current at $t = 0$ and

$$\delta \approx p_1 \frac{T}{2} \quad (11\text{-}29)$$

The coupling and emitter bypass circuits produce the sag, which is smaller if the lower 3 db frequency is lower. The sag for each type of low-frequency circuit is given in Table 11-1.

TABLE 11-1 APPROXIMATE FRACTIONAL SAG δ

	Bipolar	FET
Input Coupling	$\dfrac{T/2}{C_1[R_1 + R_B\|h_{ie}]}$	$\dfrac{(T/2)}{C_1[R_i + R_g]}$
Output Coupling (R_0 is resistance to the right of C_2)	$\dfrac{(T/2)}{C_2(R_L + R_0)}$	$\dfrac{(T/2)}{C_2(R_d + R_0)}$
Emitter Bypass (Source Bypass)	$\dfrac{(T/2)(R_B + R_E + h_{ie})}{C_E R_E(R_B + h_{ie})}$	$\dfrac{(T/2)[r_{ds} + R_d\|R_L + (1+\mu)R_s]}{C_s R_s(r_{ds} + R_d\|R_L)}$

If there are several RC coupled identical stages, the gain for the complete low-frequency circuit can be written as

$$A_i(s) = \frac{A_i(\infty)s^n}{(s+p_1)^n} \quad (11\text{-}30)$$

and the output current for a unit step input current is

$$I_L(s) = \frac{A_i(\infty)s^{n-1}}{(s+p_1)^n} \quad (11\text{-}31)$$

The zero state or time response is

$$i_L(t) = \frac{A_i(\infty)}{(n-1)!}\frac{d^{n-1}}{dt^{n-1}}(e^{-p_1 t}(t)^{n-1}) \quad (11\text{-}32)$$

which can be approximated as

$$i_L(t) \approx -A_i(\infty)nt \quad (11\text{-}33)$$

and

$$sag/sec. = -\left.\frac{di_L(t)}{dt}\right|_{t=0^+} = +A_i(\infty)n \quad (11\text{-}34)$$

This shows that the sag increases linearly with the number of stages. Comparing Eq. (11-21) with Eq. (11-34), we observe that ω_1 and δ increase with n. Therefore, there is no direct relationship between low-frequency cutoff and sag when n is unknown.

High-Frequency Response

The high-frequency response of common-emitter or common-source amplifiers is determined by the internal capacitance of the transistors and external stray capacitances. The high-frequency models for the circuits of Fig. 11-2a and b are given in Fig. 11-10a and b.

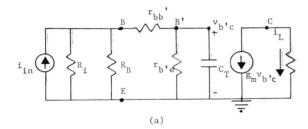

(a)

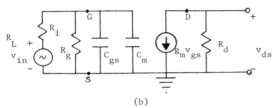

(b)

Fig. 11.10 High frequency models.

The transfer functions for these two circuits can be derived as before

$$A_i(s) = \frac{I_L(s)}{I_{in}(s)} = \frac{\dfrac{-g_m R}{(r_{bb'} + R)C_T}}{s + p_T + \dfrac{1}{C_T(R + r_{bb'})}} = \frac{A_i(0)p_2}{s + p_2}$$

(11-35)

where

$$R = R_B \| R_i; \quad p_T = \frac{1}{C_T r_{b'e}} \quad \text{and} \quad p_2 = p_T + \frac{1}{C_T(R + r_{bb'})}$$

$$A_v(s) = \frac{V_{ds}(s)}{V_{in}(s)} = \frac{\dfrac{-g_m R_d}{C_F}}{s + \dfrac{1}{C_F}\left(\dfrac{1}{R_g} + \dfrac{1}{R_i}\right)} = \frac{A_v(0)p_2'}{s + p_2'}$$

(11-36)

where

$$C_F = C_{gs} + C_M \quad \text{and} \quad p_2' = \frac{1}{C_F}\left(\frac{1}{R_g} + \frac{1}{R_i}\right)$$

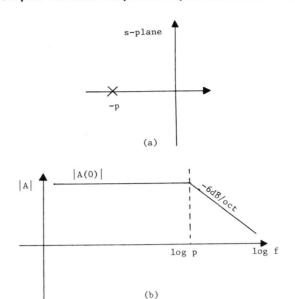

Fig. 11.11 Pole-zero diagram and Bode asymptotic plot.

Both transfer functions have the identical single pole form

$$A(s) = \frac{A(0)p}{s + p}$$

(11-37)

The s-plane and asymptotic plot of gain are shown in Fig. 11-11a and b.

The magnitude of the high-frequency pole (p_2 or p_2') is generally many times larger than the magnitude of the low-frequency pole (p_1 or p_1').

This large separation of pole locations allows the high-frequency and low-frequency models to be considered separately, as described in this experiment. On the other hand, if p_2 is not much larger than p_1, the combined effect can be considered in a single transfer function including p_1 and p_2.

Very often a number of identical stages are coupled together, so that the overall transfer function has the form

$$A(s) = \frac{A(0)p_2^n}{(s + p_2)^n}$$

(11-38)

The high-frequency cutoff ω_2 is determined from

$$\frac{A(0)p_2^n}{|(j\omega_2 + p_2)^n|} = \frac{A(0)}{\sqrt{2}}$$

(11-39)

and the high-frequency cutoff is given by

$$\omega_2 = p_2 \sqrt{2^{\frac{1}{n}} - 1}$$

(11-40)

Eq. (11-40) shows that the upper 3 db frequency cutoff decreases as n increases. This means that the $BW(\omega_2 \gg \omega_1)$ decreases as the number of stages increases.

We again consider the case where the input is a unit step

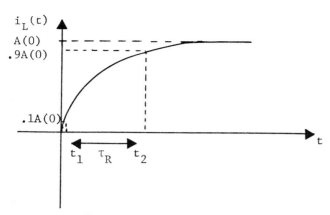

Fig. 11.12 Output time response.

function and the output current is given by

$$I_L(s) = \frac{A(0)p_2}{s(s+p_2)} = \frac{A(0)}{s} - \frac{A(0)}{s+p_2} \qquad (11\text{-}41)$$

and

$$i_L(t) = A(0)(1 - e^{-p_2 t})u(t) \qquad (11\text{-}42)$$

The output current $i_L(t)$ is shown in Fig. 11-12.

The rise time is, by definition, the time required for the response to rise from 10 to 90% of the steady state value; therefore

$$t_2 - t_1 = \tau_R = \frac{2.3}{p_2} - \frac{.1}{p_2} = \frac{2.2}{p_2} \qquad (11\text{-}43)$$

The rise time is inversely proportional to the BW. That is, the bandwidth (p_2) must be increased in order to decrease the rise time. Very often it is desirable that the output of the amplifier resemble the step input. In this case, a small rise time is desired, and the amplifier should be designed with a large bandwidth.

If there are several identical stages, the gain for the complete high-frequency circuit can be written as

$$A_i(s) = \frac{A_i(0)p_2^n}{(s+p_2)^n} \qquad (11\text{-}44)$$

and the output current for a unit step input current as

$$I_L(s) = \frac{A_i(0)p_2^n}{s(s+p_2)^n} \qquad (11\text{-}45)$$

The zero state or time response is

$$i_L(t) = A_i(0)p_2^n \left[1 - \sum_{k=0}^{n-1} \frac{e^{-p_2 t} t^k}{k!} \right] \qquad (11\text{-}46)$$

It can be shown for certain responses (nonovershooting) that the overall rise time is

$$\tau_{R0} = \sqrt{\tau_{R1}^2 + \tau_{R2}^2 + \cdots} \qquad (11\text{-}47)$$

and for identical stages that

$$\tau_{R0} = \tau_R \sqrt{n} \qquad (11\text{-}48)$$

If we substitute Eq. (11-43) into Eq. (11-48), we obtain

$$\tau_{R0} = \frac{2.2}{p_2} \sqrt{n} \qquad (11\text{-}49)$$

We have shown that the rise time increases with the number of stages and that there is a direct relationship between the rise time and the high-frequency cutoff.

Up to now, the discussion has centered on common-emitter and common-source amplifiers. However, common-collector (emitter-follower) and source-follower amplifiers are used when a large bandwidth (good high-frequency response) is desired. Of course, this large bandwidth is achieved at the expense of a relatively low gain.

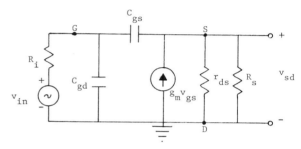

Fig. 11.13 High frequency source follower model.

The source-follower high-frequency equivalent circuit of Experiment 8 is used in Fig. 11-13. The node equations written in matrix form with

$$G_i = \frac{1}{R_i}, \quad G_s = \frac{1}{R_s}, \quad \text{and} \quad g_{ds} = \frac{1}{r_{ds}}$$

are

$$\begin{bmatrix} G_i + s(C_{gs} + C_{gd}) & -sC_{gs} \\ -g_m - sC_{gs} & g_m + g_{ds} + G_s + sC_{gs} \end{bmatrix} \begin{bmatrix} V_{gs}(s) \\ V_{sd}(s) \end{bmatrix}$$
$$= \begin{bmatrix} G_i V_{in}(s) \\ 0 \end{bmatrix}$$

The voltage gain is

$$A_v(s) = \frac{V_{sd}(s)}{V_{in}(s)}$$

$$= \frac{G_i(g_m + sC_{gs})}{(g_m + g_{ds} + G_s + sC_{gs})(G_i + sC_{gd}) + (g_{ds} + G_s)sC_{gs}} \qquad (11\text{-}50)$$

If we assume that $\omega \ll \dfrac{g_m}{C_{gs}}$, then the voltage gain sim-

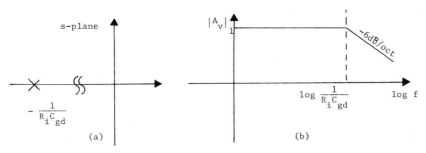

Fig. 11.14 Pole-zero diagram and Bode plot of gain.

plifies to

$$A_v(s) \approx \cfrac{1}{1 + R_i C_{gd}\left[1 + \left(1 + \cfrac{C_{gs}}{C_{gd}}\right)\left(\cfrac{g_{ds} + G_s}{g_m}\right)\right]s}$$

(11-51)

which contains a simple pole. The pole moves far to the left of the s-plane, and the gain approaches 1 as $R_i \to 0$.

For frequencies $\omega \gg \dfrac{g_m + G_s + g_{ds}}{C_{gs}}$, the voltage gain

simplifies to

$$A_v(s) \approx \cfrac{1}{R_i C_{gd}\left[s + \cfrac{g_{ds} + G_s + G_i}{C_{gd}}\right]}$$

(11-52)

The pole-zero diagram and asymptotic plot of gain for Eq. (11-52) are shown in Fig. 11-14 when $\omega \ll \dfrac{g_m}{C_{gs}}$ and $\dfrac{g_{ds} + G_s}{g_m} \ll 1$.

Part Two

OBJECTIVE

The frequency and phase response of single and two stage RC-coupled amplifiers will be examined in this experiment. In particular, the effect of various circuit components on rise time, sag, and the upper and lower cutoff frequencies will be investigated.

REFERENCES

Alley, C. L., and Atwood, K. W., *Electronic Engineering*. New York: Wiley, 1966, Chapters 7 and 9.

Angelo, E. J., *Electronics: BJTs, FETs, and Microcircuits*. New York: McGraw-Hill, 1969, Chapter 14.

Chirlian, P. M., *Electronic Circuits: Physical Principles, Analysis, and Design*. New York: McGraw-Hill, 1971, Chapters 8 and 9.

Fitchen, F. C., *Transistor Circuit Analysis and Design*. New York: Van Nostrand Reinhold, 1966, Chapters 6 and 8.

Ghausi, M. S., *Electronic Circuits: Devices, Models, Functions, Analysis, and Design*. New York: Van Nostrand Reinhold, 1971, Chapters 4 and 5.

Gray, P. E., and Searle, C. L., *Electronic Principles: Physics, Models, and Circuits*. New York: Wiley, 1967, Chapter 14.

Millman, J., and Halkias, C. C., *Electronic Devices and Circuits*. New York: McGraw-Hill, 1967, Chapters 11, 12, and 13.

Schilling, D. L., and Belove, C., *Electronic Circuits: Discrete and Integrated*. New York: McGraw-Hill, 1968, Chapters 7, 12, and 13.

LABORATORY PREPARATION

1. Design a common-emitter amplifier (Fig. 11-2a) which has a lower 3 db frequency of about 100 Hz and an upper 3 db frequency of approximately 100 kHz. Specify values for R_1, R_2, C_1, R_L, and V_{CC}. Select values of C_2 and R_0 which do not influence the lower 3 db frequency ($R_0 = \infty$, open circuit). The values of R_1, R_2, and R_L will also be determined by which bipolar transistor you choose and the Q point that you specify. Transistors such as the 2N526 or 2N697 have an f_β of greater than 100 kHz and can be used to meet the 100 kHz specification. Of course, other transistors could be used which give a lower or higher ω_2 than specified. Be certain that your test equipment can accurately measure the upper 3 db frequency which you designed for. In addition, you should *calculate the Q point and maximum output swing for all* the amplifiers which you design.

2. Calculate the numerical values of $f_1 \left(f_1 = \dfrac{\omega_1}{2\pi}\right)$ and the midband current and voltage gains ($A_i(\infty)$ and $A_v(\infty)$ when using your low-frequency common-emitter circuit models). Calculate $A_i(0), A_v(0)$, and ω_2 for your high-frequency equivalent circuit. Draw the pole-zero diagrams and asymptotic plots of gain and phase in each case. Consider stray

capacitance to be between 1 and 10 pf. Where would the stray capacitance have the most effect?

3. What are the sag and rise time of your amplifier? What components influence the sag and rise time the most? What should the period of the input signal be to clearly exhibit the sag and rise time effects?

4. Place an emitter resistor and bypass capacitor between the emitter and ground as shown in Fig. 11–5a. Select a value of R_E and C_E which dominates the low-frequency transfer function. Namely, the lower 3 db frequency should now be determined mainly by the value of C_E, R_E, h_{fe}, R_B, and h_{ie} as given by Eq. (11–15). What are $A_i(0)$, $A_v(0)$, $A_i(\infty)$, and $A_v(\infty)$? (See Eqs. [11–16] and [11–17].) What is the bandwidth (BW) of your amplifier?

5. Connect a second identical common-emitter transistor amplifier stage by means of capacitor C_2 to your first stage. Repeat steps 2 and 3 for this two-stage amplifier. Be sure to clearly indicate the effects on rise time and sag when the second stage is added. (Include R_E and C_E for both stages.)

6. (optional) Design a common-collector (emitter-follower) amplifier with a voltage gain close to 1 and a Q point similar to the one you designed in Experiment 10. Connect the emitter follower between the output of your first stage and the input of your second stage. Use coupling capacitors where necessary. Repeat steps 2 and 3 for the three stages. Explain how your second-stage emitter follower isolates the first-stage common-emitter from the third-stage common-emitter. Does the introduction of the buffer stage (emitter-follower) change the frequency response of the two-stage amplifier designed in step 5?

7. (optional) Select an integrated circuit amplifier such as the MC1550, CA3028A, or SN5510 and obtain the manufacturer's specifications and circuit diagrams. Try to describe the use of each resistor and transistor for the linear integrated amplifier of your choice. In particular, note the wide frequency response of these amplifiers and compare the integrated circuits to similar amplifiers with discrete components. Can you think of any uses for the linear integrated amplifier you have chosen?

8. Design a common-source amplifier which has a BW of 100 kHz or larger. Specify values of R_g, R_d, C_1, and V_{LD}. Select values of C_2 and R_0 which do not influence the lower 3 dbv frequency ($R_0 = \infty$). Select a JFET such as the 2N3819 or 2N3820 which you used in Experiment 9. Be certain that you include the effect of stray capacitances due to wiring and the test equipment. They are usually in the range of 1 to 10 pf. If larger, you probably have a badly wired circuit or are not using good testing equipment. Be sure to calculate the Q point and specify the maximum output swing for your design of Fig. 11–3b.

9. Repeat steps 2 and 3 for your common-source amplifier.

10. Place a source resistor and bypass capacitor between the source connection and ground. Select a value of R_s and C_s which dominates the low-frequency transfer function. What are $A_i(0)$, $A_v(0)$, $A_i(\infty)$, $A_v(\infty)$? What is the BW of this amplifier?

11. Couple a second identical common-source transistor amplifier stage by means of capacitor C_2 to your first stage. Repeat steps 2 and 3 above. Be sure to clearly indicate the effects on rise time and sag of adding a second stage. (Include R_s and C_s for both stages.)

12. (optional) Design a common-drain (source-follower) amplifier with a voltage gain close to 1 and a Q point within the active region which allows for small-signal linear operation. Connect the source-follower to your single-stage common-source amplifier by means of coupling capacitor C_2, and repeat steps 2 and 3 for these two stages. If a third common-source stage is added to the second-stage source follower, would the source follower act as a good buffer (isolation) between the first and third stages? Would the FET source-follower be a better isolation stage than an equivalent bipolar emitter-follower stage? Explain your answer.

LABORATORY PROCEDURE

1. Construct the circuit of Figure 11–2a which you have designed. Measure the Q point and the maximum output swing for a sinusoidal input. Compare with your calculated values. Make appropriate measurements to plot a frequency response of gain and phase. Most of your data should be taken close to the lower and upper 3 db frequencies. You should use a sensitive ac voltmeter to measure the output. This voltmeter should be left on the circuit throughout all measurements, because the voltmeter will have a small capacitance which could change the frequency response measurements. If the input capacitance of the voltmeter is known, be sure to include its effect in explaining the frequency response you measured. The output should be monitored with an oscilloscope to insure that your circuit is operating linearly. (Sinusoidal input yields a sinusoidal output.)

2. You should make voltage measurements at appropriate points in the circuit to obtain the voltage and current gains from simple calculations. One simplification is to keep the ac voltage from base to ground at a convenient value such as .01, .1, or 1. Why? Another is to measure ac voltages across known resistances so that the ac current can be easily calculated. If an ac voltmeter is available with a db scale, use it. Take the midband gain as the 0 db reference so that f_1 and f_2 are the frequencies at which the output voltage is 3 dbv down from the reference level. The phase characteristics can be measured by simultaneously applying the input and output signals to the vertical and horizontal inputs of the oscilloscope. (Another method is explained in Experiment 1.) The resulting pattern on the scope will

be an ellipse. The phase shift can be measured directly from the ellipse as explained in Experiment 1.

3. Change the input signal from a sine-wave to a square-wave and measure the sag and rise time of your amplifier. Compare with calculated values. Vary the amplitude and frequency of the input square-wave and record the results.

4. Construct and test the circuit of Fig. 11–5a which you designed. Perform the measurements described in steps 1, 2, and 3, above.

5. Connect a second identical common-emitter transistor stage by means of a capacitor to your first stage and repeat the measurements of steps 1, 2, and 3, above. Compare your calculated and measured values.

6. (optional) Construct an emitter-follower amplifier and insert it between your first and second stages. Repeat steps 1, 2, and 3 and make any other measurements which you think necessary.

7. (optional) Test the integrated amplifier circuit which you have chosen. Make measurements similar to those of steps 2 and 3, above. Note all input and output connections for your amplifier and apply test signals to those inputs which are specified by the manufacturer. If more than one output terminal is available, measure the output at these terminals and compare them.

8. Construct and test the common-source amplifier which you have designed. Note the effect of your test equipment on the amplifier gain and bandwidth.

9. Compare the gain and bandwidth of your FET amplifier with your bipolar transistor amplifier. Be sure you know which circuit elements most influence the midband gain and bandwidth for the FET amplifier.

10. Place a source resistor and a bypass capacitor between the source connection and ground. Make appropriate measurements to verify the calculations you made in the preparation.

11. (optional) Construct a second identical common-source transistor amplifier stage by means of a capacitor C_2 to your first stage. Make the measurements described in steps 2 and 3, above.

12. (optional) Construct and test the common-drain (source-follower) amplifier which you have designed. Connect it to your common-source amplifier and test the two stages together as described in steps 2 and 3.

LIST OF EQUIPMENT

1. Cathode-ray oscilloscope
2. General-purpose voltmeters or ac and dc voltmeters and ohmmeters
3. Signal sources: Function generator or sine-wave and square-wave oscillator, dc power supply
4. Circuit board
5. Components: resistors, capacitors, transistors (bipolar and FET's), and linear integrated amplifiers (optional)

Experiment 12/Computer-Aided Circuit Analysis and Design (ECAP and SCEPTRE)

Part One

INTRODUCTION

The analysis of integrated circuits containing large numbers of transistors and other circuit elements requires numerous and often tedious calculations to achieve a desirable design. There are now several digital computer programs available to the designer for analyzing these complex electronic circuits. These programs allow the computer to perform routine calculations and allow the designer to concentrate his attention on the more important overview of the design.

Among the several automated digital computer programs, this experiment will study the use of ECAP (Electronic Circuit Analysis Program) for ac and dc analysis of linear circuits and SCEPTRE (System for Circuit Evaluation and Prediction of Transient Radiation Effects) for transient analysis of linear and nonlinear circuits. In addition, this experiment is intended to help the designer become acquainted with computers, computer language, and the procedures for dealing with computing centers.

THEORY

ECAP

It is advisable that the designer consult the IBM User's Manual (#H20-0170-1) to supplement the ECAP program description contained in this experiment. In addition, it is helpful but not necessary that the designer be familiar with the FORTRAN computer language.

Data are entered into ECAP by means of a special input language which is similar to FORTRAN but does not follow FORTRAN rules. The user simply describes the network in the ECAP language on punched cards and enters this information into the computer. Only data are entered—not a program. The ECAP program must be stored somewhere in the computer and is called for by the user by means of punched cards or from a time-sharing teletype terminal.

The performance of a given network is often characterized by its response either to a constant dc voltage or to a sinusoidal voltage.

The dc analysis involves the measurements of dc voltages at various points in the network, especially dc bias voltages in electronic circuits. The ac analysis involves the determination of frequency response, which is the variation of the magnitude and phase of the output when the frequency of the sinusoidal input is varied. ECAP can perform the dc analysis of any linear network which has only the following types of elements (DC ANALYSIS): resistors; fixed voltage sources; fixed current sources; dependent current sources. ECAP can perform the ac analysis of any linear network which has only the following types of elements (AC ANALYSIS): resistors; capacitors; inductors; mutual inductances; fixed rms voltage sources; fixed rms current sources; dependent current sources.

A typical maximum network size that can be analyzed by ECAP is: 50 nodes; 200 branches; 200 dependent current sources; 50 parameter changes in a particular parameter modification; 25 mutual inductances; 50 inductive branches when there are mutual inductances. The standard set of units used with ECAP are: current—amperes; voltage—volts; resistance—ohms; capacitance—farads; inductance—henries; time—seconds; frequency—cycles per second. In addition, the following requirements must be met by the network: minimum of one branch; non-zero passive element in each branch; minimum of two nodes; the graph must be connected—mutual inductances are not considered to complete an electric path.

Each branch of any network analyzed by ECAP must contain a passive element, the value of which must be non-zero. The branch can also contain a voltage source in series and one or more dependent current sources in parallel as well as an independent current source in parallel. The minimum configuration of the standard circuit branch consists of the passive element alone. A standard circuit branch is shown in Fig. 12-1, and the direction of current in the branch is assigned in the way shown.

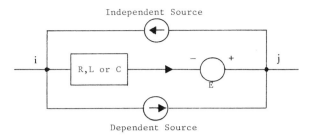

Fig. 12.1 A standard circuit branch.

DC and AC ANALYSIS

First, the actual network must be replaced by an equivalent network which contains only the elements recognized by the DC ANALYSIS or AC ANALYSIS programs. Next, all the nodes (other than ground nodes) and all the branches are consecutively numbered, starting with the number 1. The ground nodes are assigned the number 0. Positive current directions are chosen, the choice being arbitrary for any branch which does not have a current source across it. Otherwise, the convention shown in Fig. 12-1 is used.

We will designate two major types of cards that the user will have to have keypunched. First are the Control Cards which are unique to each computing center. These cards typically contain information such as the user's name, charge numbers, and symbols calling up the ECAP program from the computer's program library. The information to be punched on these cards should be obtained from the user's computing center.

The second major type consists of the Input Cards. These cards consist of the following.

1. Comment cards: "C" is placed in column 1, and the text of the comment in columns 2 through 72. Comment cards may appear anywhere among the input cards.

2. Continuation cards: These cards are denoted by an * in column 6, and must be the first character of the card. A comma must be the last character of the card preceding a continuation card.

3. Analysis command card: DC ANALYSIS and AC ANALYSIS. The analysis command is the first program instruction. Only comment cards can precede it.

4. Branch cards: The branch cards follow the analysis command card. A general branch card has the following form

$$\underbrace{\text{B n n}}_{\substack{\text{columns} \\ 1\text{-}5}} \underbrace{\text{N(i, j), X = aa, E = vv, I = cc}}_{\substack{\text{columns} \\ 7\text{-}72}}$$

The letter B is placed in column 1, and the sequential branch number (nn) in columns 2 through 5 (e.g., B23). Next, the letter N in column 7 and the node interconnections (i, j) starting with the left parenthesis in column 8

(e.g., N(23,30)). Note that positive current is defined from node i to node j and passing through element Bnn. The node interconnection N(i, j) is followed by a comma. Next, X may be R, L or C having passive element value aa. (e.g., R = 330E3). The passive element value aa is followed by a comma. Next, E is the voltage source in the circuit branch with voltage source value vv. (e.g., E = 0.1 for dc or E = 0.1/20 for ac). For DC ANALYSIS, vv is the dc value of the voltage; and for AC ANALYSIS, vv is rms/phase angle. The voltage source value is followed by a comma. Next, I is the independent current source in parallel with the circuit branch with the current source value cc. (e.g., I = 3.0E2 for DC ANALYSIS and I = 2.3/32 for AC ANALYSIS).

5. Trans-element cards: These cards are used to designate the dependent current sources. All dependent current sources are numbered T1, T2.... A general Trans-element card (T card) has the following form

$$\underbrace{\text{T x x}}_{\substack{\text{columns} \\ 1\text{-}5}} \underbrace{\text{B(i, j), BETA = vv}}_{\substack{\text{columns} \\ 7\text{-}72}}$$

The letter T is placed in column 1, and the sequential trans-element number (xx) in column 2 through 5 (e.g., T21). Next, the letter B in column 7 and the branch designation (i, j) starting with the left parenthesis in column 8 (e.g., B(2,3)). Note that i is the reference branch and j the affected branch. The branch designation B(i, j) is followed by a comma. Next, BETA is the current gain with value vv (e.g., BETA = 1.23). An alternate form for the trans-element card is to replace BETA = vv by GM = aa where GM is the transconductance of the dependent current source, with transconductance value = aa.

6. Mutual inductance cards: The mutual inductance cards are sequentially marked M1, M2 .... A general mutual inductance card has the following form

$$\underbrace{\text{M x x}}_{\substack{\text{columns} \\ 1\text{-}5}} \underbrace{\text{B(i, j), L = vv}}_{\substack{\text{columns} \\ 7\text{-}72}}$$

The letter M is placed in column 1, and the sequential mutual inductance number xx in columns 2 through 5 (e.g., M24). Next, the letter B in column 7, and the branch designation (i, j) starting with the left parenthesis in column 8 (e.g., B(21,24)). Note that since the mutual inductance is bilateral, the ordering of the coupled branches (i, j) is unimportant.

7. Solution control cards: The statement on these cards always appears in columns 7 through 72. No solution control card is needed for DC ANALYSIS. FREQUENCY = vv is the solution control card which must be used for

AC ANALYSIS. The vv is the value of frequency for which the first AC ANALYSIS is performed.

8. Output specification cards: The statement on these cards should appear in columns 7 through 72. A general output specification card has the following form

PRINT, NV, CA

columns
7-72

The PRINT statement must be followed by a comma and then as many output indicators as desired, each separated by a comma. The following output indicators are available

NV or VOLTAGES	Node voltages
CA or CURRENTS	Element currents
CV	Element voltages
BA	Branch currents
BV	Branch voltages
BP	Element power loss

9. MODIFY command card: This card allows the user to repeat an immediately preceding network with modified input data. Specific element values may be changed by specification of the desired modifications. However, the topology of the network remains unchanged. A maximum of fifty parameter data subgroups may be entered per modify run. Output specification cards are not allowed after the modify command card. Thus, any required output must have been called for in the nominal solution.

10. Parameter variation cards: In order to vary a parameter over a range of values (e.g., the frequency in AC ANALYSIS) and to obtain solutions for each of these values, the following procedure is used. Note that only one parameter may be varied per modify run but that the frequency variation is unlimited. Three cards are used, with the statement starting in column 7 of each card as shown.

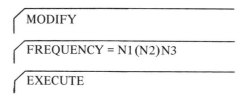

MODIFY

FREQUENCY = N1(N2)N3

EXECUTE

N1 is the starting value of the parameter; N2 multiplies N1 by its value until N3 is exceeded. N3 is the final value of the parameter.

11. EXECUTE command card: This card signifies the end of data, output control, and specification cards. The execution of the program begins with this card.

EXECUTE

12. END card: This card signifies the end of all ECAP jobs. A few examples of DC and AC ANALYSIS programs are included to serve as guides for the ECAP user.

Examples of DC ANALYSIS—The dc equivalent circuit of Fig. 12-3 is obtained after replacing the transistor in Fig. 12-2 by its low-frequency equivalent model. Note

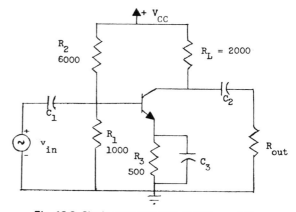

Fig. 12.2 Single-stage common emitter amplifier.

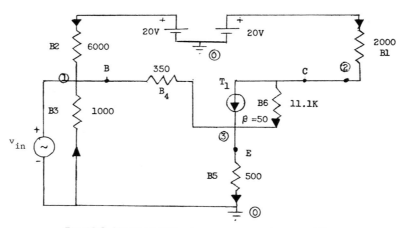

Fig. 12.3 Model of single stage common emitter amplifier.

that all capacitive branches are open-circuited. The current directions are arbitrary except in the 11.1 k resistor.

The input data deck could be as follows

C   EXPERIMENT NUMBER
C   SINGLE STAGE COMMON EMITTER AMPLIFIER
         DC ANALYSIS
B1   N(0,2), R = 2000, E = 20
B2   N(0,1), R = 6000, E = 20
B3   N(0,1), R = 1000
B4   N(1,3), R = 350
B5   N(3,0), R = 500
B6   N(2,3), R = 11.1 E3
T1   B(4,6), BETA = 50
         PRINT, VOLTAGES, CURRENTS
         MODIFY
B1   R = 400
B2   R = 12000
B3   R = 2000
         EXECUTE
         END

Examples of AC ANALYSIS

$$\beta_1 \cong \frac{N_2}{N_1}, \ \beta_2 \cong \frac{N_1}{N_2}, \ R_1 \cong R, R_2 \cong \left(\frac{N_2}{N_1}\right)^2 R$$

Each dependent current source in Fig. 12-4 is controlled by the current flowing in the opposite resistor. The dependent

current sources must therefore be assigned to branches other than those containing R_1 and R_2.

As an example, let $N_1/N_2 = 0.5$ and let $R = 0.1 \ \Omega$, which is small enough so that the voltage change across it is negligible compared with that across the transformer coils. Dummy resistors of high value (10 megohms) are assigned to the current sources. The equivalent circuit is shown in Fig. 12-5. The input data for this example could be

C   IDEAL TRANSFORMER
         AC ANALYSIS
B1   N(0,1), R = 10 E6
B2   N(0,2), R = 10 E6
B3   N(0,1), R = 1000, E = 1/0
B4   N(1,2), R = 1000
B5   N(1,0), R = 0.1
B6   N(2,0), R = 0.4
T1   B(6,1), BETA = 2.
T2   B(5,2), BETA = 0.5
         FREQUENCY = 1000
         PRINT, VOLTAGES, CURRENTS
         EXECUTE
         END

The final example could be used to study the frequency response of a single-stage common-emitter transistor amplifier when the transistor is replaced at first with a small-signal hybrid pi circuit model and then with a unilateral

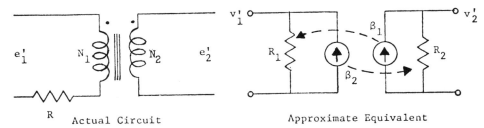

Fig. 12.4 Equivalent circuit of a two-coil transformer.

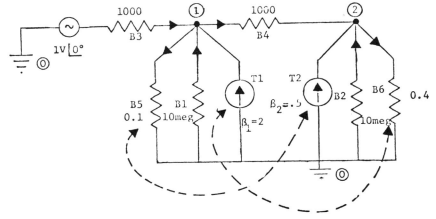

Fig. 12.5 Equivalent circuit.

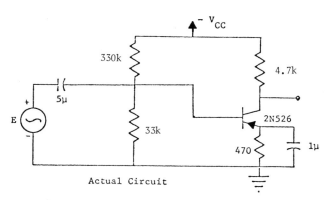

Fig. 12.6 A single stage-common emitter amplifier.

model (see Experiment 8). The actual circuit is shown in Fig. 12–6, and each model is shown in Fig. 12–7a and 12–7b. The parameter values chosen are typical values for the 2N526 transistor biased at V_C = 10 V and I_C = 3.0 mA.

C	SINGLE STAGE AMPLIFIER FREQUENCY
C	RESPONSE
C	HYBRID PI EQUIVALENT
	AC ANALYSIS
B1	N(0,1), C = 5E-6, E = 0.1/0
B2	N(1,0), R = 330E3
B3	N(1,0), R = 33E3
B4	N(1,2), R = 160
B5	N(2,4), C = 5.4E-9
B6	N(2,4), R = 705
B7	N(2,3), C = 18E-12
B8	N(2,3), R = 4E6
B9	N(4,0), R = 270
B10	N(4,0), C = 100E-6
B11	N(3,4), R = 20.2E3
B12	N(0,3), R = 4.7E3

B13	N(3,5), C = 10E-6
B14	N(5,0), R = 400
T1	B(6,11), GM = 0.115
	FREQUENCY = 10
	PRINT, VOLTAGES
	MODIFY
	FREQUENCY = 10(1.41421)1E6
	EXECUTE

C	SINGLE STAGE AMPLIFIER FREQUENCY
C	RESPONSE
C	UNILATERAL EQUIVALENT
	AC ANALYSIS
B1	N(0,1), C = 5E-6, E = 0.1/0
B2	N(1,0), R = 330E3
B3	N(1,0), R = 33E3
B4	N(1,2), R = 160
B5	N(2,4), R = 705
B6	N(2,4), C = 15.11E-9
B7	N(4,0), R = 470
B8	N(4,0), C = 100E-6
B9	N(3,4), R = 20.2E3
B10	N(3,4), C = 18E-12
B11	N(0,3), R = 4.7E3
B12	N(3,5), C = 10E-6
B13	N(5,0), R = 400
T1	B(5,9), GM = 0.115
	FREQUENCY = 10
	PRINT, VOLTAGES
	MODIFY
	FREQUENCY = 10(1.41421)1E6
	EXECUTE

ECAP has recently been updated and improved, and the new version is known as ECAP II. ECAP II is presently available on many computers.

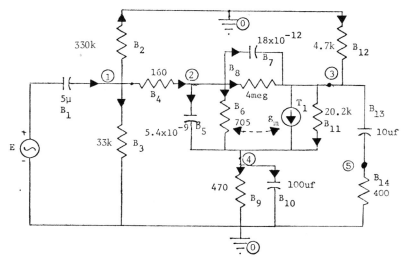

Fig. 12.7a Single stage common-emitter amplifier using hybrid pi model.

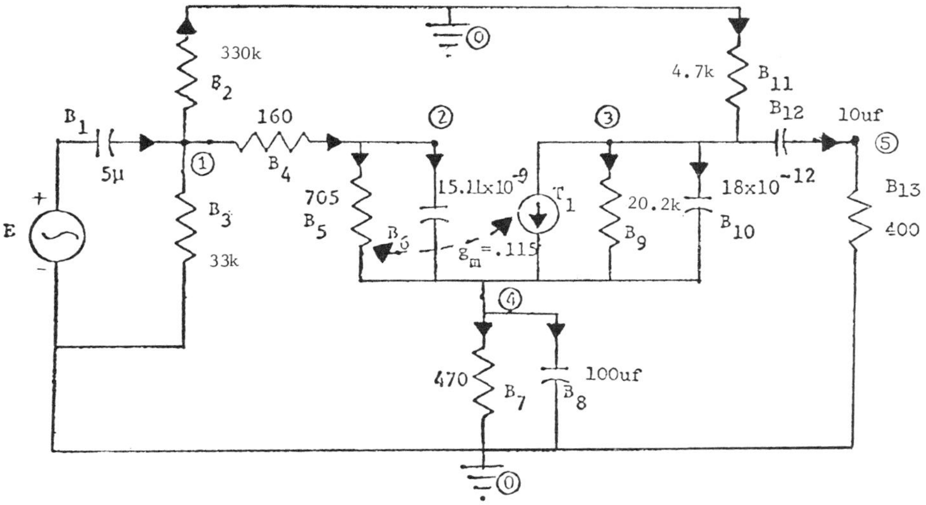

Fig. 12.7b Single stage common emitter amplifier using unilateral model.

SCEPTRE

The performance of a network is very often characterized by another type of response, known as the "transient response." The transient response can be thought of as the variations of the output of a network when there are sudden changes in the input. The SCEPTRE program is well suited for the analysis of this type of response. In fact, the SCEPTRE program has some attractive features not found in the ECAP program.

1. The program is written entirely in FORTRAN IV, and the user familiar with computer programming may write FORTRAN subroutines and insert them in otherwise conventional SCEPTRE runs.

2. Time-varying and nonlinear network elements can be handled conveniently.

3. Any active element (e.g., a transistor model) or interconnected group of elements can be stored on tape and called into use for any part of a network.

The following set of units is most often used with SCEPTRE: resistance—kilohms; capacitance—picofarads; inductance—microhenries; current—milliamperes; voltage—volts; time—nanoseconds.

The following step-by-step procedure has been found helpful in setting up the network for analysis by the SCEPTRE program.

1. Draw an equivalent circuit comprised only of resistors, capacitors, inductors, and voltage and current sources.

2. Assign a name or number to all nodes in the network.

3. Give a name to each network element. The first character of the name must be R, C, L, E, or J corresponding to the element type (i.e., resistor, capacitor, inductor, voltage source, or current source, respectively).

4. Assume arbitrary current flow directions in each passive network element.

5. Indicate the direction of positive current flow in each voltage and current source.

6. Choose and record network element values in a consistent set of units, preferably the one given above for electronic circuits.

The set of control cards required to run your job and to call the SCEPTRE program from the computer's program library should be specified by the user's computing center.

A brief description of the format for inputs is given next. However, it is advisable that the designer consult the SCEPTRE User's Manual (Defense Documentation Center number AD 808583). In addition, it is very helpful if the designer is familiar with the FORTRAN language when using SCEPTRE.

The Input Data Cards begin with a card containing the word ELEMENTS starting in the first column. *All data cards may begin in column 1 and can contain information up to and including column 72.*

1. ELEMENTS card: The following are examples of cards that can follow the ELEMENTS card.

(a)
> Xnn, i-j = aa

Xnn is the element name, as specified in step 3, above (e.g., C23). Next comes a comma, and i-j is the positive current direction from node i to node j and passing through element Xnn (e.g., 6–1). aa is the value of element Xnn in the set of units chosen.

(b)
> J18, 10-3 = DIODE TABLE 1

DIODE TABLE 1 gives the current-voltage characteristics of the current source J18.

(c)
> J6, 14-2 = DIODE EQUATION (1.E-7,30)

This is a special card for diodes. The diode current source obeys the following law

$$I = 1 \times 10^{-7} [e^{30V} - 1]$$

where V is the voltage across the diode source and I is the diode current.

(d)

$$C1, 7-8 = (10. + 80. * J1)$$

This card indicates that capacitor C1 is current-dependent, so that C1 = 10. + 80. $\times$ (current in source J1). Note that the decimal points are required for the constants 10 and 80.

(e)

$$LX3, 9-3 = EQUATION\ 15X(ILX3,TIME)$$

This card indicates that inductor LX3 is current- and time-dependent, so that EQUATION 15X is a relation between LX3, TIME, and the current ILX3 flowing through LX3.

(f)

$$T4, 2-3-7 = MODEL\ 2N526$$

This card indicates that element T4 is a stored model of transistor 2N526 with 2-3-7 corresponding to base, emitter, and collector terminals, respectively.

(g)

$$MX, L1-L2 = TABLE\ 1\ (TIME)$$

The mutual inductance MX between inductors L1 and L2 is tabulated in TABLE 1, where TIME is the independent variable of TABLE 1. If nothing is indicated with a parenthesis, then TIME is assumed to be the independent variable.

(h)

$$C1, 7-8 = (6. + 47. * TABLE\ (T7,VC1))$$

The capacitor C1 between nodes 7 and 8 has a value equal to 6. + 47. $\times$ (TABLE 7), where TABLE 7 is a function of VC1.

2. Source derivative cards: The time derivative of the source must be furnished whenever a variable voltage source is connected in a loop containing only capacitors and other voltage sources, or whenever a variable current source is connected in a cut-set containing only inductors and other current sources. The time derivative will be assumed zero for a constant source.

$$DE7 = TABLE\ 2$$

The derivative of voltage source E7 is furnished in TABLE 2 with TIME as the independent variable in the table.

3. Defined parameter cards: Each card indicates a variable that can be described in terms of any network variable. The SCEPTRE program format requires that the first letter of such a parameter be P. For example,

$$P8 = TABLE\ 1(VC7)$$

The parameter P8 is tabulated in TABLE 1 with the voltage across capacitor C7 as the independent variable.

$$P14 = EQUATION\ 2(VC7,VR1)$$

The parameter P14 is given by Equation 2 which involves voltages across C7 and R1. Finally,

$$P8 = VCC + VCE$$

The parameter P8 is the sum of voltages CC and CE.

4. Output cards: The following quantities can be obtained as outputs:

Voltages or currents associated with any passive elements such as VR1, VC4, IL3, IR9, etc.

Voltages or currents associated with any source such as E1, J2, IE1, VJ2, etc.

Any element value such as C1, R2, L3, etc.

Any defined parameter such as P12, P8, etc.

Most outputs will use TIME as the independent variable and can be plotted if requested. For example,

$$OUTPUTS$$
$$VR2, VC1, P14, PLOT$$

This example plots the variables VR2, VC1, and P14 against TIME. If any other independent variable is required, it may be included in parentheses following PLOT.

5. Initial condition cards: The complete solution of a transient analysis problem requires that all independent initial conditions be supplied. Any initial conditions not specified will be taken as zero. The format is

$$VXnn = bb,\ IYnn = cc, \ldots$$

Xnn is the element which has initial voltage value bb, and Ynn is the element name which has initial current value cc.

6. FUNCTION cards:

a) Equations: If an element card appears as

$$LX3, 9-3 = EQUATION\ 15X(ILX3,TIME,VC1)$$

and if the equation is

$$LX3 = ILX3 + (4)(TIME)(VC1)$$

then the function must be defined after the FUNCTIONS heading card. For example

FUNCTIONS

EQUATION 15X(A, B, C) = (Mathematical expression)

The dummy variables in this example are A, B, and C, which replace ILX3, TIME, and VC1, respectively. The mathematical expression must be included in the parentheses, and must be defined in terms of A, B, and C, and any other constants or subprograms which apply. The dummy variables A, B, and C need not be reserved for EQUATION 15X alone. Another example is, if under ELEMENTS, the user enters C2, 9-10 = EQUATION 2(TABLE 7(VC1)), then EQUATION 2 must be explicitly defined under FUNCTIONS, and could be

EQUATION 2(A) = (8. + 22.*A)

All mathematical operations which are allowed in FORTRAN IV are allowed in SCEPTRE, and the same symbols are used.

  b) Tabular definition sequence cards: Every table name that has been referenced under ELEMENTS or in DEFINED PARAMETER cards must be explicitly defined under the FUNCTIONS subheading. The format is DIODE TABLE NAME or TABLE NAME NUMBER, NUMBER, NUMBER. . . . For example,

DIODE TABLE 2

0,0,.13,0,.62,.4,.64,1

The tabular data are represented by a series of paired numbers, each number separated by a comma. For each pair, the number representing the independent variable comes first, with the dependent variable following. Any number of point pairs can be supplied per card. However, the point pair must be supplied in such a way that the independent variable is in increasing algebraic order. Two consecutive independent variable values may be equal but have different independent variable values when it is required to produce step functions. Linear interpolation is performed between points supplied. For example, suppose that EVIN is given by Fig. 12-8.

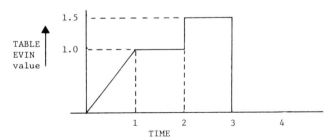

Fig. 12.8 Voltage vs. time.

The tabular definition sequence cards for Fig. 12-8 are

TABLE EVIN

0,0,1,1,2,1,2,1.5,3,1.5,3,0,4,0

  7. Run control cards: These cards contain all the auxiliary information needed to control the run. The information does not directly affect the network, and most of these quantities have automatically preset values. Two important ones are STOP TIME and MINIMUM STEP SIZE.

RUN CONTROLS

STOP TIME = xxx

MINIMUM STEP SIZE = yy

The xxx has to be specified where the value of xxx is in the TIME units chosen. The yy must also be specified. If nothing is specified for MINIMUM STEP SIZE (card left out), then 10^{-5} × STOP TIME will be assumed. In addition, MINIMUM, MAXIMUM ABSOLUTE, and RELATIVE ERRORS may be specified if necessary. Note that STOP TIME must be specified.

  8. Stored model feature: Repeated use is made of certain models of active devices or of standard combinations of passive elements such as filter sections, biasing networks, and so on. These situations can always be handled by inserting the components under ELEMENTS. A more convenient approach is to describe the network once and store it for future use. A model may be stored permanently or temporarily. The stored model feature is best illustrated by an example.

  Suppose it is required to store the transistor model shown in Fig. 12-9. $J1$ and $J2$ are diodes in Fig. 12-9. The dependent current sources JA and JB are equal to .1 × $J2$ and .98 × $J1$, respectively. The input deck will begin with the MODEL DESCRIPTION card, as shown on page 120.

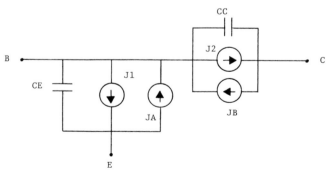

Fig. 12.9 Transistor model.

MODEL DESCRIPTION
MODEL TTLNAND (B-E-C)
ELEMENTS
CE, B-E=EQUATION1(5.,80.,TABLE1(VCE))
CC,B-C=EQUATION1(10.,200.,TABLE2(VCC))
J1,B-E=DIODE TABLE1
JA,E-B=.1*J2
J2,B-C=DIODE TABLE2
JB,C-B=.98*J1
FUNCTIONS
DIODE TABLE1
0,0,.3,0,.65,.05,.7,.6,.72,1.4,.73,2,.74,3.4,.8,10,.82,15
DIODE TABLE2
0,0,.58,0,.62,.4,.64,1,.66,2,.67,3,.69,7,.7,12
EQUATION1(A,B,C)=(A+B*C)

If a transistor $T1$ is to be modeled as above, the following card appears in the ELEMENTS group and uses the MODEL DESCRIPTION above provided it has been originally stored by the user.

T1, 14-21-23 = MODEL TTLNAND

with 14-21-23 corresponding to the base (B), emitter (E), and collector (C) nodes of the transistor, respectively.

9. END card: This card signifies the end of all SCEPTRE jobs.

There are additional features, such as changes in initial conditions, changes in output, temporary and permanent storage, and rerun features, available with SCEPTRE which are completely described in the SCEPTRE User's Manual.

An example of a common-emitter transistor amplifier is given to show how the transient response is obtained with the SCEPTRE program when the combined effects of emitter bypass, coupling, and transistor capacitance are included. The example is the circuit of Fig. 12-6 with the unilateral model of Fig. 12-7b. In this case, E is a square-wave input voltage with amplitude .1 and period $20\,\mu$ sec. The coupling capacitor values are different, and an additional RC coupling circuit appears on the output.

CIRCUIT DESCRIPTION
HIGH AND LOW FREQUENCY RESPONSE OF
  COMMON-EMITTER AMPLIFIER
ELEMENTS
E,0-5=TABLE 1 (TIME)
JT1,3-4=(115,*VRB5)
CB1,5-1=.02E6
RB2,1-0=330
RB3,1-0=33
RB4,1-2=.160
RB5,2-4=.705
CB6,2-4=15.11E3
RB7,4-0=.470
CB8,4-0=.8E6
RB9,3-4=20.2
CB10,3-4=18
RB11,0-3=4.7
CB12,3-6=.02E6
RB13,6-0=.400
OUTPUTS
VRB13,PLOT
FUNCTIONS
TABLE 1
0,0,0,.1,10000,.1,10000,-.1,20000,-.1,20000,.1,30000,
  .1,30000,-.1,
40000,-.1,40000,.1,50000,.1,50000,-.1,60000,-.1,60000,0
RUN CONTROLS
STOP TIME=60000
MINIMUM STEP SIZE=0.0001
END

The output voltage across resistor B_{13}, which is 400 Ω, is plotted versus time by the computer and is shown in Fig. 12-10.

The pole-zero analysis approach used in Experiment 11 to obtain the rise time and sag (tilt) for electronic circuits can be performed when high- and low-frequency effects (poles and dipole locations) are orders of magnitude apart or when there are relatively few stages to analyze. It can be seen from this example that the combined effect of all the capacitors upon the transient response can be easily obtained by the use of the SCEPTRE program.

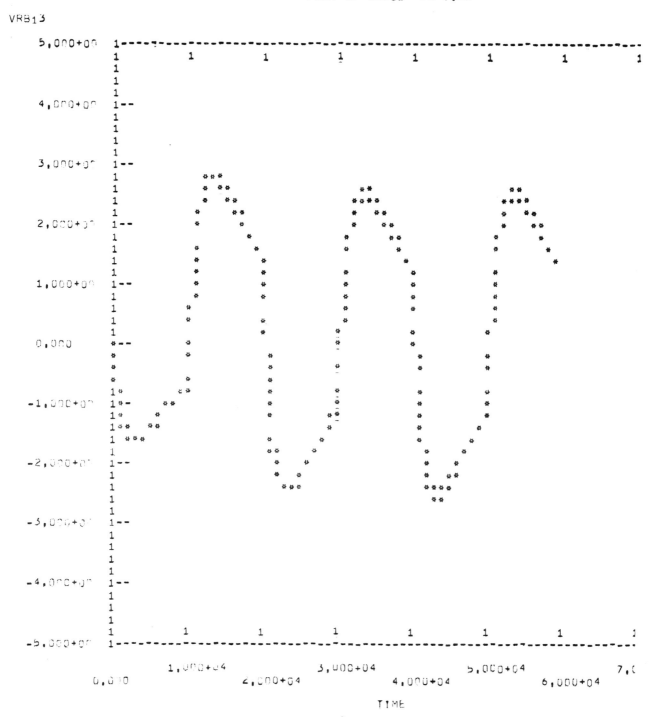

Fig. 12.10 Computer plot of output voltage vs. time.

Part Two

OBJECTIVE

The analysis and design of some passive and active circuits will be accomplished with the aid of ECAP and SCEPTRE computer programs. Furthermore, this experiment should help the designer become acquainted with computers, computer language, and procedures for dealing with computing centers.

REFERENCES

Alley, C. L., and Atwood, K. W., *Electronic Engineering*. New York: Wiley, 1966, Chapters 7 and 9.

Angelo, E. J., *Electronics: BJTs, FETs, and Microcircuits*. New York: McGraw-Hill, 1969, Chapter 13 and 14.

Chirlian, P. M., *Electronic Circuits: Physical Principles, Analysis, and Design*. New York: McGraw-Hill, 1971, Chapters 8 and 9.

Fitchen, F. C., *Transistor Circuit Analysis and Design*. New York: Van Nostrand Reinhold, 1966, Chapters 6 and 8.

Ghausi, M. S., *Electronic Circuits: Devices, Models, Functions, Analysis, and Design*. New York: Van Nostrand Reinhold, 1971, Chapters 1, 2, 4, and 5.

Gray, P. E., and Searle, C. L., *Electronic Principles: Physics, Models, and Circuits*. New York: Wiley, 1967, Chapters 15 and 16 and Appendix C.

Millman, J., and Halkias, C. C., *Electronic Devices and Circuits*. McGraw-Hill, 1967, Chapters 11, 12, and 13.

Schilling, D. L., and Belove, C., *Electronic Circuits: Discrete and Integrated*. New York: McGraw-Hill, 1968, Chapters 7, 12 and 13.

LABORATORY PREPARATION

ECAP

1. Become familiar with the rules and regulations governing the use of the digital computer in your computing center. Be sure that you know how to punch IBM cards on a keypunching machine. Obtain the information that you need to punch on your control cards (name, charge numbers, etc.) from the personnel in your computing center or from your laboratory instructor. Be sure to obtain the calling name of the ECAP program which is stored in your computer's library. Punch this information on IBM cards. These cards will always precede your input deck. You should ask for help from your laboratory instructor if this is the first time that you are using a digital computer or if you are having difficulty with any of the above steps. Also, consult the ECAP User's Manual.

2. Write an ECAP program for the dc analysis of the network shown in Fig. 12–11. This network has thirteen branches and six nodes (including ground). Your ECAP program should print all voltages and currents and should include a MODIFY statement to change resistors R_1, R_2, R_3, and R_4 to 100, 250, 20, and 7, respectively.

3. Write an ECAP program for the ac analysis of the teletype filter shown in Fig. 12–12.

The network of Fig. 12–12 has nine branches and six nodes (including ground). The input frequency is 10. Print all voltages and currents. Modify the program so that the input frequency is varied from 10 to 2000 by doubling each preceding frequency (i.e., 10, 20, 40, 80, 160, etc.).

4. Write an ECAP program for the ac analysis of the networks shown in Fig. 12–7a and b. If you performed Experiment 8, then use your particular transistor and quiescent point. Vary the input frequency from a few cycles to a few megacycles. Be sure to cover the frequency

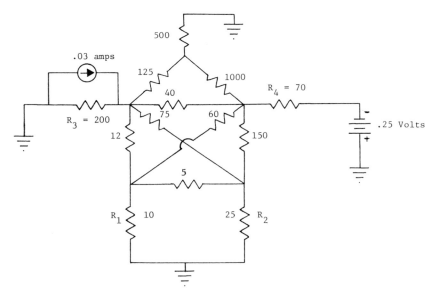

Fig. 12.11 A dc circuit.

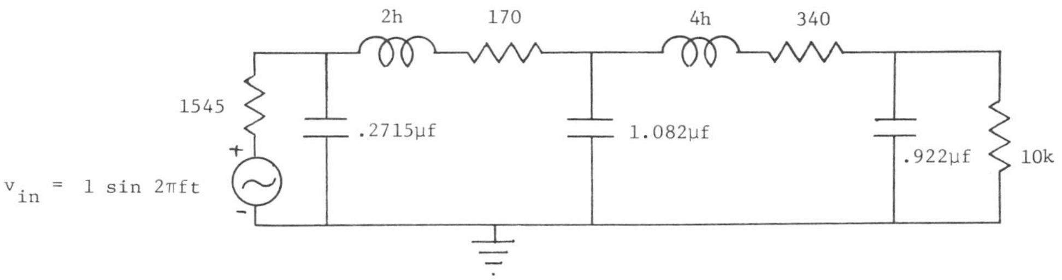

Fig. 12.12 An ac circuit.

range which includes both lower and upper 3 db frequencies of your amplifier.

5. Experiments 8 through 11 contain many networks which can be analyzed using the ECAP program. Select one or more of these circuits, and write ECAP programs which will ac analyze these circuits for you. Try to select networks and component values which you used in earlier experiments, to compare your computer results with any experimental results you obtained earlier.

6. (optional) Select an electronic network from either this manual or from any reference book and try to analyze it with the aid of an ECAP program. Change component values in order to redesign the network to either improve its performance or modify the overall function of the network. Some integrated circuit packages could serve as a start for this project. Use the ECAP program to perform routine calculations while you concentrate your efforts on the more important aspects of the design. *Note, however, that it is the user's responsibility to choose the proper equivalent circuit and the correct parameter values, no matter what device is used or what network is analyzed.* Also note that modifications of ECAP I are now available.

SCEPTRE

7. Be sure to obtain the calling name of the SCEPTRE program which is stored in your computer's library. Prepare the control cards which will precede your input decks. Consult the SCEPTRE User's Manual and your laboratory instructor if you are having any difficulties.

8. Write a SCEPTRE program to obtain the output voltage response for the network of Fig. 12–7b under small-signal conditions. The input voltage E should be a step function with an amplitude of .1 volt and a duration of 20 μ sec.

9. Experiments 2, 3, 4, and 8, 9, 10, and 11 contain many networks which can be analyzed using the SCEPTRE program. Select one or more of these networks, and write SCEPTRE programs which will analyze these circuits for you. Try to select networks and component values which you used in earlier experiments, in order to compare your computer results with any experimental results you obtained from the breadboarded versions of these circuits.

10. Experiments 13 through 17 contain many electronic networks amenable to analysis by the SCEPTRE program. Some of these experiments contain examples of SCEPTRE programs which should be helpful in preparing this experiment. Select an electronic network from one of the later experiments, and see if you can write a SCEPTRE program for it. You may not as yet understand the function of these networks, but you may still be able to write a program to analyze it.

11. (optional) Select an electronic network from any of the reference books cited in this manual under "References," and try to obtain its transient response with the aid of a SCEPTRE program. Change component values in order either to redesign the network or to modify the function of the network. Some integrated circuit packages could serve as a start for this project. The designer can go as far with this project as his ambition, imagination, and interest will carry him. This optional part is intended to encourage well-motivated individuals to begin to explore the myriad uses and complexities of modern electronic networks once they have acquired some appreciation of fundamental concepts.

LABORATORY PROCEDURE

ECAP

1. Be sure that the control cards you have punched which precede your input decks are correct.

2. Submit your complete ECAP program deck for the network of Fig. 12–10 to your computing center. If you have made any errors, continue to submit your program until you get the correct results. Check with your instructor.

3. Run your ECAP program deck for the analysis of the network of Fig. 12–11. Discuss the results.

4. Run your ECAP program deck for the network of Fig. 12–7a and b. Compare the results and discuss the differences in the upper 3 db frequencies for the hybrid pi and unilateral models.

5. Run the ECAP programs for the network you selected in step 5 of the preparation. Compare your computer results with any experimental results you have obtained previously.

6. (optional) Run the ECAP programs you have written for the networks you selected in step 6 of the preparation.

SCEPTRE

7. Be sure that the control cards you have punched which precede your input decks are correct.

8. Run the complete SCEPTRE program that you have written for step 8 of the preparation. Measure the rise time for this network from the computer output data. How does this compare with the results you would obtain by using the method discussed in Experiment 11? Also, note that ECAP II could be used for this part of the experiment.

9. Run the SCEPTRE programs that you have written for step 9 of the preparation.

10. Run the SCEPTRE programs that you have written for step 10 of the preparation. Save the computer output data, to be used in comparing with experimental results you may obtain later on.

11. (optional) Run the SCEPTRE programs that you have written for step 11 of the preparation. Discuss your project with your laboratory instructor. He may be able to suggest changes and improvements in your programs. You may have discovered a new application of a well-known network or a new and better electronic network to perform a common and well-known function.

LIST OF EQUIPMENT

1. ECAP User's Manual
2. SCEPTRE User's Manual
3. Computing center
4. Cathode-ray oscilloscope
5. General-purpose voltmeters
6. Signal sources
7. Circuit board
8. Components: Resistors, capacitors, inductors, transistors, and integrated circuits

Experiment 13/Transistor Feedback Amplifiers

Part One

INTRODUCTION

An electronic feedback amplifier is one in which an electrical signal is transmitted in some manner from output to input as well as from input to output. Generally, the analysis of feedback amplifiers is more complex than their non-feedback equivalents because of the fundamental differences in a signal transmission from output to input. Nevertheless, feedback amplifiers can be analyzed using standard loop and node equations without even utilizing the fact that feedback is present. The approach usually requires the solution of a large number of simultaneous equations, and is undesirable in a preliminary analysis phase. Recently, an increased emphasis on studying simple techniques of analysis and design which focus attention on the important manifestations of feedback circuits has arisen.

The analysis technique described in this experiment will be used to reveal some of these basic feedback principles. Of course, an exact or improved design can be achieved from a computer-aided analysis once the fundamental feedback principles are understood. An example of where this approach would be helpful is in the analysis of linear integrated amplifiers which maintain temperature and frequency stabilization by the use of feedback circuits. The approximate or first phase of analysis of these amplifiers would be followed by a more exact and preferably computer-aided phase, especially if the integrated amplifiers are to be produced in large quantities.

THEORY

It should be pointed out that all electronic circuits have some feedback present, which may or may not be intentional. We will assume throughout this experiment that linear models adequately describe the small-signal behavior of the solid state devices and that their associated parameter values are known. Consequently, a linear analysis employing Laplace transforms will be used for the calculation of gains, sensitivities, and impedances.

A simple block diagram representing a single-loop feedback amplifier is shown in Fig. 13-1.

The open-loop gain or forward-loop gain without feedback is $G(s)$, and the feedback circuit gain is $H(s)$, which are defined as

$$G(s) \triangleq \frac{O(s)}{E(s)}$$

$$H(s) \triangleq \frac{F(s)}{O(s)} \qquad (13\text{-}1)$$

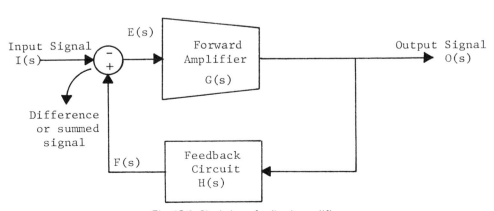

Fig. 13.1 Single loop feedback amplifier.

The quantities $G(s)$ or $H(s)$ can represent the ratio of either two currents or two voltages, depending upon the circuit configuration.

The effects of feedback on amplifier performance all depend upon the loop gain or return ratio $T(s)$, which is the product of $G(s)$ and $H(s)$. The gain, impedance, and sensitivity with feedback can all be easily calculated, and depend explicitly upon $T(s)$. The overall gain with feedback is defined as

$$A_f(s) \triangleq \frac{0(s)}{I(s)} \qquad (13\text{-}2)$$

The error signal $E(s)$ is simply the difference between the input signal $I(s)$ and the feedback signal $F(s)$ (or their sum), as given by

$$E(s) = I(s) \pm F(s) \qquad (13\text{-}3)$$

Substituting Eqs. (13-1) and (13-3) into (13-2) yields the basic feedback equation

$$A_f(s) = \frac{G(s)}{1 \pm G(s)H(s)} = \frac{G(s)}{1 - T(s)} \qquad (13\text{-}4)$$

The basic feedback equation contains the plus sign in the denominator if the difference signal (Eq. [13-3]) has the minus sign in it, and the minus sign appears in the denominator of Eq. (13-4) if the difference signal has the plus sign. The quantity $1 \pm G(s)H(s)$ is called the return difference, and is very important because the roots of $1 \pm G(s)H(s) = 0$ determine the natural frequencies of the feedback amplifier (see Experiment 4). These roots must be in the left half of the s-plane for a stable amplifier. Furthermore, the magnitude of $1 \pm G(j\omega)H(j\omega)$ determines the amount of feedback. If $|1 - T(j\omega)|$ is smaller than unity, the amplifier is said to have *positive* (or regenerative) feedback, and if $|1 - T(j\omega)|$ is greater than unity, it is said to have *negative* (or degenerative) feedback. Positive feedback is the cause of instability.

The sensitivity of the closed-loop gain A_f with respect to variations in the open-loop gain $G(s)$ is the ratio of the fractional (or percentage) change in A_f to the fractional (or percentage) change in $G(s)$—namely,

$$S_G^{A_f} = \frac{dA_f/A_f}{dG/G} \qquad (13\text{-}5)$$

We can calculate the sensitivity by differentiating Eq. (13-4) with respect to G

$$\frac{dA_f}{dG} = \frac{1}{1-T} - \left[\frac{1}{(1-T)^2}\right] G \frac{d(1-T)}{dG} \qquad (13\text{-}6)$$

Eq. (13-6) can be simplified by observing that

$$G \frac{d(1-T)}{dG} = -T \qquad (13\text{-}7)$$

and that Eq. (13-6) is simply

$$\frac{dA_f}{dG} = \frac{1}{(1-T)^2} \qquad (13\text{-}8)$$

Substituting Eq. (13-8) into Eq. (13-5) yields

$$S_G^{A_f} = \frac{1}{1-T} \qquad (13\text{-}9)$$

The sensitivity also explicitly depends upon the return difference $1 - T(s)$. Note that if $|1 - T(j\omega)| \gg 1$, then a 10 percent change in the open-loop gain G will appear as a $\frac{10}{|T|}$ percent change in the closed-loop gain A_f.

The input and output impedances of a feedback amplifier are also either multiplied or divided by the factor $1 - T(s)$. In particular, the "no-feedback" input impedance $Z_i(s)$ and output impedance $Z_o(s)$ are multiplied or divided by $1 - T(s)$ to obtain the feedback impedances $Z_f(s)$ and $Z_{of}(s)$. A knowledge as to whether the feedback is of the current or voltage type and the type of error is required to determine whether the factor $1 - T(s)$ multiplies or divides the no-feedback impedance. If the output voltage is sampled and fed back, then the output impedance is divided by $1 - T(s)$; while if the output current is sampled and fed back, the output impedance is multiplied by $1 - T(s)$. On the other hand, the type of error is required to determine the input impedance. If the portion of the output which is fed back is compared to the input signal by summing currents at a node, then we have a current error signal and the input impedance is divided by $1 - T(s)$. If the comparison is via voltages in series, we have a voltage error signal and the input impedance is multiplied by $1 - T(s)$.

A few practical feedback amplifier circuits will now be presented and related to the block diagram of Fig. 13-1. A design-oriented analysis technique applicable to each of these feedback circuits will be employed. The technique involves the identification of the ideal forward amplifier as well as the identification of the feedback circuit.

There are four basic types of feedback amplifier configurations, known as shunt-shunt, series-series, series-shunt, and shunt-series. All four of these configurations are used, and will be presented in order.

Shunt-Shunt Feedback Amplifiers

A shunt-shunt configuration is shown in Fig. 13-2, and an example of this configuration is shown in Fig. 13-3.

It is important to note the similarities between the single-loop feedback circuit shown in block diagram form in Fig. 13-1 and the circuits shown in Figs. 13-2 and 13-3. Also note that the ideal amplifier shown in Fig. 13-3 is characterized by input impedance Z_i looking into the first

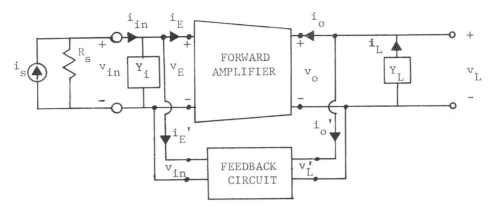

Fig. 13.2 Shunt-shunt configuration.

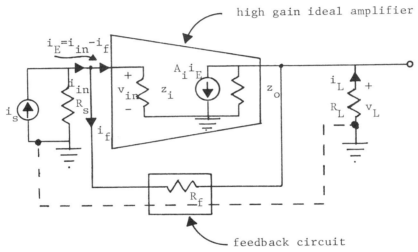

Fig. 13.3 Shunt-shunt configuration with resistive feedback.

stage, an output impedance Z_o seen looking into the output of the last stage, and a total current gain (A_i or voltage gain A_v) for the cascaded stages of the forward amplifier. When using linear integrated circuits, these values are specified at midband frequencies by the manufacturer, and typically vary as follows: $Z = 1 \text{ k} - 100 \text{ k}\Omega$, $Z_o = 1 - 10 \ \Omega$, $A_v = 1$ to 100,000.

The feedback network of Fig. 13-3 consists of a single resistor R_f. Clearly, it is the output voltage v_L that is sampled and fed back through R_f. Note that, on the one hand, if we short-circuit R_L, so that $v_L = 0$, the feedback would be zero. If we open-circuit R_L, so that the load current $i_L = 0$, then the feedback would not be seriously affected. Thus, this circuit has *voltage feedback*. Furthermore, the current i_E is produced by comparing i_{in} with the current i_f, and this circuit is classified as having *current error*.

Now we are ready to begin the analysis of Fig. 13-2. We first recall that the feedback circuit and ideal amplifier can be represented in terms of two-port parameters. In particular, the inputs and outputs of Fig. 13-2 are connected

in parallel (shunt-shunt), which implies that the y-parameters would be convenient for analysis. The application of Kirchhoff's current and voltage laws to Fig. 13-2, with all currents and voltages defined in terms of their Laplace transform variables, yields

$$V_{in}(s) = V_E(s) = V'_{in}(s) \tag{13-10}$$

$$V_L(s) = V_o(s) = V'_L(s) \tag{13-11}$$

$$I_{in}(s) = I_E(s) + I'_E(s) \tag{13-12}$$

$$I_L(s) = I_o(s) + I'_o(s) \tag{13-13}$$

The two-port y-admittance matrix representation for the ideal amplifier is

$$\begin{bmatrix} I_E(s) \\ I_o(s) \end{bmatrix} = \begin{bmatrix} y_{11} & y_{12} \\ y_{21} & y_{22} \end{bmatrix} \begin{bmatrix} V_E(s) \\ V_o(s) \end{bmatrix} \tag{13-14}$$

and for the feedback circuit is

$$\begin{bmatrix} I'_E(s) \\ I'_o(s) \end{bmatrix} = \begin{bmatrix} y'_{11} & y'_{12} \\ y'_{21} & y'_{22} \end{bmatrix} \begin{bmatrix} V'_{in}(s) \\ V'_L(s) \end{bmatrix} \tag{13-15}$$

By using Eqs. (13-10), (13-11), (13-12), (13-13), (13-14), (13-15), a representation for the complete shunt-shunt connection can now be written, leaving off the Laplace transform variable for notational simplicity. Thus

$$\begin{bmatrix} I_{in} \\ I_L \end{bmatrix} = \begin{bmatrix} y_{11} + y'_{11} & y_{12} + y'_{12} \\ y_{21} + y'_{21} & y_{22} + y'_{22} \end{bmatrix} \begin{bmatrix} V_{in} \\ V_L \end{bmatrix} \qquad (13-16)$$

also define the sum of the elements of the admittance matrices as

$$[y_{ij}^T] = [y_{ij}] + [y'_{ij}] \qquad (13-17)$$

The input and load connections yield the additional relationships

$$I_L = -Y_L V_L \qquad (13-18)$$

$$I_{in} = I_s - G_s V_{in} \qquad (13-19)$$

Solving for $-(I_L/I_s)$

$$A_{if}(s) = \frac{-I_L(s)}{I_s(s)} = \frac{-y_{21}^T Y_L}{(y_{11}^T + G_s)(y_{22}^T + Y_L) - y_{12}^T y_{21}^T} \qquad (13-20)$$

Suppose that $-i_L$ is the current flowing through a resistor in the last stage of the ideal amplifier, as shown in Fig. 13-3. The expression for the current gain with feedback becomes

$$A_{if}(s) = \frac{-I_L(s)}{I_s(s)} = \frac{\dfrac{-y_{21}^T G_L}{(y_{11}^T + G_s)(y_{22}^T + G_L)}}{1 - \dfrac{y_{12}^T y_{21}^T}{(y_{11}^T + G_s)(y_{22}^T + G_L)}} \qquad (13-21)$$

To obtain the input admittance, we solve for I_s/V_{in}, which yields

$$Y_{if}(s) = \frac{I_s}{V_{in}} = (y_{11}^T + G_s)\left[1 - \frac{+y_{12}^T y_{12}^T}{(y_{22}^T + G_L)(y_{11}^T + G_s)}\right] \qquad (13-22)$$

Eq. (13-22) is obtained by eliminating I_L and V_L from the second equation of Eq. (13-16). Similarly, the output admittance is obtained from Eq. (13-16) by eliminating I_{in} and V_{in} and solving for I_L/V_L, with $I_s = 0$

$$Y_{of} = \frac{I_L}{V_L} = y_{22}^T - \frac{y_{21}^T y_{12}^T}{y_{11}^T + G_s} \qquad (13-23)$$

The question remaining is how to identify the terms in Eqs. (13-21), (13-22), and (13-23) with the terms in the basic feedback Eq. (13-4). If no approximations are made, we can at once identify $G(s)$ and $H(s)$ as

$$G(s) = \frac{-y_{21}^T G_L}{(y_{11}^T + G_s)(y_{22}^T + G_L)} \qquad (13-24)$$

$$H(s) = -\frac{y_{12}^T}{G_L} \qquad (13-25)$$

and

$$T(s) = +G(s)H(s) = \frac{+y_{12}^T y_{21}^T}{(y_{11}^T + G_s)(y_{22}^T + G_L)} \qquad (13-26)$$

It is generally assumed that $H(s)$ is only a function of the parameters (y'_{ij}) of the feedback circuit, and that a signal is fed from the input through the ideal forward amplifier and then back again through the feedback circuit to the input. Therefore, in order to appropriately define an ideal forward amplifier circuit and a feedback circuit, as shown in Fig. 13-1, the following assumptions are made

$$y_{21} \gg y'_{21}$$

$$y_{12} \ll y'_{12}$$

These two assumptions are now consistent with the idealized situation depicted in Fig. 13-1 because the signal flow for the actual circuit of Fig. 13-3 is from input to output through the ideal forward amplifier only. The signal flow from output to input is through the feedback circuit only. However, also note that $G(s)$ will depend upon the feedback circuit due to y_{11}^T and y_{22}^T. If the values of the elements in the feedback circuit are known, then y'_{11} and y'_{22} are simply added to those of y_{11} and y_{22}.

Normally, in a design problem, the values of y'_{11} and y'_{22} are to be determined, and are usually assumed to be much smaller than y_{11} and y_{22}, respectively.

The input admittances using the assumptions given are

$$Y_{if} = (y_{11} + G_s)\left[1 - \frac{y'_{12} y_{21}}{(y_{22} + G_s)(y_{11} + G_L)}\right]$$

$$= (y_{11} + G_s)[1 - T(s)] \qquad (13-27)$$

and

$$Y_{of} = (y_{22}^T + G_L)[1 - T(s)] \qquad (13-28)$$

Eqs. (13-27) and (13-28) are consistent with what was said earlier, because the output voltage is sampled and fed back for the shunt-shunt configuration. Similarly, the portion of the output which is fed back is compared with the input signal by summing currents at a node (current error signal) and, therefore, the admittance is multiplied by $1 - T(s)$.

It can easily be shown that if R_f is much larger than both R_L and the input impedance of the transistor amplifier of Fig. 13-4, the following results are obtained

$$H(s) = -R_L y'_{12} = -R_L \left.\frac{I'_E}{V'_L}\right|_{V'_{in}=0} = -R_L \left(-\frac{1}{R_f}\right) \qquad (13-29)$$

and

$$G(s) = \frac{A_i(0)p_2}{s + p_2} \qquad (13-30)$$

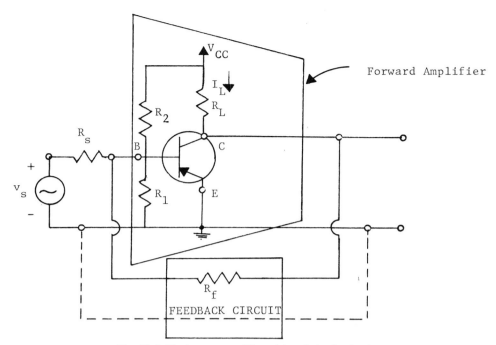

Fig. 13.4 Single stage amplifier with resistive feedback.

Eq. (13-30) is the high-frequency current gain of the forward amplifier (see Eq. [11-35] of Experiment 11). The overall gain with feedback can now be simply calculated as

$$A_{if} = \frac{G(s)}{1 - T(s)} = \frac{\dfrac{A_i(0)p_2}{s + p_2}}{1 - \dfrac{A_i(0)p_2\left(\dfrac{R_L}{R_f}\right)}{s + p_2}} \qquad (13\text{-}31)$$

Note that we use the unilateral model approximation to obtain $G(s)$ for the forward amplifier instead of using Eq. (13-24) directly. This simplifies the analysis, but can be checked using a hybrid pi model for the transistor and Eq. (13-24) if a more precise analysis is warranted. Also note that $A_i(0)$ is a negative quantity for the amplifier shown in Fig. 13-4.

The sensitivity for the amplifier of Fig. 13-4 has the form given by Eq. (13-9), and has the following important characteristic. Since

$$T(0) = A_i(0)\frac{R_L}{R_f} \qquad (13\text{-}32)$$

a smaller value of R_f will increase $T(0)$ and decrease the sensitivity, which at first appears desirable. Further reflection reveals that the overall gain A_{if} is also reduced, which may not be desirable—that is, the desensitivity is achieved at the expense of a lower overall midband gain. This is generally the case with negative feedback. More important,

however, is the possibility in some amplifiers of achieving high-frequency instability by reducing R_f. This instability may be totally undesirable when designing for a stable feedback amplifier but highly desirable when designing an oscillator.

Series-Series Feedback Amplifiers

The series-series configuration is shown in Fig. 13-5. A common-emitter amplifier with an unbypassed emitter-resistor is shown in Fig. 13-6, and is an example of a series-series configuration exclusive of biasing circuitry.

Since the load current in Fig. 13-6 is sampled via the voltage across R_f, the circuit exhibits current feedback and voltage error. The circuits of Figs. 13-5 and 13-6 can be conveniently analyzed by choosing the z-parameters. The

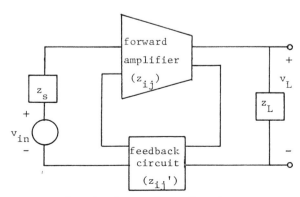

Fig. 13.5 Series-series configuration.

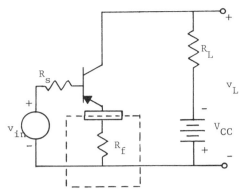

Fig. 13.6 Example of series-series configuration.

overall voltage gain in this case is

$$A_{vf} = \frac{V_L(s)}{V_{in}(s)} = \frac{z_{21}^T Z_L}{(z_{11}^T + Z_s)(z_{22}^T + Z_L) - z_{12}^T z_{21}^T} \quad (13\text{-}33)$$

where

$$[z_{ij}^T] = [z_{ij}] + [z_{ij}'] \quad (13\text{-}34)$$

The exact return ratio for this case is

$$T(s) = \frac{z_{12}^T z_{21}^T}{(z_{11}^T + Z_s)(z_{22}^T + Z_L)} = +G(s)H(s) \quad (13\text{-}35)$$

We note that, as in the previous case, we make two important assumptions, which are

$$z_{21} \gg z_{21}'$$

$$z_{12} \ll z_{12}'$$

This enables us to identify $G(s)$ and $H(s)$ using the approximations, and we have

$$G(s) = \frac{z_{21} Z_L}{(z_{11}^T + Z_s)(z_{22}^T + Z_L)} \quad (13\text{-}36)$$

$$H(s) = \frac{+z_{12}'}{Z_L} \quad (13\text{-}37)$$

and

$$A_{vf}(s) = \frac{G(s)}{1 - T(s)} \quad (13\text{-}38)$$

It can be shown that for the series-series configuration the input and output impedances are given by

$$Z_{in} = (z_{11}^T + Z_s)(1 - T(s)) \quad (13\text{-}39)$$

$$Z_o = (z_{22}^T + Z_L)(1 - T(s)) \quad (13\text{-}40)$$

Therefore, the series-series connection increases the input and output impedances. Once again considering the example of Fig. 13-6 and replacing the transistor with a unilateral high-frequency model

$$G(s) = \frac{+A_v(0)p_1}{s + p_1} \quad (13\text{-}41)$$

where

$$A_v(0) = \frac{-g_m R_L r_{b'e}}{R_s + R_f + h_{ie}} \quad (13\text{-}42)$$

$$p_1 = \frac{R_s + R_f + h_{ie}}{C_T r_{b'e}(R_s + R_f + r_{bb'})} \quad (13\text{-}43)$$

and

$$H(s) = \frac{+z_{12}'}{R_L} = \frac{+R_f}{R_L} \quad (13\text{-}44)$$

The closed-loop gain is

$$A_{vf} = \frac{A_v(0)p_1}{s + p_1\left(1 - A_v(0)\dfrac{R_f}{R_L}\right)} \quad (13\text{-}45)$$

and the midband transmission function is

$$T(0) = -\frac{R_f}{R_L}\frac{g_m R_L r_{b'e}}{(R_s + R_f + h_{ie})} = \frac{-h_{fe} R_f}{R_f + R_s + h_{ie}} \quad (13\text{-}46)$$

Because the error is of the voltage type, the midband input impedance is

$$Z_{if} = (R_f + R_s + h_{ie})\left(1 + \frac{h_{fe} R_f}{R_f + R_s + h_{ie}}\right) \quad (13\text{-}47)$$

Because the feedback is of the current type, the midband output impedance is

$$Z_{of} = (R_o + R_f + R_L)\left(1 + \frac{h_{fe} R_f}{R_f + R_s + h_{ie}}\right) \quad (13\text{-}48)$$

where R_o is the output impedance of the hybrid pi model.

Series-Shunt Feedback Amplifiers

The series-shunt configuration is shown in Fig. 13-7, and an example of this connection, exclusive of coupling and biasing circuitry, is given in Fig. 13-8. Note that the circuit of Fig. 13-8 is an example of voltage feedback since v_e is sampled and fed back. The circuit is sometimes called a voltage feedback pair. In addition, this circuit exhibits a voltage error since v_{in} and v_e form a series circuit.

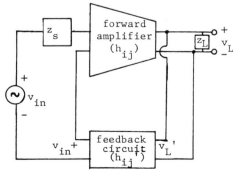

Fig. 13.7 Series-shunt configuration.

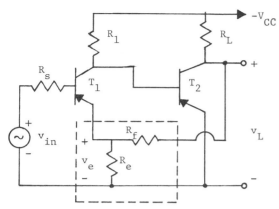

Fig. 13.8 Example of series-shunt configuration.

The series-shunt type of connection is most conveniently analyzed using the h-parameters. The overall voltage gain in this case is

$$A_{vf} = \frac{V_L(s)}{V_{in}(s)} = \frac{h_{21}^T}{(h_{11}^T + Z_s)(h_{22}^T + Y_L) - h_{12}^T h_{21}^T} \quad (13\text{-}49)$$

Once again for identification purposes, we make the two basic assumptions that

$$h_{21} \gg h'_{21}$$

$$h_{12} \ll h'_{12}$$

From these two assumptions, we obtain

$$G(s) = \frac{h_{21}}{(h_{11}^T + Z_s)(h_{22}^T + Y_L)} \quad (13\text{-}50)$$

and

$$H(s) = -h'_{12} \quad (13\text{-}51)$$

Remembering that $G(s)$ represents approximately the open-loop gain of the circuit of Fig. 13-8, we can replace the transistors by their unilateral high-frequency models to calculate $G(s)$ in a simple manner. That is,

$$G(s) = \frac{V_L(s)}{V_{in}(s)} = \frac{A_v(0)p_1 p_2}{(s + p_1)(s + p_2)} \quad (13\text{-}52)$$

If we assume identical transistor parameters, then

$$A_v(0) = \frac{R_1 R_L \beta^2}{(R_s + h_{ie})(R_1 + h_{ie})} \quad (13\text{-}53)$$

and

$$p_1 = \frac{(R_s + h_{ie})}{r_{b'e} C_T (R_s + r_{bb'})} \quad (13\text{-}54)$$

$$p_2 = \frac{(R_1 + h_{ie})}{r_{b'e} C_T (R_1 + r_{bb'})} \quad (13\text{-}55)$$

The feedback circuit gain can be calculated from

$$H(s) = -h'_{12} = \frac{-v'_{in}}{v'_L} = \frac{R_e}{R_e + R_f} \quad (13\text{-}56)$$

$$A_{vf} = \frac{G(s)}{1 - T(s)} = \frac{A_v(0)p_1 p_2}{s^2 + (p_1 + p_2)s + p_1 p_2 \left(1 + A_v(0)\frac{R_e}{R_e + R_f}\right)} \quad (13\text{-}57)$$

Note that the low-frequency gain with feedback is

$$A_{vf}(0) = \frac{A_v(0)}{1 + A_v(0)\dfrac{R_e}{R_e + R_f}} \quad (13\text{-}58)$$

When $\dfrac{A_v(0)R_e}{R_e + R_f} \gg 1$, the gain simplifies to

$$A_{vf} \approx \frac{R_e + R_f}{R_e} \quad (13\text{-}59)$$

A complete circuit for a voltage feedback pair is shown in Fig. 13-9. A small-signal circuit model with typical transistor parameters is shown in Fig. 13-10. (These parameters are for a 2N526 *pnp* transistor biased at $I_E = 5$ m.a. and $V_{CE} = 6.8$V.) Observe that the circuit of Fig. 13-10 contains a large number of elements. Thus the determination of the effect on the gain or bandwidth of changing R_f would require numerous and lengthy calculations. This

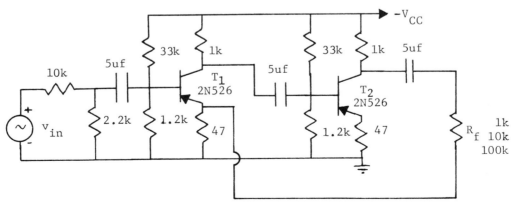

Fig. 13.9 Voltage feedback pair.

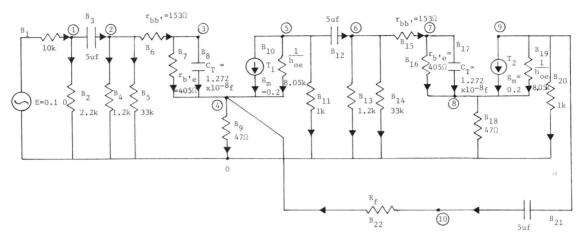

Fig. 13.10 Model of voltage feedback pair amplifier.

problem, as mentioned earlier, could be handled by a computer program such as ECAP or SCEPTRE. An example of an ECAP program which can be used to compare the gain and bandwidth as a function of the feedback resistor is shown following Figs. 13–9 and 13–10. A more accurate analysis could be achieved by using the hybrid pi model in Fig. 13–10 instead of the unilateral model.

```
C     TWO STAGE COMMON-EMITTER AMPLIFIER
C        WITH FEEDBACK
C     COMPARISON OF MIDBAND GAIN AND
C        BANDWIDTH AS A FUNCTION OF THE
C     FEEDBACK RESISTOR
      AC ANALYSIS
B1    N(0,1), R = 10E3,E = 0.1/0
B2    N(1,0), R = 2.2E3
B3    N(1,2), C = 5E-6
B4    N(2,0), R = 1.2E3
B5    N(2,0), R = 33E3
B6    N(2,3), R = 153
B7    N(3,4), R = 405
B8    N(3,4), C = 1.272E-8
B9    N(4,0), R = 47
B10   N(5,4), R = 8.05E3
B11   N(5,0), R = 1E3
B12   N(5,6), C = 5E-6
B13   N(6,0), R = 1.2E3
B14   N(6,0), R = 33E3
B15   N(6,7), R = 153
B16   N(7,8), R = 405
B17   N(7,8), C = 1.272E-8
B18   N(8,0), R = 47
B19   N(9,8), R = 8.05E3
B20   N(9,0), R = 1E3
B21   N(9,10), C = 5E-6
B22   N(10,4), R = 100E3
T1    B(7,10), GM = 0.2
```

```
T2    B(16,19), GM = 0.2
      FREQUENCY = 10
      PRINT,VOLTAGES
      MODIFY
      FREQUENCY = 10(1.5)1.3E6
      EXECUTE
```

Another example of the series-shunt connection is the single-stage emitter-follower shown in Fig. 13–11 exclusive of biasing. As explained in a previous experiment, the unilateral model is not valid for the emitter-follower configuration. The midband model shown in the circuit of

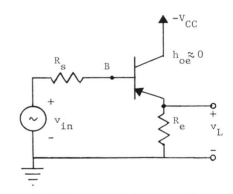

Fig. 13.11 Emitter follower amplifier.

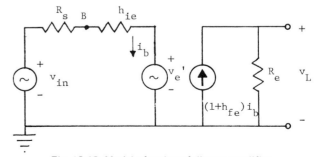

Fig. 13.12 Model of emitter follower amplifier.

Fig. 13-12 will be used. Note that v'_e represents the voltage fed back from the output. Therefore, the voltage gain without feedback is

$$G(0) = \frac{V_L}{V_{\text{in}}}(0)\bigg|_{v'_e=0} = \frac{(h_{fe}+1)R_e}{R_s + h_{ie}} \quad (13\text{-}60)$$

and

$$H(0) = +h'_{12} = +1 \quad (13\text{-}61)$$

$$A_{vf} = \frac{G(0)}{1 - T(0)} = \frac{R_e(h_{fe}+1)}{R_s + h_{ie} + (h_{fe}+1)R_e} \quad (13\text{-}62)$$

The output impedance, noting that this circuit employs voltage feedback, is

$$Z_{of} = \frac{R_e}{1-T} = \frac{R_e}{1 + \dfrac{(h_{fe}+1)R_e}{R_s + h_{ie}}} \quad (13\text{-}63)$$

Since there is voltage error in this circuit, the input impedance is

$$Z_{if} = (R_s + h_{ie})(1-T) = (R_s + h_{ie})\left(1 + \frac{(h_{fe}+1)R_e}{R_s + h_{ie}}\right) \quad (13\text{-}64)$$

Very often it is desirable to increase the input impedance of the emitter-follower. This increase can be achieved by using an external feedback resistor to provide controlled positive feedback, as shown in Fig. 13-13. This procedure

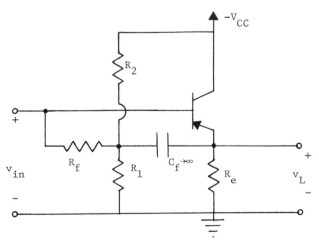

Fig. 13.13 Shunt-shunt amplifier.

is often called "bootstrapping." Note that setting $R_f = 0$ and $C_f = 0$ reduces the bootstrapped circuit to the ordinary emitter-follower circuit of Fig. 13-11.

The circuit of Fig. 13-13 operates with voltage feedback and current error and has a shunt-shunt configuration when redrawn as in Fig. 13-14 with $R_B = R_1 || R_2$.

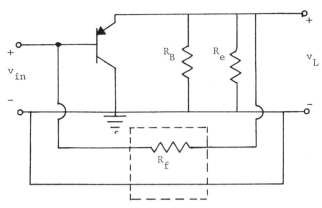

Fig. 13.14 Fig. 13.13 redrawn.

It can be easily shown that

$$T(0) = \frac{(1 + h_{fe})R'_e}{R_f + h_{ie} + (1 + h_{fe})R'_e} \quad (13\text{-}65)$$

with $R'_e = R_B || R_e || R_f$. Note that $|T(0)| < 1$, which is positive feedback. The input impedance with feedback is simply

$$Z_{if} = \frac{R_f || [h_{ie} + (1 + h_{fe})R'_e]}{1 - T}$$

$$= \frac{R_f[h_{ie} + (1 + h_{fe})R'_e]}{R_f + h_{ie}} \quad (13\text{-}66)$$

This input impedance is generally greater than the input impedance for the circuit of Fig. 13-11.

Shunt-Series Feedback Amplifiers

The shunt-series configuration is shown in Fig. 13-15, and an example of this connection is given in Fig. 13-16.

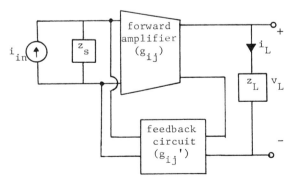

Fig. 13.15 Shunt-series configuration.

Once again, biasing and coupling circuitries are omitted from Fig. 13-16. This circuit is sometimes called a current feedback pair. The g-parameters are the most convenient for the connections shown in Figs. 13-15 and 13-16. In

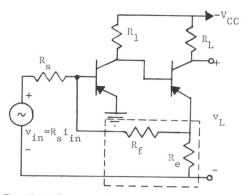

Fig. 13.16 Example of shunt-series configuration.

this case, the overall current gain with feedback is

$$A_{if} = \frac{I_L}{I_{in}} = \frac{-g_{21}^T}{(g_{11}^T + Y_s)(g_{22}^T + Z_L)} \qquad (13\text{-}67)$$

Employing the two assumptions that $g_{21} \gg g_{21}'$ and $g_{12} \ll g_{12}'$ allows the following identification

$$G(s) = \frac{I_L}{I_s} = \frac{-g_{21}}{(g_{11}^T + Y_s)(g_{22}^T + Z_L)} \qquad (13\text{-}68)$$

and

$$H(s) = \left. \frac{+I_{in}}{I_L} \right|_{v_{in}' = 0} = +g_{12}' \qquad (13\text{-}69)$$

For the circuit of Fig. 13-13, it can be shown that under reasonable assumptions the two-stage high-frequency transfer functions $G(s)$ and $H(s)$ can be approximated as

$$G(s) = \frac{A_i(0)p_1 p_2}{(s + p_1)(s + p_2)} \qquad (13\text{-}70)$$

$$H(s) = \frac{R_e}{R_e + R_f} \qquad (13\text{-}71)$$

then

$$A_{if} = \frac{A_i(0)p_1 p_2}{s^2 + (p_1 + p_2)s + p_1 p_2 \left(1 + A_i(0)\dfrac{R_e}{R_e + R_f}\right)} \qquad (13\text{-}72)$$

Note that the denominator polynomial of A_{if} can have complex roots. The frequency response of this amplifier will depend upon the location of the poles of $A_{if}(s)$. The input impedance at midband is simply

$$R_{if} = \frac{R_f \| h_{ie}}{1 - T(0)} \qquad (13\text{-}73)$$

R_{if} is generally low because $1 - T(0) \gg 1$. The output impedance with feedback is simply

$$R_{of} = \frac{R_L + R_e + R_o}{1 - T(0)} \qquad (13\text{-}74)$$

when R_o is the output impedance of the hybrid pi model.

Part Two

OBJECTIVE

A design-oriented analysis of several transistor feedback amplifiers will be studied. Overall gains, sensitivities, and impedances will be considered, including their frequency responses. Computer-aided analysis will also be employed to exhibit fundamental differences between feedback amplifiers and their non-feedback equivalents.

REFERENCES

Alley, C. L., and Atwood, K. W., *Electronic Engineering.* New York: Wiley, 1966, Chapter 11.

Angelo, E. J., *Electronics: BJTs, FETs, and Microcircuits.* New York: McGraw-Hill, 1969, Chapter 13.

Chirlian, P. M., *Electronic Circuits: Physical Principles, Analysis, and Design.* New York: McGraw-Hill, 1971, Chapter 13.

Fitchen, F. C., *Transistor Circuit Analysis and Design.* New York: Van Nostrand Reinhold, 1966, Chapter 10.

Ghausi, M. S., *Electronic Circuits: Devices, Models, Functions, Anal-*

ysis, and Design. New York: Van Nostrand Reinhold, 1971, Chapter 6.

Gray, P. E., and Searle, C. L., *Electronic Principles: Physics, Models, and Circuits.* New York: Wiley, 1967, Chapter 18.

Millman, J., and Halkias, C. C., *Electronic Devices and Circuits.* New York: McGraw-Hill, 1967, Chapter 17.

Schilling, D. L., and Belove, C., *Electronic Circuits: Discrete and Integrated.* New York: McGraw-Hill, 1968, Chapter 15.

LABORATORY PREPARATION

Shunt-Shunt Feedback Amplifiers

1. The circuit of Fig. 13-4 is to be analyzed using a transistor which is available in your laboratory. We will select the 2N526, which was used previously. Typical values for a 2N526 transistor might be: $V_{CC} = -12$ V, $R_L = 1$ k, $R_s = 1.3$ k, $R_1 = 33$ k, $R_2 = 330$ k, and R_f varies between 1 and 100 k. Determine the dc quiescent point for your transis-

tor. Use a high-frequency unilateral model for the transistor and calculate $G(s)$ and $H(s)$ for this circuit.

2. Calculate the sensitivity and input and output impedances at midband frequencies for your amplifier.

3. Can the overall transfer function $A_{if}(s)$, which you derived in step 1, have a pole in the right half s-plane for positive values of R_f ($R_f > 0$)? What happens to the bandwidth and midband gain of this amplifier as R_f is decreased towards zero?

4. (optional) Write a simple computer program similar to the one included in the experiment to determine the frequency response of your amplifier. If ECAP is used, you should print out the output voltages for a wide range of input frequencies. If SCEPTRE is used, a plot of the output voltage versus time is easily obtained. This means that input signals other than sinusoids could be applied and various responses analyzed as a function of R_f.

Series-Series Feedback Amplifiers

5. Design and analyze the circuit of Fig. 13-6. Be sure to include all necessary biasing and coupling circuitry. Use a unilateral transistor model. Of course, your design should include the selection of a transistor, determination of Q points, and the determination of $G(s)$, $H(s)$, and associated input and output impedances at midband frequencies.

6. Compare your midband analysis with an analysis which replaces the transistor with a hybrid pi model. Compare with the amplifiers you designed in Experiment 10.

7. (optional) Write a computer program to analyze your circuit. Compare your design with those circuits you designed in Experiment 12.

Series-Shunt Feedback Amplifiers

8. Design and analyze the circuit of Fig. 13-8. Be sure to include biasing and coupling circuitry. Include the same

calculations as required in step 5. Explain why this circuit exhibits negative feedback.

9. Design and analyze the circuit of Fig. 13-11, including all coupling and biasing circuitry. Compare your results with Experiment 10.

10. Design and analyze the shunt-shunt amplifier of Fig. 13-13, and compare it with the circuit of Fig. 13-11.

11. (optional) Write a computer program to analyze any series-shunt amplifier you desire. Vary any feedback resistors, and note their effect on gains, impedances, and sensitivities. Use the example in Figs. 13-9 and 13-10 or Fig. 13-17 as a guide. The following ECAP program is given for the circuit of Fig. 13-17.

```
C      SINGLE STAGE FEEDBACK AMPLIFIER FRE-
C         QUENCY RESPONSE
C         CIRCUIT–FIG. 13–17
       AC ANALYSIS
B1     N(0,1), E = 0.1/0,R=330E3
B2     N(1,2), C = 5E-6
B3     N(2,0), R = 17.68E3
B4     N(2,3), R = 130
B5     N(0,4), R = 560
B6     N(3,5), R = 480
B7     N(5,0), R = 330
B8     N(5,6), C = 5E-6
B9     N(6,0), R = 1E3
B10    N(4,5), C = 18E-12
B11    N(4,5), R = 12.6E3
B12    N(3,5), C = 9.85E-9
B13    N(2,7), R = 10E3
B14    N(7,5), C = 25E-6
T1     B(6,11), GM = 0.173
       FREQUENCY = 10
       PRINT,VOLTAGES
       MODIFY
       FREQUENCY = 10(1.41421)1E6
       EXECUTE
```

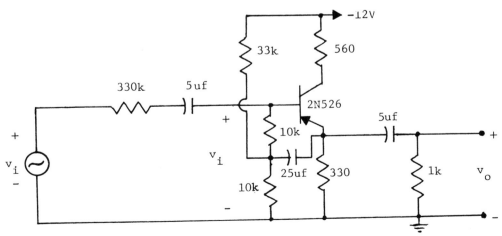

Fig. 13.17 A series-shunt amplifier.

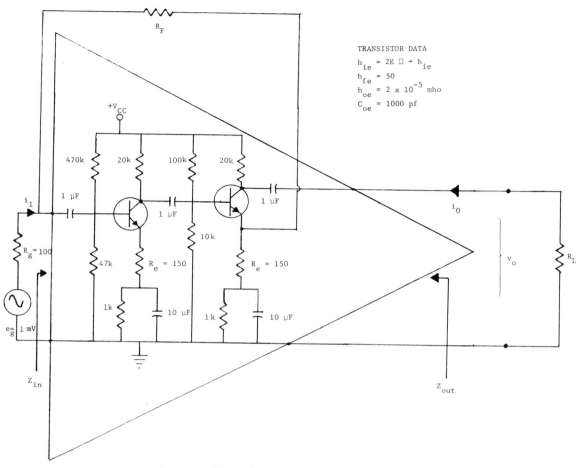

Fig. 13.18 Shunt-series amplifier.

Shunt-Series Feedback Amplifiers

12. Design and analyze the current feedback pair of Fig. 13–16. Vary R_f and note the effect on pole locations and frequency response.

13. (optional) Write a computer program to analyze the shunt-series amplifier shown in Fig. 13–18.

LABORATORY PROCEDURE

Shunt-Shunt Feedback Amplifiers

1. Construct the circuit you designed in step 1 of the preparation and measure all the dc quiescent voltages.

2. Make a frequency response measurement and measure the input and output impedances of your amplifier. Change R_L by 10% and note the effect on the overall midband gain. What is the relation between this effect and the sensitivity of the amplifier?

3. Change R_f and measure the effect on midband gain and bandwidth.

4. (optional) Compare your measurements with the results obtained from your computer program. Apply a

square-wave input to your amplifier and compare with your computer results.

Series-Series Feedback Amplifiers

5. Construct the circuit of Fig. 13–6 and make all measurements to verify your calculations in step 5 of the preparation.

6. Note that changing R_f changes the Q point as well as the amount of ac feedback in this circuit. Therefore, R_f is also used as a dc stabilizing resistor (see Experiment 7).

7. (optional) Compare your computer results with measurements made on your circuit.

Series-Shunt Feedback Amplifiers

8. Construct the circuit you designed for step 8 of the preparation. Show by direct measurements at the midband frequencies that your circuit exhibits negative feedback. Measure all important quantities.

9. Construct the shunt-shunt amplifier of Fig. 13–13 and measure the input impedance. Compare with your calcu-

lated values. Compare this amplifier's performance with the series-shunt amplifier of Figure 13-11.

10. (optional) Compare your computer-aided analysis with measurements made on your series-shunt amplifiers.

Shunt-Series Feedback Amplifiers

11. Construct the current feedback pair you designed and completely test this circuit out. Vary R_f and measure the frequency response. It is important to carefully measure the frequency response at frequencies close to the upper 3 dbv frequency. Why?

12. (optional) Construct the circuit of Fig. 13-18 and compare measurements with predicted values.

13. (optional) Test some linear integrated high-frequency amplifiers which employ feedback, such as the MC 1552G (series-series) video amplifier.

LIST OF EQUIPMENT

1. Cathode-ray oscilloscope
2. General-purpose voltmeters or ac and dc voltmeters
3. Signal sources: Function generator or sine- and square-wave oscillators, dc power supplies
4. Circuit board
5. Components: Resistors, capacitors, bipolar transistors, FET's, and integrated circuits

Experiment 14/Linear Differential and Compound Amplifiers

Part One

INTRODUCTION

The differential or difference amplifier is the basic building block in most integrated circuit linear amplifiers and many other types of amplifiers as well. The basic linear differential amplifier is made up of two transistors, and has an output signal which is linearly proportional to the difference of the input signals applied to the two transistors. It has a frequency response extending from dc up into the megacycle range. Additional advantages of differential amplifiers include freedom of output level drift, relatively high gain, gain as a function of resistance ratios rather than actual values, use of a minimum number of capacitors, and stabilized dc operating points. Of course, there are some disadvantages, which include critical transistor matching and possible instabilities under certain conditions. However, the disadvantages can generally be overcome, and the advantages and versatility of differential amplifiers are the reasons for their popularity. This experiment will also study other types of compound amplifiers, including the Darlington and Cascode amplifiers. These amplifiers will be studied in both their discrete and integrated circuit forms.

THEORY

Differential Amplifiers

The function of a linear differential amplifier is to amplify the difference between two signals. The basic linear differential amplifier circuit is shown in Fig. 14-1.

We will analyze the circuit of Fig. 14-1 under the assumption that perfect symmetry exists. This means that the transistors and certain external elements are identical. In addition, we assume that the balance resistor R_B is equal to zero. In practical circuits, R_B is between 1 and 100 Ω to balance off any unsymmetrical effects between the two halves of the circuit.

The quiescent currents and voltages can be calculated assuming identical transistors and that $R_B = 0$. Therefore,

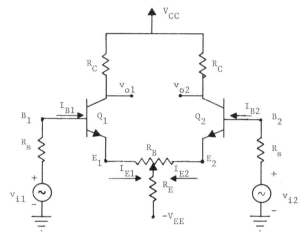

Fig. 14.1 Linear differential amplifier.

$I_{E1} = I_{E2} = I_E$, and the base-emitter loop equation for silicon type transistors is

$$-V_{EE} + .7 + (I_{E1} + I_{E2})R_E + R_s I_{B1} = 0 \quad (14\text{-}1)$$

Thus

$$I_E = I_{E1} = I_{E2} = \frac{V_{EE} - .7}{2R_E + \dfrac{R_s}{h_{fe}}} \quad (14\text{-}2)$$

The collector-emitter loop equation is

$$-V_{CC} + I_{C1}R_C + V_{CE1} + 2I_{E1}R_E - V_{EE} = 0 \quad (14\text{-}3)$$

Rearranging Eq. (14-3), we obtain

$$V_{CE1} = V_{CE2} = V_{CC} - I_C R_C - 2I_E R_E + V_{EE} \quad (14\text{-}4)$$

The importance of the difference amplifier, as mentioned previously, is its ability to amplify the difference between two signals. The output can be taken in a double-ended form, such as $v_{o1} - v_{o2}$, or in a single-ended form from the collector of Q_2 to ground. Suppose that the single-

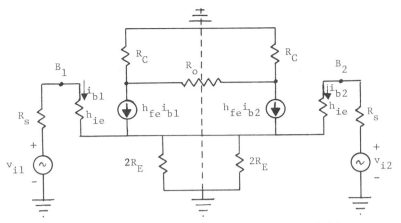

Fig. 14.2 Model of linear differential amplifier with symmetrical inputs.

ended output signal v_{o2} with respect to ground is given by

$$v_{o2} = A_d(v_{i1} - v_{i2}) + A_c(v_{i1} + v_{i2}) \qquad (14\text{-}5)$$

with A_d defined as the differential mode gain, and A_c as the common-mode gain. In addition, suppose that an input differential-mode signal v_d and an input common-mode signal v_c are defined as

$$v_d \triangleq v_{i1} - v_{i2} \qquad (14\text{-}6)$$

$$v_v \triangleq v_{i1} + v_{i2} \qquad (14\text{-}7)$$

Thus Eq. (14-5) becomes

$$v_{o2} = A_d v_d + A_c v_c \qquad (14\text{-}8)$$

Note that if $v_{i1} = v_{i2} = v_i$, then $v_d = 0$, $v_c = 2v_i$, and $v_{o2} = 2A_c v_i$, and if $v_{i1} = -v_{i2} = v_i$, then $v_d = 2v_i$, $v_c = 0$ and $v_{o2} = 2A_d v_i$. Clearly, it is desirable to have A_d large and A_c small. The ratio of A_d to A_c is called the common-mode rejection ratio, and defined as

$$CMRR \triangleq \left| \frac{A_d}{A_c} \right| \qquad (14\text{-}9)$$

Substituting Eq. (14-9) into Eq. (14-8) yields

$$v_{o2} = A_d v_d \left(1 + \frac{A_c}{A_d} \frac{v_c}{v_d}\right) = A_d v_d \left(1 + \frac{1}{CMRR} \frac{v_c}{v_d}\right) \qquad (14\text{-}10)$$

Thus if $v_c/v_d = 10$, then $CMRR$ must be greater than 10 in order for $v_o \approx A_d v_d$. In order to obtain expressions for A_d and A_c in terms of the small-signal parameters of the circuit of Fig. 14-1, let us use the midband unilateral model for a transistor introduced in Experiment 8. The circuit of Fig. 14-2 contains two symmetrical parts as shown, with R_o representing any load introduced by the following amplifier stage.

The circuit of Fig. 14-2 is symmetrical, and can be replaced by the circuit of Fig. 14-3 for purposes of analysis.

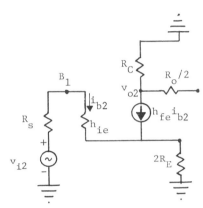

Fig. 14.3 One-half of symmetrical circuit of Fig. 14.2.

For the common-mode gains, we have

$$A_c = \frac{v_{o2}}{v_{i2}} = \frac{-h_{fe}R_C}{R_s + h_{ie} + 2R_E(1 + h_{fe})} \qquad (14\text{-}11)$$

If $v_{i2} = -v_{i1}$, then the circuit of Fig. 14-2 is called anti-symmetrical, and can be replaced by the circuit of Fig. 14-4.

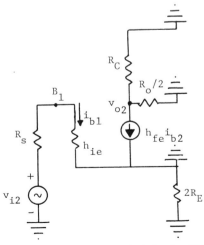

Fig. 14.4 One-half of antisymmetrical circuit of Fig. 14.2.

In this case, the differential-mode gain is

$$A_d = \frac{v_{o2}}{v_{i2}} = -\frac{h_{fe}}{h_{ie} + R_s}\left(\frac{R_C\frac{R_o}{2}}{R_C + \frac{R_o}{2}}\right) \quad (14\text{-}12)$$

Note that in the circuit of Fig. 14-4, $2R_E$ is effectively short-circuited and, consequently, does not appear in the expression for the gain A_d.

The $CMRR$ value for $R_o/2 \gg R_C$ is

$$CMRR = \frac{|A_d|}{|A_c|} = \frac{R_s + h_{ie} + 2R_E(1 + h_{fe})}{h_{ie} + R_s} \quad (14\text{-}13)$$

Equation (14-13) implies that R_E should be large for a large value of $CMRR$. This generally requires the use of a separate power supply $-V_{EE}$ in series with the resistor R_E. However, there are practical considerations which limit the size of R_E and V_{EE}. The quiescent dc voltage across R_E will increase if R_E is increased, and then V_{EE} must be increased to maintain the quiescent current at its proper value. If R_E is increased and I_{E1} or I_{E2} decreased, then h_{ie} will increase and h_{fe} will decrease, causing $CMRR$ to decrease. Thus what is really required is a large ac resistance from pin E_1 or E_2 to ground and a constant dc current supply for transistors Q_1 and Q_2. A constant current source with these properties is shown in Fig. 14-5.

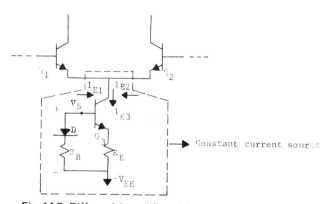

Fig. 14.5 Differential amplifier with constant current source.

The identical quiescent emitter currents for the differential amplifier are determined as

$$I_{E1} = I_{E2} = \frac{1}{2}\,I_{E3} = \frac{1}{2}\left(\frac{V_{EE} - V_B - .7}{R_E}\right) \quad (14\text{-}14)$$

Then since

$$V_{CC} = I_{C1}R_C + V_{CE1} - V_{BE1} - \frac{R_sI_{C1}}{h_{fe}} \quad (14\text{-}15)$$

and if $V_{CC} \gg .7$ and $R_C \gg \dfrac{R_s}{h_{fe}}$, the collector-emiiter voltages are

$$V_{CE1} = V_{CE2} \approx V_{CC} - I_{C1}R_C \quad (14\text{-}16)$$

The diode D_1 is used for thermal compensation. The tendency of the emitter current of Q_3 to increase with temperature is counterbalanced by a reduction of the diode forward resistance and a reduction of the forward base bias of the transistor. This tends to decrease the emitter current, and excellent compensation is obtained by matching the diode resistance characteristics to those of the base-emitter diode of Q_3. This matching is easily achieved, and often used in integrated circuits.

The voltage V_B is the voltage drop from the base of transistor Q_3 to ground. Eq. (14-16) indicates that V_{CE1} and V_{CE2} are independent of V_{BE} and h_{fe}.

The basic difference between the circuit of Fig. 14-5 and that of Fig. 14-1 is that in Fig. 14-5 the impedance from the emitters of Q_1 and Q_2 to ground is $(1 + h_{fe})/h_{oe}$ instead of R_E, the passive resistance shown in Fig. 14-1. The quantity $(1 + h_{fe})/h_{oe}$ is generally much larger than R_E, and consequently provides a large value of $CMRR$.

Compound Amplifiers

The Darlington amplifier shown in Fig. 14-6 operates as a single transistor, and has a voltage gain approaching $-R_L/r_{e2}$ and an input impedance of $2h_{ie}$.

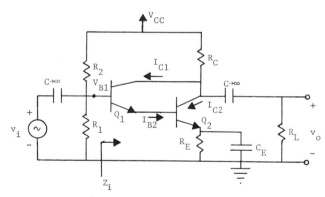

Fig. 14.6 A Darlington amplifier.

The quiescent point for the compound amplifier shown in Fig. 14-6 can be obtained in the usual way. Observe that for silicon type transistors

$$V_{CE2} = V_{CE1} + V_{BE2} \approx V_{CE1} + .7 \quad (14\text{-}17)$$

and that since $I_{C1} \approx I_{B2}$, then

$$I_{C2} \approx h_{fe2}I_{B2} \gg I_{B2} \quad (14\text{-}18)$$

Also $I_{E2} \approx I_{C2} = h_{fe2}I_{B2} \approx h_{fe2}I_{E1}$.

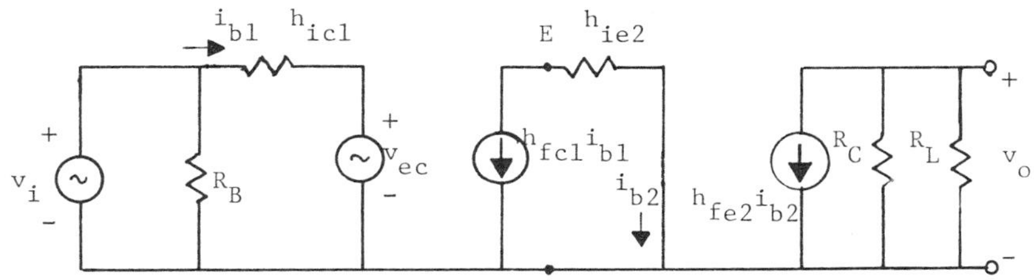

Fig. 14.7 Small signal model of Darlington amplifier.

The dc load line for Q_2 is

$$V_{CC} \approx V_{CE2} + R_C\left(I_{C2} + \frac{I_{C2}}{h_{fe2}}\right) + I_{C2}R_E$$

$$\approx V_{CE2} + I_{C2}(R_C + R_E) \qquad (14\text{-}19)$$

The base-to-emitter loop equation of Q_1 is given by

$$-\frac{R_1 V_{CC}}{R_1 + R_2} + \left(\frac{R_1 R_2}{R_1 + R_2}\right)I_{B1} + .7 + .7 + I_{C2}R_E = 0$$
$$(14\text{-}20)$$

or by

$$\frac{-R_1 V_{CC}}{R_1 + R_2} + \left(\frac{R_1 R_2}{R_1 + R_2}\right)\frac{I_{C1}}{h_{fe1}} + 1.4 + h_{fe2}I_{B2}R_E = 0$$
$$(14\text{-}21)$$

If $\frac{R_1 R_2}{R_1 + R_2}\left(\frac{1}{h_{fe1}}\right) \ll h_{fe2}R_E$, then Eq. (14-21) reduces to

$$\frac{-R_1 V_{CC}}{R_1 + R_2} + 1.4 + h_{fe2}I_{C1}R_E = 0 \qquad (14\text{-}22)$$

The small-signal midband voltage gain of this amplifier can be obtained by replacing Q_1 by its emitter-follower model and Q_2 with its common-emitter model, as shown in Fig. 14-7 (see Experiment 8).
Now

$$v_{ec} = -h_{fc1}h_{ie2}i_{b1} = h_{ie2}i_{b2} \qquad (14\text{-}23)$$

and

$$i_{b1} = \frac{v_i - v_{ec}}{h_{ic1}} \qquad (14\text{-}24)$$

Therefore, the output voltage is

$$v_o = \frac{R_C R_L}{R_C + R_L}(-h_{fe2}i_{b2}) = \left(\frac{R_C R_L}{R_C + R_L}\right)\left(\frac{-h_{fe2}h_{fc1}v_i}{h_{ic1}-h_{fe1}h_{ie2}}\right)$$
$$(14\text{-}25)$$

and the voltage gain, using the h-parameter identities of Experiment 8, is

$$A_v = \frac{v_o}{v_i} = +\left(\frac{R_C R_L}{R_C + R_L}\right)\frac{(1+h_{fe1})h_{fe2}}{(h_{ic1}-h_{fe1}h_{ie2})}$$
$$(14\text{-}26)$$

Since $h_{fe1}h_{ie2} \gg h_{ic1}$ and $h_{fe1} \gg 1$

$$A_v \approx -\left(\frac{R_C R_L}{R_C + R_L}\right)\frac{h_{fe2}}{h_{ie2}} \qquad (14\text{-}27)$$

In practice, it is generally true that $R_L \ll R_C$ and $h_{ie2} \approx h_{fe2}r_{e2}$. Therefore, Eq. (14-27) becomes

$$A_v \approx -\frac{R_L}{r_{e2}} \qquad (14\text{-}28)$$

which is the voltage gain of a single-stage common-emitter amplifier. The input impedance is simply

$$Z_i = \frac{v_i}{i_{b1}} = h_{ic1} - h_{fc1}h_{ie2}$$

$$= h_{ic1} + (1+h_{fe1})h_{ie2} \approx h_{ie1} + h_{fe1}h_{ie2} \quad (14\text{-}29)$$

We also know that

$$h_{ie2} = \frac{h_{fe2}(.026)}{I_{E2}} \approx \frac{.026}{I_{E1}} = h_{ib1} \qquad (14\text{-}30)$$

and that

$$Z_i \approx h_{ie1} + \frac{(1+h_{fe1})h_{ie1}}{(1+h_{fe1})} = 2h_{ie1} \qquad (14\text{-}31)$$

Thus the input impedance of a Darlington circuit is twice the input impedance of a single-stage common-emitter amplifier.

A differential amplifier in integrated circuit form containing the Darlington configuration as well as the constant current source is shown in Fig. 14-8.

Another common type of compound amplifier is the cascode configuration shown in Fig. 14-9. One of its primary purposes in direct coupled amplifiers is to shift the dc level of an input signal such as v_{o1} to the zero or ground level at the output v_{o3} without much attenuation.

If I_{B3} is very small, then

$$V_{B3} = \left(\frac{R_7}{R_7 + R_6}\right)(-V_{EE}) \qquad (14\text{-}32)$$

and

$$V_{E3} = V_{B3} + V_{EB3} \qquad (14\text{-}33)$$

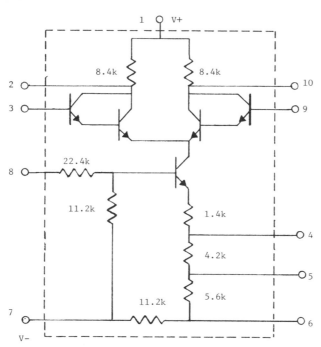

Fig. 14.8 IC differential amplifier with Darlington inputs.

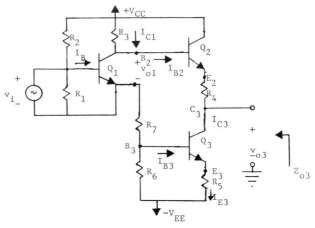

Fig. 14.9 Cascode amplifier.

$V_{EB3} = -.7V$ for the *npn* silicon transistor Q_3. Thus

$$I_{E3} = \frac{V_{E3}}{R_5} \approx I_{C3}$$

If V_{o3} is to be 0 volts, then

$$V_{E2} = R_4 I_{C3} + 0$$

and

$$V_{o1} = V_{B2} = .7 + V_{E2}$$

Therefore, if I_{B2} is small, then

$$V_{o1} = V_{CC} - R_3 I_{C1}$$

and I_{C1} can be adjusted by the biasing resistors R_1 and R_2. Thus the dc level of the output voltage V_{o3} can be shifted by adjusting R_1 and R_2, which controls V_{o1}, which, in turn, controls V_{E2} and V_{o3}.

The small signal gain of this level-shifting amplifier can be calculated using the small-signal equivalent circuit shown

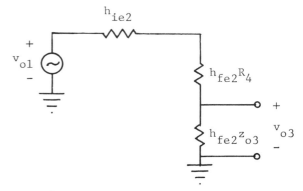

Fig. 14.10 Model of level shifting amplifier.

in Fig. 14-10. Since $Z_{o3} \approx \dfrac{v_{o3}}{h_{ob3}}$, the gain is

$$A_v = \frac{v_{o3}}{v_{o1}} = \frac{h_{fe2}/h_{ob3}}{\dfrac{h_{fe2}}{h_{ob3}} + h_{fe2} R_4 + h_{ie2}}$$

In this circuit, it is generally true that

$$\frac{h_{fe2}}{h_{ob3}} \gg h_{fe2} R_4 + h_{ie2}$$

and then the gain $A_v \approx 1$.

The output stage of the integrated circuit operational amplifier discussed in the next experiment is a level-shifting circuit similar to the one shown in Fig. 14-9.

Part Two

OBJECTIVE

The purpose of this experiment is to investigate the operation of the linear differential amplifier, the Darlington amplifier, and the level-shifting amplifier. Both the discrete circuit and integrated circuit forms of these amplifiers will be studied.

REFERENCES

Alley, C. L., and Atwood, K. W., *Electronic Engineering*. New York: Wiley, 1966, Chapter 9.

Angelo, E. J., *Electronics: BJTs, FETs, and Microcircuits*. New York: McGraw-Hill, 1969, Chapter 12.

Chirlian, P. M., *Electronic Circuits: Physical Principles, Analysis, and Design*. New York: McGraw-Hill, 1971, Chapter 9.

Fitchen, F. C., *Electronic Integrated Circuits and Systems*. New York: Van Nostrand Reinhold, 1970, Chapter 5.

Ghausi, M. S., *Electronic Circuits: Devices, Models, Functions, Analysis, and Design*. New York: Van Nostrand Reinhold, 1971, Chapter 5.

Gray, P. E., and Searle, C. L., *Electronic Principles: Physics, Models, and Circuits*. New York: Wiley, 1967, Chapters 7 and 16.

Millman, J., and Halkias, C. C., *Electronic Devices and Circuits*. New York: McGraw-Hill, 1967, Chapter 12.

Schilling, D. L., and Belove, C., *Electronic Circuits: Discrete and Integrated*. New York: McGraw-Hill, 1968, Chapter 7.

LABORATORY PREPARATION

1. Design a linear differential amplifier as shown in Fig. 14-1. Choose transistors which are readily available in your laboratory. For example, if a 2N697 transistor is available, then $R_C = 1$ k, $R_B = 50$, $R_E = 800$, $R_s = 500$, $V_{CC} = +15$ V, and $V_{EE} = -15$ V would be suitable values. Calculate all quiescent voltages and the differential-mode and common-mode gains.

2. Calculate *CMRR* for your amplifier. What is maximum output voltage swing for the common-mode and differential-mode configurations?

3. If a sinusoidal signal is applied to one input and the other signal source is grounded, then what do you expect to happen to the dc level of either v_{o1} or v_{o2} when the amplitude of the input signal is increased upward from 0 volts? This is known as the dc level shift.

4. Estimate the gain and frequency response of your amplifier when one input is grounded and the output is measured from one collector to ground. For the 2N697 and the values given in step 1, you should expect a roll-off occurring somewhere between 100 kHz and 1 MHz.

5. Design a constant current source circuit as shown in Fig. 14-5 that can be connected to your differential amplifier. Calculate all quiescent voltages and the ac impedance "looking" into the collector of your constant current source.

6. What is the value of *CMRR* for your circuit with a constant current source? Compare with the linear differential amplifier without a constant current source.

7. Are the two symmetrical halves of the differential amplifier in series or parallel? Compute the input and output impedances for the differential- and common-mode configurations.

8. (optional) Use one of the computer-aided circuit programs to analyze your differential amplifier.

9. (optional) Select an integrated linear differential amplifier and obtain the manufacturer's specifications. Since Experiment 15 deals with operational amplifiers whose basic building blocks are differential amplifiers, the differential portion of some operational amplifiers could be used for this part.

10. Design and analyze the Darlington amplifier shown in Fig. 14-6. Determine all quiescent points, gains, and impedances.

11. Obtain the manufacturer's specifications for an integrated differential amplifier similar to the MC 1429 shown in Fig. 14-8. Observe that this amplifier has Darlington inputs and a constant current source.

12. Design the cascode (level-shifting) amplifier of Fig. 14-9. Be sure that the dc level of the output signal v_{o3} is close to zero ($\leqslant .1$ V).

13. What are the gain and output impedances of your cascode amplifier? What percent changes in R_1 and R_2 will cause a factor of 10 change in V_{o3} (assume V_{o3} is nominally .1 V)?

14. (optional) Identify and study the level-shifting amplifiers contained in some integrated operational amplifiers. See, for example, the level-shifting amplifier discussed in Experiment 15. Note that the gain of some level shifters is slightly greater than 1.

15. (optional) Analyze your level-shifting amplifier of Fig. 14-9 using digital computer programs that you are familiar with.

LABORATORY PROCEDURE

1. Construct and test your linear differential amplifier of Fig. 14-1. In order to provide a small output impedance and a dc path to ground, a shunt resistance R_{SH} should be placed across your input source, as shown in Fig. 14-11.

2. Measure *CMRR* for your amplifier and the maximum output voltage swing for the common-mode and differential-mode configurations.

3. Measure the dc level shift of your differential amplitude as a function of the amplitude of your sinusoidal input signal.

4. Measure the dc gain and frequency response of your

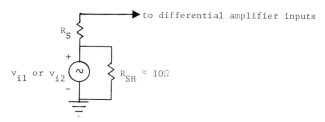

Fig. 14.11 Circuit for reducing output impedance of source.

differential amplifier for both the common-mode and differential-mode configurations. For the common-mode configuration, the inputs can be tied together and the same ac source can be applied to both inputs. For the differential mode, two signals 180° out of phase must be applied to the inputs. If only one dc source is available, there are a number of ways of obtaining two signals 180° out of phase. For example, a phase-inverting stage or a phase-shifting network can be used.

5. Construct your constant current source circuit as shown in Fig. 14-5 and connect it to your differential amplifier. Measure all important voltages and compare with your calculated values.

6. Measure the *CMRR* of your circuit with a constant current source and compare with your computed value.

7. Measure the input and output impedances of your differential amplifier in each configuration.

8. (optional) Using the results of your computer programs, compare the results of your experimental measurements with those from your computer-aided analyses. Can you improve the design of your differential amplifier now?

9. (optional) Test the integrated differential amplifier you have chosen. Compare its performance with your dis-

crete form of a differential amplifier. Be certain that your comparison is a fair one in the sense that the number of active devices in each circuit form is comparable and that important parameters in each circuit are, to the best of your knowledge, of comparable values.

10. Test your Darlington amplifier of Fig. 14-6. Measure all quiescent points, gains, and impedances.

11. Test your integrated differential amplifier which has Darlington inputs and a constant current source. Measure offset voltages, single-ended voltage gain, bandwidth, and so on.

12. Test your level-shifting amplifier of Fig. 14-9. Compare all measurements with your calculated values. Discuss all discrepancies.

13. Measure the gain and output impedances of your level-shifting amplifier. Vary R_1 and R_2 by small amounts and measure the dc output level shift.

14. (optional) Test some integrated circuit amplifiers containing level shifters and observe the dc output level under various input conditions.

15. (optional) Run your digital computer program which analyzes your level-shifting amplifier. Compare the computer results with your measurements.

LIST OF EQUIPMENT

1. Cathode-ray oscilloscope
2. General-purpose voltmeter or ac and dc voltmeter and ohmmeter
3. Signal sources: Function generator or sine-wave oscillator, dc power supply
4. Circuit board
5. Components: Resistors, capacitors, bipolar transistors, integrated circuits

Experiment 15/Operational Amplifiers: Discrete and Integrated

Part One

INTRODUCTION

An operational amplifier usually contains both a high-gain dc amplifier and a special feedback circuit to perform a linear operation such as addition, subtraction, integration, or differentiation. The high-gain dc amplifier is very often a linear differential amplifier with a large bandwidth. The feedback circuit is comprised of resistors and capacitors to help perform a specific linear operation.

Operational amplifiers are commercially available in discrete and integrated circuit form. They are used mainly in analog computers to perform mathematical operations and computation. They are also used as comparators, and are finding widespread usage in the synthesis of desired transfer functions. This is due mainly to the fact that high-performance integrated operational amplifiers are available commercially at reasonable prices.

THEORY

This experiment will first study a simple direct-coupled amplifier and its use in the design of an operational amplifier. The four mathematical operations of inversion (sign change), scale change (amplification), addition (summation), and integration will be demonstrated using the direct-coupled amplifier. The second part of this experiment will study a few integrated circuit operational amplifiers (IC op amp). This will be accomplished by explaining the detailed dc and ac operation of the linear differential amplifiers making up the operational amplifier package. After the circuitry is explained, the integrated amplifiers are applied to four basic operational amplifier applications: a summing amplifier, a dc comparator, an integrator, and a transfer function simulation.

The circuit of Fig. 15-1 is a direct-coupled transistor amplifier. The direct-coupled amplifier derives its name from the fact that the signal coupling from one stage to another is achieved without the use of direct current (dc) blocking capacitors or transformers. Therefore, the same elements that bias the output junction of one stage must

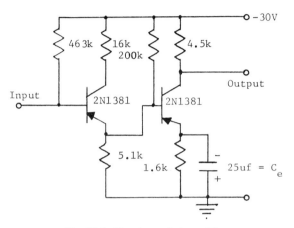

Fig. 15.1 Direct coupled amplifier.

properly bias the input junction of the following stage as well as couple the alternating current (ac) signal.

The circuit of Fig. 15-1 may be capable of amplifying very slowly varying signals because of the direct method of coupling. This is certainly an advantage, but it means that any direct current changes, such as those due to heating in one transistor, are amplified by the following transistors, which may cause unsatisfactory operation due to Q point shifts. Nevertheless, the circuit of Fig. 15-1 without emitter bypass capacitor C_e is capable of uniform gain down to dc; its single-block diagram representation is shown in Fig. 15-2.

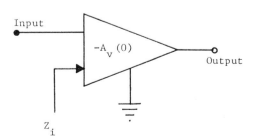

Fig. 15.2 Schematic representation.

145

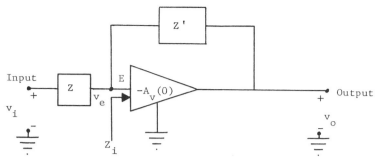

Fig. 15.3 Operational amplifier.

In other practical direct-coupled amplifiers, the voltage gain A_v is large ($A_v \geqslant 10^3$), the input impedance Z_i is of the order of 500 k, and the output impedance Z_o is small and approximately 50 Ω. The bandwidth is large enough so that the amplifier gain A_v is a constant over the range of input frequencies starting at 0 Hz.

An equivalent circuit for an operational amplifier is shown in Fig. 15-3. There are now two additional external circuits Z and Z' connected to the direct-coupled amplifier of Figs. 15-1 and 15-2.

The sum of the currents at node E of Fig. 15-3 is obtained by applying Kirchhoff's current law

$$\frac{V_i - V_e}{Z} + \frac{V_o - V_e}{Z'} + \frac{V_o - V_e}{Z_i} = 0 \qquad (15\text{-}1)$$

It is also known that the output voltage is related to the error voltage V_e by

$$\frac{V_o}{V_e} = -A_v(0) \qquad (15\text{-}2)$$

Substituting Eq. (15-2) into Eq. (15-1) and solving for the overall voltage gain with feedback yields

$$A_{vf}(s) = \frac{V_o(s)}{V_i(s)} = \frac{-\dfrac{1}{Z}}{\left(\dfrac{1}{Z'} + \dfrac{1}{Z_i}\right) + \dfrac{1}{A_v(0)}\left(\dfrac{1}{Z'} + \dfrac{1}{Z_i} + \dfrac{1}{Z}\right)}$$

$$(15\text{-}3)$$

If the midband gain $A_v(0)$ and the input impedance Z_i are very large (approach ∞), we obtain

$$A_{vf}(s) \approx \frac{Z'(s)}{Z(s)} \qquad (15\text{-}4)$$

Eq. (15-4) states that the overall voltage gain is independent of the direct-coupled amplifier, and depends only upon the impedances Z' and Z. Eq. (15-4) is very important in circuits employing operational amplifiers.

The basic configurations for operational amplifiers are

derived from Eq. (15-4), and are

Inverter (sign changer)

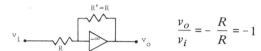

$$\frac{v_o}{v_i} = -\frac{R}{R} = -1$$

Scale changer (amplifier)

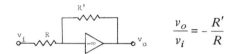

$$\frac{v_o}{v_i} = -\frac{R'}{R}$$

Adder (summer)

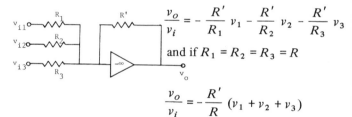

$$\frac{v_o}{v_i} = -\frac{R'}{R_1}v_1 - \frac{R'}{R_2}v_2 - \frac{R'}{R_3}v_3$$

and if $R_1 = R_2 = R_3 = R$

$$\frac{v_o}{v_i} = -\frac{R'}{R}(v_1 + v_2 + v_3)$$

Integrator

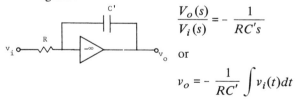

$$\frac{V_o(s)}{V_i(s)} = -\frac{1}{RC's}$$

or

$$v_o = -\frac{1}{RC'}\int v_i(t)dt$$

(The initial condition for the capacitor can be supplied by the use of a battery and switch in shunt with C'.)

Differentiator

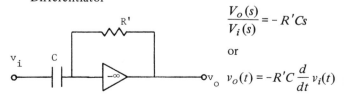

$$\frac{V_o(s)}{V_i(s)} = -R'Cs$$

or

$$v_o(t) = -R'C\frac{d}{dt}v_i(t)$$

The four basic configurations (inverter, adder, scale changer, and integrator) are used in analog computers to simulate

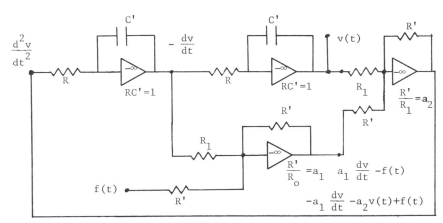

Fig. 15.4 Second-order system.

and solve differential equations. As a simple example, consider the second-order linear differential equation given by Eq. (15-5)

$$\frac{d^2v(t)}{dt^2} + a_1 \frac{dv(t)}{dt} + a_2 v(t) = f(t) \qquad (15\text{-}5)$$

We want to solve Eq. (15-5) to obtain $v(t)$. We start by assuming that d^2v/dt^2 is available. Since d^2v/dt^2 is the sum of three components, we need to generate $-a_1(dv/dt)$ and $-a_2 v(t)$ by integrating d^2v/dt^2 and $-(dv/dt)$, as shown in Fig. 15-4.

The only signals that need to be applied to the circuit of Fig. 15-4 are $f(t)$ and the initial conditions for the differential equation. Observe that the circuit has two integrators and that the differential equation is of second order. Also observe that if $f(t) = 0$ and $a_1 = 0$, the differential equation becomes $d^2v(t)/dt^2 + a_2 v(t) = 0$. The solution of this equation is a sinusoid, and thus an oscillator can be built using operational amplifiers.

Integrated operational amplifiers are becoming very popular because of their low drift and offset characteristics which can be achieved with component matching by monolithic circuit fabrication techniques. The low drift is achieved because critical dc levels within the circuit can be made functions of resistor ratios and not absolute values. In addition, low output voltage offset is achieved for integrated circuits because the β and V_{BE} of the input transistors can be matched very closely. Since output offset voltage is a measure of the difference in potential between two output terminals when no signal is applied to either input transistor, the low output offset is due to the proximity of the input transistors on the monolithic chip and the similarity of their diffusion profiles when in close proximity.

The balanced differential amplifier studied in Experiment 14 is the basic circuit configuration used for a broad line of monolithic silicon integrated circuit operational amplifiers. In general, IC op amps are composed of three

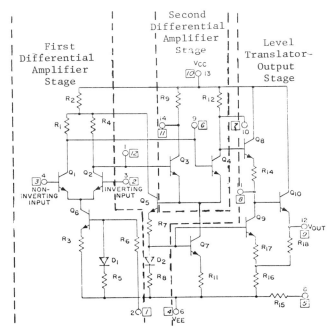

Fig. 15.5 IC operational amplifier.

basic sections: an input differential amplifier, a second differential amplifier, and a level translator-output stage. A schematic diagram of a typical IC op amp is shown in Fig. 15-5. Note that boxed pin numbers refer to CA 3010, CA 3015, and the other pin numbers to the CA 3008, CA 3016, CA 3029, CA 3030, CA 3037, and CA 3038 types.

The input differential amplifier is composed of a pair of emitter-coupled transistors, Q_1 and Q_2. The inverting and noninverting input signals are applied to the bases of Q_2 and Q_1, respectively. These transistors develop the driving signals for the second differential amplifier stage. A dc constant current source transistor Q_6 is also included in the first differential amplifier stage to provide bias stabilization for transistors Q_1 and Q_2 and thus a high common-mode rejection. Diode D_1 provides thermal compensation for the first stage.

The dc currents in each emitter of the first differential amplifier are generally in the range of .1 to 1.0 mA. Let us assume that the emitter currents in transistors Q_1 and Q_2 are equal at about .1 mA. The emitter resistance of Q_1 is then

$$r_{e1} = \frac{.026}{|I_{E1}|} = 260\Omega \qquad (15\text{-}6)$$

The differential impedance of the second differential amplifier stage is approximately $2\beta r_{e3} \approx 2(40)\left(\frac{.026}{.0005}\right) \approx$ 4 kΩ. Note that we have assumed that I_{E3} = .5 mA. Also, if $R_1 = R_4$ = 10 k, R_2 = 4.1 k, and $R_9 = R_{12}$ = 7.5 k, then the effective load resistance in parallel with $R_1 + 2R_2$ or $R_4 + 2R_2$ is

$$R_{L1} = \frac{(4\text{ k})(10\text{ k} + 8.2\text{ k})}{4\text{ k} + 10\text{ k} + 8.2\text{ k}} \approx 3.3 \text{ k}\Omega \qquad (15\text{-}7)$$

The midband voltage gain of the first amplifier stage is approximately

$$A_{v1}(0) \approx \frac{R_{L1}}{r_{e1}} = \frac{3.3 \text{ k}}{260} \approx 13 \qquad (15\text{-}8)$$

The emitter-coupled transistors Q_3 and Q_4 in the second differential amplifier are driven push-pull by the output from the first differential amplifier. Bias stabilization for the second stage is provided by the constant current source transistor Q_7. Compensating diode D_2 provides the thermal stabilization for the second differential amplifier stage and also for the constant current source transistor Q_9 in the output stage. The single-ended difference gain of the second stage with R_{L2} = 7.5 k is

$$A_{v2}(0) = \frac{1}{2} \frac{7.5 \text{ k}}{52} = 72 \qquad (15\text{-}9)$$

The overall gain of the first two differential stages is

$$A_v(0) = A_{v1}(0) A_{v2}(0) = (13)(72) \approx 930 \qquad (15\text{-}10)$$

Transistor Q_5 develops the negative feedback to reduce common-mode error signals that are produced when identical input signals are applied to both input terminals of the IC op amp. Transistor Q_5 samples the voltage that is developed at the emitters of transistors Q_3 and Q_4. Since the second differential stage is driven push-pull, the signal at this point will be zero if the first differential stage and the base-emitter circuits of the second stage are matched and there is no common-mode input. This error signal appearing at the emitter of transistors Q_3 and Q_4 is fed back through Q_5 and back across R_2 with the proper phase to reduce the error. The emitter circuit of transistor Q_5

also reflects a portion of the same error signal into the constant current source transistor Q_7 in the second differential stage, so that the activating error signal is further reduced. In a similar manner, Q_5 develops the compensating feedback to cancel the effects produced by variations in the supply voltages.

In addition to their function in the cancellation of supply voltage variations, transistors Q_8, Q_9, and Q_{10} are used in an emitter-follower type of single-ended output circuit. The output signal from the op amp is taken at the emitter of output transistor Q_{10}, so that the dc level of the output signal is substantially lower than that of the differential amplifier output at the collector of transistor Q_4. In this way, the output circuit shifts the dc level of the output, so that it is effectively the same as that at the input when no input signal is applied. This translating level circuit generally has a voltage gain of one (see Experiment 14). However, a small amount of signal gain in the level translator output circuit of Fig. 15–5 is made possible by the bootstrap connection from the emitter of the output transistor Q_{10} to the emitter circuit of transistor Q_9. The gain is approximately 1.5 from the collector of the differential amplifier transistor Q_4 to the output terminal. Although this configuration realizes a small gain, it also increases the output swing capabilities of the operational amplifier. The total midband gain for the operational amplifier is approximately

$$A_T(0) \approx A_{v1}(0) A_{v2}(0) \times 1.5 = 1400 \approx 60 \text{ db}$$
$$(15\text{-}11)$$

All IC op amps have pin connections to be used for open-loop frequency compensation. External elements, which are usually resistors and/or capacitors, must be connected between these pins to insure that when a feedback loop is closed around an IC op amp it remains stable. These open-loop frequency-compensating circuits provide the required phase shifts to stabilize the IC op amp for various feedback configurations. The criterion for unconditional stability when resistive negative feedback is used is that the open-loop voltage gain must have a 6 db/octave slope when passing through 0 db.

A brute-force method of frequency compensation is to apply a large capacitor between two frequency-compensating terminals (roll-off terminal), which will cause a steady fall of 6 db/octave from some frequency f_1 below the upper 3 db open-loop frequency of the IC op amp. This capacitor is

$$C_1 = \frac{1}{2\pi f_1 R_0}$$

where R_0 is the output resistance across the roll-off terminals. This method is simple, but severely restricts the amplifier bandwidth and the voltage swing.

Another method is to place a resistor R_1 in series with a capacitor C_1 across the roll-off terminals. The values of R_1 and C_1 can be simply computed. Suppose we plot the magnitude of the closed-loop response in decibels $\left(\text{i.e.,} \right.$ $20 \log_{10} \left| -\dfrac{Z'}{Z} \right| \left. \right)$ on the same graph with the uncompensated open-loop frequency response. Then f_c is defined as the frequency where the open-loop and closed-loop frequency-response curves intersect. Next project a line with a slope of -6 db/octave from f_c up until it intersects the open-loop frequency-response curve $(20 \log_{10} A_v(0))$. This will give the first desired break point f_1, which can be used to calculate the capacitor C_1

$$C_1 = \frac{1}{2\pi f_1 R_0}$$

The resistor R_1 is calculated as

$$R_1 = \frac{1}{2\pi f_0 C_1}$$

where f_0 is the lowest break frequency of the open-loop response curve.

It is not always possible to frequency compensate an IC op amp by applying an RC combination to an internal roll-off point, since not all amplifiers have this point brought out to a terminal. An alternate method is to connect R_1 in series with C_1 from the inverting to the non-inverting input terminal of the op amp. The method for computing R_1 and C_1 is the same as described above.

The CA 3008 op amp does have internal roll-off pins and a 2000 Ω resistor in series with a 27 pf capacitor connected between pins 1 and 14 and between pins 9 and 10 causes the closed-loop response of the CA 3008 or CA 3008A op amp to meet the stability criterion. These values of compensating elements are sufficient to stabilize the amplifier for all resistive feedback applications, including unity gain. However, it is important to emphasize that each type of IC op amp requires its own compensating circuits, and the manufacturer's specification sheets should be consulted for this information if the compensating elements cannot be easily computed as described previously.

The applications of IC op amps are numerous, and just a few will be discussed here in order to familiarize the student with some basic applications.

Figs. 15–6 and 15–7 show the basic schematic diagrams for the use of IC op amps in the inverting and noninverting feedback configurations, respectively.

The gain for the inverting configuration of Fig. 15–6 is $A_v = -\dfrac{Z'}{Z}$ and the resistor R_r is equal to $Z' \| Z$ at $\omega = 0$,

so that each input is returned to ground through dc paths that are effectively identical, which insures a minimum off-

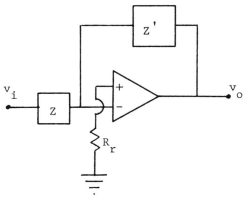

Fig. 15.6 Inverting feedback configuration.

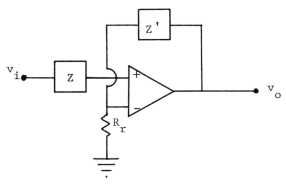

Fig. 15.7 Noninverting feedback configuration.

set voltage. The noninverting configuration of Fig. 15–7 has a gain $A_v = 1 + \dfrac{Z'}{Z}$ with $R_r = Z' \| Z$ at $\omega = 0$.

A summing amplifier is shown in Fig. 15–8 with pin connections for power supplies and open-loop frequency-compensating elements.

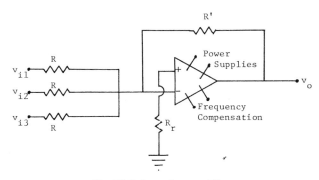

Fig. 15.8 Summing amplifier.

If $R' = R = 10\,\text{k}$, then $R_r = \dfrac{(10)(10)\text{k}}{10 + 10} = 5\,\text{k}$. A small value of R_r is actually used to minimize the offset, because there is one resistor R for each input. The output for the sum-

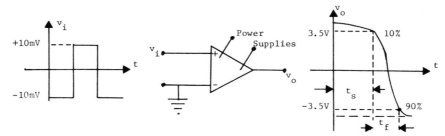

Fig. 15.9 Voltage comparator.

ming amplifier is

$$v_o = \frac{R'}{R} (v_{i1} + v_{i2} + v_{i3}) \qquad (15\text{-}12)$$

Another important application for IC op amps is the voltage comparator shown in Fig. 15-9 with associated input and output voltages.

The comparator circuit of Fig. 15-9 compares the input voltage to the ground potential 0, but could also be used to compare the input voltage with a reference voltage other than ground. However, the reference voltage cannot exceed the maximum common-mode voltage swing. The output-input curve for a comparator is shown in Fig. 15-10.

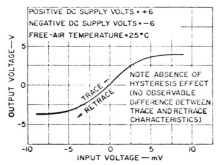

Fig. 15.10 Trace and retrace characteristics of comparator.

It takes a comparator circuit a storage time t_s to respond to the application of the −10 to +10 mV input change. The circuit responds from 10 to 90% of its maximum output change in a fall time t_f. Note that the output starts to drop from 3.5 volts after the input exceeds 0 mV. That is, as long as the input remains below 0 mV, the output will not respond, which shows that this circuit compares the input to a ground potential. At an input of approximately 7.5 mV, the output has changed its full amount to −3.5 volts in a time $t_s + t_f$, which is generally in the order of a few hundred nanoseconds.

An integrator circuit is shown in Fig. 15-11.

The resistor $R_r = R$, and the purpose of resistor R' is to provide a dc feedback path so that an offset (error) voltage cannot continuously charge the feedback resistor C', which

TABLE 15.1 IC OPERATIONAL AMPLIFIERS.

Manufacturer	Type	Z_{in} diff. (typ) ohms	A_v (typ)	Drift $\mu V/°C$ (typ)	Pwr sup volts
Amelco	709BE	400 k	45 k	3	±15
	806CE	1 meg	60 k	10	±12
	809CE	200 k	40 k	10	±15
	809CJ	200 k	40 k	10	±15
Burr Brown	3056/01	300 k	65 k	5	±15
	3057/01	200 k	50 k	10	±15
Fairchild	μA702C	32 k	3.4 k	3	±12-6
Semiconductor	μA709C	250 k	45 k	3	±15
GE	PA223	2.5 meg	7 k	10	±12
Motorola	MC1430G	15 k	5 k	5	±6
	MC1431G	600 k	3.5 k	10	±6
	MC1433G	600 k	60 k	10	±15
	MC1439G	300 k	100 k		±15
	MC1709CG	250 k	45 k	3	±15
	MC1712G	35 k	3.4 k	2.5	±12
NSC Microcircuits	LH201[1]	400 k	150 k	10	±15
	LM201	400 k	150 k	6	±5 to ±15
Philbrick/Nexus	T52[2]	200 k	40 k	20	±15
Research	S52[3]	200 k	40 k	20	±15
RCA	CA3008[4]	15 k	1 k	4	±6
	CA3008A[4]	20 k	1 k	4	±6
	CA3010[4]	14 k	1 k	4	±6
	CA3010A[4]	20 k	1 k	4	±6
	CA3015[4]	7.8 k	3.2 k	4	±12
	CA3015A[4]	10 k	3.2 k	4	±12
	CA3016[4]	7.8 k	3.2 k	4	±12
	CA3016A[4]	10 k	3.2 k	4	±12
	CA3029	14 k	1 k	4	±6
	CA3029A	20 k	1 k	4	±6
	CA3030	7.8 k	3.2 k	4	±12
	CA3030A	10 k	3.2 k	4	±12
	CA3037[4]	14 k	1 k	4	±6
	CA3037[4]	20 k	1 k	4	±6
	CA3038[4]	7.8 k	3.2 k	4	±12
	CA3038A[4]	10 k	3.2 k	4	±12
	CA3031/ 702A[4]	25 k	3.2 k	4	+12,−6
	CA3032/ 702C	20 k	3.2 k	4	+12,−6
	CA3033[4]	1.5 M	31.6 k	6.6	±12
	CA3033A[4]	1.0 M	63.3 k	6.6	±18
Signetics	NE515K	2.3 k	3.2 k	5	+6,−3
Texas Instruments	SN524A	1000 k	1.4 k	25	±15
	SN724L	1 meg	1.2 k	25	±5
	SN724N	800 k	1.2 k	30	±15
	SN52702N	25 k	2 k	5	
	SN52709N	400 k	45 k	3	±15
	SN72702L	32 k	3.4 k	5	+12,−6
	SN72702N	20 k	2 k		
	SN72709L	250 k	45 k	10	±15
	SN72709N	250 k	45 k		±15
	SN7241N	200 k	200 k		±15
	SN72748	200 k	200 k		±15
Union Carbide	UC709	3 meg	50 k	6	±18
	UC4000C	3 meg	50 k	5	±15
	UC4001C	3 meg	50 k	10	±15
	UC4002C	3 meg	50 k	20	±15
	UC4002[4]	3 meg	50 k	20	±15

[1] Internally frequency-compensated
[2] TO-t case
[3] Dual in-line package
[4] Mil. temp. range −55 to +125°C

TABLE 15.2 TECHNOLOGY COMPARISON.

Technology	Advantages	Disadvantages
Discrete	Wide range of performance characteristics Uses widest range of available components Shortest lead time from design to production Lowest cost for short runs having unique performance features Inherently high yield Diversity of circuit types, chopper, FET, parametric, etc. Permits committed amplifier designs	Heavy weight Large size Large number of interconnections reduces predicted reliability Too much performance for simple applications Price "floor" too high in large quantity applications
Hybrid	Smaller size than discrete Shorter lead time than IC's Fewer interconnections and discrete elements for same performance level Easily hermetically sealed Low cost in moderate quantity Wider range of performance characteristics than monolithics Can be intermediate design step from discrete to monolithic pacing state of the art Permits committed amplifier designs	More expensive than monolithics because of labor content More expensive than discretes (short runs) because of yields and need for subminiature components Circuit ramification limited by substrate; less versatile than discretes Longer lead time than discretes Packages usually larger than monolithics because of increased circuit complexity
Monolithic IC	Smallest size (chips) Lowest cost in long runs for optimum specs vs yield Fewest interconnections Hermetic seals usual Excellent matching of internal device parameters and essentially isothermal construction available Devices may employ many transistors for some configurations at little extra cost	Longest lead time for new designs High cost in low volume High cost for premium low-yield selection Inflexibility of designs Lowest single-package performance Size and complexity can be worse than hybrids (and possibly discretes) if additional circuitry necessary for compensation, biasing, etc.

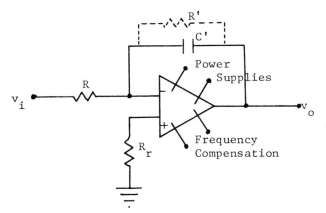

Fig. 15.11 Op amp integrator.

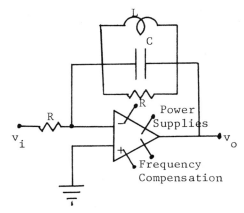

Fig. 15.12 Op amp synthesizing a transfer function.

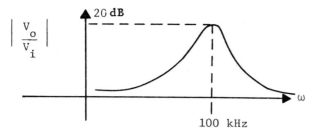

Fig. 15.13 Response of circuit in Fig. 15.12.

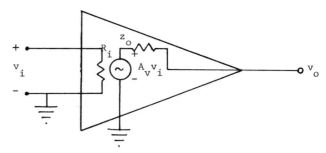

Fig. 15.14 Simple model of IC op amp.

would otherwise cause the amplifier to be driven to saturation. The required value of R' is determined so that the time constant $R'C'$ is substantially longer than the periods of the input signal v_i. Usually the integrator time constant RC' is ten times larger than $R'C'$. In this way, the input signals are integrated by the effect of R and C, and R' does not affect the overall gain.

An IC op amp can also be used very effectively in both RC filters and in transfer function simulations. Using the closed-loop expression $A_v(s) = -Z'/Z$, a large number of transfer functions can be generated. As a representative example, the IC op amp of Fig. 15-12 will be used to simulate Eq. (15-13).

$$\frac{v_o}{v_i}(s) = \frac{\dfrac{R'}{CR}s}{s^2 + \dfrac{1}{R'C}s + \dfrac{1}{LC}} \qquad (15\text{-}13)$$

If $R' = 60$ k, $C = 300$ pf and $L = 10$ mh, then the center frequency of this amplifier is approximately 100 kHz and the gain at 100 kHz is about 20 db. The amplifier shown in Fig. 15-12 is known as a bandpass amplifier, and its frequency response is shown in Fig. 15-13.

To conclude the theory concerning IC op amps, a simple model representation of an IC op amp is shown in Fig. 15-14. This model is adequate for dc or low-frequency operation.

A few commercially available IC op amps are listed in Table 15-1. The data in this table are useful for the circuit model shown in Fig. 15-1. In addition to discrete and integrated IC op amps, there are some available which are composed of both discrete and integrated components, and are called hybrid circuits. Table 15-2 compares discrete, hybrid, and monolithic IC op amps.

Part Two

OBJECTIVE

The purpose of this experiment is to assist the student in evaluating the performance of a number of operational amplifiers. This is accomplished by first explaining the operation of a discrete circuit form of op amp and then some monolithic integrated circuit forms.

REFERENCES

Alley, C. L., and Atwood, K. W., *Electronic Engineering*. New York: Wiley, 1966. Chapter 11.

Angelo, E. J., *Electronics: BJTs, FETs, and Microcircuits*. New York: McGraw-Hill, 1969, Chapter 13.

Chirlian, P. M., *Electronic Circuits: Physical Principles, Analysis, and Design*. New York: McGraw-Hill, 1971, Chapter 13.

Fitchen, F. C., *Electronic Integrated Circuits and Systems*. New York: Van Nostrand Reinhold, 1970, Chapters 6 and 7.

Ghausi, M. S., *Electronic Circuits: Devices, Models, Functions, Analysis, and Design*. New York: Van Nostrand Reinhold, 1971, Chapters 6 and 8.

Gray, P. E., and Searle, C. L., *Electronic Principles. Physics, Models, and Circuits*. New York: Wiley, 1967, Chapter 16.

Millman, J., and Halkias, C. C., *Electronic Devices and Circuits*. New York: McGraw-Hill, 1967, Chapters 15 and 17.

Schilling, D. L., and Belove, C., *Electronic Circuits: Discrete and Integrated*. New York: McGraw-Hill, 1968, Chapters 8 and 9.

LABORATORY PREPARATION

1. Design a direct-coupled transistor amplifier as shown in Fig. 15-1. If your laboratory does not have the 2N1381 transistor, redesign the circuit to suit your transistor. Calculate the value of all quiescent currents and voltages to be expected in your design.

2. Calculate the midband voltage gain $A_v(0)$ and the input and output impedances.

3. What is the approximate power gain of the amplifier you have designed? $\left(\text{Power gain} = \dfrac{P_L}{P_{in}} = \dfrac{P_L}{v_{in}^2/R}, \text{where } R \text{ is the input impedance seen by the input drive } v_{in}.\right)$

4. Discuss the relationship between the maximum output voltage swing available and your quiescent values of V_{CE} and V_{CC} for the last stage.

5. If you were to decrease the value of the collector load resistance of the last stage, then what would happen to the voltage gain and the maximum output swing?

6. Estimate the bandwidth of your direct-coupled amplifier.

7. Using the direct-coupled amplifier you have designed, modify it so that it can be used as an inverter, scale changer, and adder. What values of R and R' could be used in each case?

8. Design an integrator circuit using your direct-coupled amplifier. If a square-wave were applied to your integrator, what would the output look like? Over what range can the frequency of the input square-wave be varied and still cause the output to be the integral of the input?

9. Design a differentiator circuit using your direct-coupled amplifier. An ideal differentiator has $Z' = R'$ and $Z = \dfrac{1}{sC}$.

What happens to the gain as the frequency of the input signal is increased?

10. Design a differentiator with $Z' = C' \| R'$ and $Z = R + \dfrac{1}{sC}$. Choose $RC = R'C' \ll R'C$. Can you explain how this differentiator would operate more satisfactorily than the ideal differentiator?

11. Select an IC op amp that is available in your laboratory and study the manufacturer's specifications for this op amp. Try to understand all specifications and the purpose of all the pin connections.

12. For convenience, we will assume for the remainder of this preparation that your laboratory has an RCA CA3010 IC op amp available. If not, modify the following questions to suit the IC op amp you have available. Explain in your own words how the various stages of your IC op amp work.

13. Explain how the circuit in Fig. 15–15 can be used to measure output offset voltage. From the specification sheet and the circuit shown in Fig. 15–15 can the output voltage be determined (i.e., will it be (+), (–) or zero)?

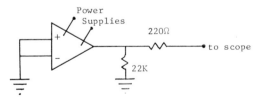

Fig. 15.15 Circuit for measuring output offset.

14. Determine the values of the resistors and capacitors that must be added to your op amp for open-loop frequency compensation. Explain how the circuit of Fig. 15–16 can be used to plot the output-input curve for your op amp at

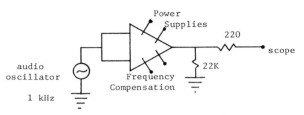

Fig. 15.16 Circuit for determining output-input curve.

1 kHz. (Hint: vary the amplitude of the input voltage v_i and measure the peak output voltage.)

15. Devise a test circuit to measure the open-loop frequency response of your op amp.

16. Design a summing amplifier using your IC op amp.

17. Discuss how your IC op amp could be used as a comparator and what connections are required for your comparator circuit. Predict the storage and fall times for your comparator. What does the output-input curve for your comparator look like?

18. Explain how the specialized comparator circuit shown in Fig. 15–17 will yield an output voltage $v_o = +V_z$ when $v_i < V_{ref}$ and $v_o = -V_z$ when $v_i > V_{ref}$.

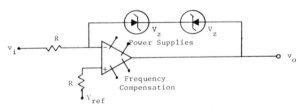

Fig. 15.17 Relay type circuit.

19. Design an integrator using your IC op amp. Choose several values of C' and R and predict the output when a sinusoid and then a square-wave are applied to your integrators.

20. Add a resistor across C' and call it R'. What do you think the effect of R' will be?

21. How can the integrator give the solution to a first-order differential equation? Design a circuit that can solve a second-order differential equation. How many integrators and op amps will you need?

22. Explain how the circuit of Fig. 15–18 operates as a sinusoidal oscillator with a frequency $f_o = \dfrac{1}{2\pi RC}$.

23. Design a bandpass amplifier using an IC op amp. The center frequency should be 100 kHz. Suppose that the center frequency (the frequency at which the gain is a maximum) is to be increased or decreased but L remains constant; then what element must be varied? Will the gain at the center frequency change?

24. (optional) Very often it is necessary to compute the frequency response of a circuit containing commercially

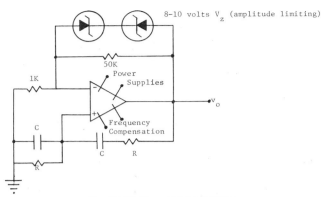

Fig. 15.18 Sinusoidal oscillator.

available IC op amps. A simple but accurate model of an IC op amp that could be used in a computer-aided design program to quickly compute the overall frequency response of the circuit would be desirable. However, IC op amps contain many different active and passive elements, and for the manufacturer to provide the detailed functional information for each active and passive device, either singly or in combination, would serve no purpose in assisting the design engineer. The manufacturer, therefore, provides curves and ratings that are applicable to the entire integrated circuit. To represent the op amp for use in computer analysis applications, the same philosophy is used. Therefore, the model shown in Fig. 15–19 is as simple as possible and still retains the operational characteristics of the device.

Using the manufacturer's specification of open-loop voltage gain versus frequency, explain how you could determine the values of R_A, R_B, C_A, and C_B for your op amp. Next write a computer program (ECAP is suggested) and compare your frequency response with the manufacturer's. Adjust R_A, R_B, C_A, and C_B until your frequency response and the manufacturer's are very similar.

25. (optional) The model of Fig. 15–20 can be used for the transient analysis of an IC op amp.

Estimate the values of R_A, R_B, C_A, C_B, and L that will yield a response to a step input which is similar to the manufacturer's specifications. Next, write a SCEPTRE program which will allow you to compare your response and the values of your model with the response given by the manufacturer.

LABORATORY PROCEDURE

1. Construct and test your two-stage direct-coupled amplifier. Measure all Q points. Explain possible causes of differences with predicted values in excess of 25%.

2. Measure the midband voltage gain and compare with your predicted value. Measure the input and output impedances of your amplifier.

3. Vary V_{CC} and note how it affects the quiescent currents, maximum undistorted output voltage, and gain of the amplifier at midband.

4. Measure how a decrease in the load resistance of the second stage effects the voltage gain and the maximum possible output voltage.

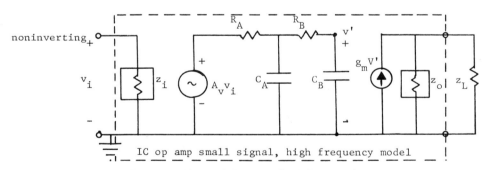

Fig. 15.19 Model of IC op amp (high frequency).

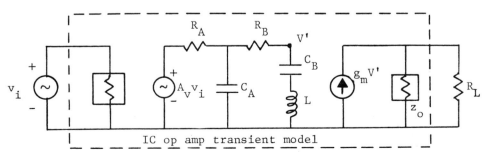

Fig. 15.20 Model of IC op amp (transient analysis).

5. Does your direct-coupled amplifier have an output offset voltage? Measure it.

6. Make a frequency response measurement of your amplifier. Also apply a square-wave with f = 1000 Hz to your amplifier and observe the output waveform. Explain the shape of the output waveform.

7. Build and test an inverter, a scale changer, and an adder.

8. Build an integrator using your amplifier and apply a sine-wave to it. Compare the output with the input (amplitude and phase). Next apply a square-wave and observe the output. Explain the output waveforms.

9. Build and test an ideal differentiator circuit. Apply a sinusoid to it and vary the frequency of the sinusoid. Observe what happens to the amplitude of the output as the input frequency is varied.

10. Build and test the differentiator you designed in step 10 of the preparation. Compare your results with the ideal differentiator you built.

11. After you have selected one or several IC op amps, become familiar with the pin connections and mount your IC op amp for testing.

12. After constructing the circuit of Fig. 15-15, measure the output offset voltage.

13. Use a voltage divider on one of the inputs to zero the output. Ground the second input. Measure the input voltage required to set the output to zero.

14. Connect the frequency-compensating resistors and capacitors to your IC op amp. Plot a frequency response curve and compare with the manufacturer's specifications. Usually at some high frequency the output of your IC op amp will be "rate-limited." This means that the amplifier is required to transfer energy at a rate that is greater than its ability to do so. The effect is to distort the input signal. One common example distorts an input sine-wave into a triangular wave. The rate limiting invalidates any further frequency response measurements. Two solutions which are generally not acceptable are: to reduce the load that the IC op amp has to drive; and to reduce the input amplitude until rate limiting no longer occurs. Be sure to have an oscilloscope connected to both the input and the output of your op amp when making this measurement.

15. Change your open-loop frequency-compensating resistors and capacitors and take data to plot a frequency response. Also, vary the load resistor and measure the maximum output swing.

16. Build and test a summing amplifier.

17. Build and test a comparator. Measure the storage and fall times of your comparator. Take data to plot an output-input curve for your comparator.

18. Build and test the special comparator of Fig. 15-17. Observe the output waveform when the input sinusoidal signal v_i is varied from 0 to $2v_{ref}$ in amplitude. Can you think of an application for this circuit?

19. Build and test an integrator. Apply a sinusoid to your circuit and then a square-wave. Observe the output waveforms and explain.

20. Add the resistor across C'. Does this improve the output waveforms? Can you now explain the use of this resistor?

21. Build and test a circuit that gives the solution to a second-order differential equation. Apply an $f(t)$ as shown in Fig. 15-4, which is a square-wave. Apply dv/dt to the horizontal input of your scope and $v(t)$ to the vertical input. The pattern that results on the scope should be similar to the results you obtained in Experiment 3. Build a circuit which solves the equation $\frac{d^2v}{dt^2} + a_2 v(t) = 0$.

You should observe a sinusoidal waveform for $v(t)$. Can you explain this?

22. Build and test the oscillator circuit of Fig. 15-18 using your IC op amp. What happens if you change one of the resistor values?

23. Build and test a band-pass amplifier. Remember that you have synthesized the transfer function given by Eq. (15-13) using an IC op amp. Change C and note the effect on the output voltage. Can you build any other simple transfer functions using your IC op amp?

24. (optional) Run the ECAP program you have written and compare your frequency responses with the manufacturer's specifications. Is the IC op amp small-signal high-frequency model given in Fig. 15-19 sufficient to describe the frequency response of your IC op amp? If not, then how would you modify it to make it compatible with your measurements?

25. (optional) Run the SCEPTRE program you have written to test the validity of the IC op amp transient model given in Fig. 15-20. Is this a good model for your IC op amp? If not, how would you modify it?

LIST OF EQUIPMENT

1. Cathode-ray oscilloscope

2. General-purpose voltmeters or ac and dc voltmeters and ohmmeters

3. Signal sources: Function generator or sine-wave oscillator, dc power supplies, and a 60 Hz Variac

4. Circuit board

5. Components: Resistors, capacitors, inductors, bipolar transistors, and IC op amps

Experiment 16/Logic Gates: Discrete and Integrated

Part One

INTRODUCTION

Logic circuits are extremely important in digital computers and in many other types of digital equipment. This equipment is generally dependent upon only a few basic operations such as addition, subtraction, data storage, data transfer, and others which are repeated very many times. These basic operations can be described by simple logic functions and realized by the use of logic circuits or gates.

Some of the most frequently employed logic circuits are the NOT, OR, NOR, AND, and NAND gates. These gates are synthesized electronically in a variety of forms, of which the most important are: diode logic (DL), resistor-transistor logic (RTL), diode-transistor logic (DTL), transistor-transistor logic (TTL), and emitter-coupled logic (ECL). The last four are common in integrated circuit form.

This experiment presents logic gates together with their physical realizations. The purpose of combining the study of logical design with physical realization is that the logic designer often has to choose one of a few possible designs, and his choice usually depends upon the cost of components. Since the cost of each design depends upon component count, component reliability, ease of manufacture, and the like, it is generally impossible to determine the least expensive logic design unless the physical realizations are known. Hence, at least one realization will be given for each of the basic logic gates presented in this experiment. Some gates have several realizations, and allow the designer to choose a unit among the commerically available devices for which the most critical defects can be minimized.

THEORY

Digital circuits generally have only two distinguishable and nonoverlapping voltage or current levels. These two levels or states are often called high and low, ON and OFF, or true and false, and are represented by the numbers 1 and 0. Since no other numbers are utilized, the arithmetic operations in digital circuits are carried out in the binary system or some variation of it. Thus in digital systems,

decimal numbers are encoded as binary numbers, and each binary digit is called a bit. A group of bits having a significance is called a bite, word, or code.

If a digital system has its most positive voltage or current levels designated as 1 and the other level as 0, it is called a *positive* logic system. On the other hand, a *negative* logic system is one which designates the more negative voltage state of the bit as the 1 level and the more positive as the 0 level.

The basic postulates of two-level logic operations, combinations, and equivalents are contained in Boolean algebra. Boolean algebra provides a simple means of expressing logic functions in the form of algebraic equations which can be manipulated by rules similar to those of ordinary algebra.

The two levels or states of a bit are called the binary or Boolean variables. For example, if a *pnp* transistor switch is driven between cutoff and saturation, then the collector voltage at cutoff is $-V_{CC}$ and is the logical 1 state, whereas the saturation voltage $V_{CE(\text{sat})}$ of the collector is the logical 0 state. The Boolean variables in this negative logic circuit are 0 and 1, and no other variables are permitted.

The basic operations of complementation (inversion), addition, and multiplication in the Boolean variables 0 and 1 are defined in Table 16-1. The bar over a variable represents the negation or complementation of the variable.

TABLE 16-1. BASIC OPERATIONS

Complementation (inversion)	Addition	Multiplication
$\bar{1} = 0$	$0 + 0 = 0$	$0 \cdot 0 = 0$
$\bar{0} = 1$	$0 + 1 = 1$	$0 \cdot 1 = 0$
	$1 + 0 = 1$	$1 \cdot 0 = 0$
	$1 + 1 = 1$	$1 \cdot 1 = 1$

NOT (Inverter) Gates

The NOT gate has a single input and single output, and performs the operation of complementation. That is the output of a NOT gate is a logical 1 if—and only if—the input

156

is a logical 0. This logical operation can be defined by tabulating all possible inputs and their corresponding outputs in the form of a table known as a "truth table." A few commonly used block diagrams of the NOT (invert) gate are given in Fig. 16-1. The associated voltage truth table and

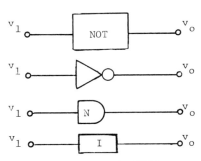

Fig. 16.1 Symbols for NOT gate.

positive logic truth table for a NOT gate are given in Tables 16-2 and 16-3, respectively.

TABLE 16-2 VOLTAGE TRUTH TABLE.	
v_1	v_o
−	+
+	−

TABLE 16-3 POSITIVE LOGIC TRUTH TABLE.	
v_1	$v_o = \overline{v}_1$
0	1
1	0

The NOT (invert) gate can be synthesized by a RTL scheme, as shown in Fig. 16-2.

The input voltage can assume either of two voltages. For a positive logic circuit, the upper level of the input voltage is denoted by $V(1)$ or by a logical 1, and the lower level by $V(0)$ or by a logical 0. The output of the NOT gate must also operate between these two voltages in order to preserve the two binary levels. If V_{CC} is equal to $V(1)$ and V_{EE} is $V(0)$, the output will be $V(1)$ when the input is $V(0)$, and vice versa. Thus inverter operation occurs pro-

vided the parameters V_{BB}, R_1, R_2, and R_B are properly chosen so that the transistor is OFF when $v_1 = V(0)$, and ON (in saturation) when the input is high, $v_1 = V(1)$. The output v_o is equal to V_{EE} if we neglect the collector-to-emitter saturation voltage $V_{CE(sat)}$. The inverter was studied in Experiment 10. Observe that the NOT circuit can also amplify the input pulse if $V_{CC} > V(1)$. The time delay t_{pd} of the output pulse is due mainly to the input capacitance of the transistor. A reduction of this delay can be achieved by placing a small capacitor C_1 across resistor R_1 so that the R_1-C_1 combination reacts with the transistors input resistance and capacitance as a compensating attenuator circuit, as explained in Experiment 2. An integrated circuit quad inverter is shown in Fig. 16-3. This

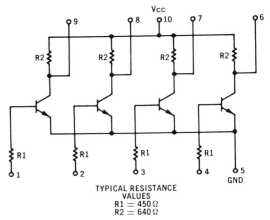

TYPICAL RESISTANCE VALUES
R1 = 450 Ω
R2 = 640 Ω

Fig. 16.3 IC NOT gates.

RTL scheme performs as four separate inverter (NOT) circuits with the inputs applied to pins 1 to 4 and the outputs from pins 9 to 6. Typical values are $V_{CC} = 3$, $V(0) = 0.0$, and $V(1) = .8$. Notice that $V(1)$ is not equal to V_{CC}, which implies that the transistor is not driven into saturation in order to reduce the storage time associated with the output pulse.

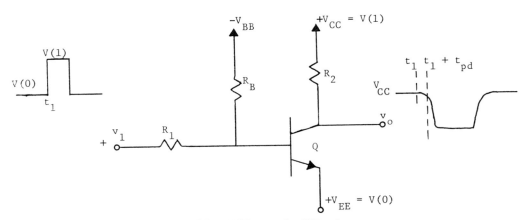

Fig. 16.2 A NOT gate using RTL scheme.

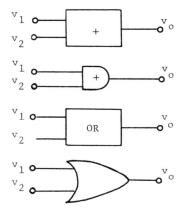

Fig. 16.4 Symbols for OR gate.

OR Gates

The OR gate performs the operation of addition. That is, the output of an OR gate is 1 when one or more of the inputs is 1. Conversely, the output is 0 only when all the inputs are 0. A few commonly used block diagrams of the OR gate are given in Fig. 16-4. The associated voltage truth table and positive logic truth table for an OR gate are given in Tables 16-4 and 16-5, respectively.

<table>
<tr><td colspan="3">TABLE 16-4 VOLTAGE TRUTH TABLE.</td><td colspan="3">TABLE 16-5 POSITIVE LOGIC TRUTH TABLE.</td></tr>
</table>

v_1	v_2	v_o	v_1	v_2	$v_o = v_1 + v_2$
−	−	−	0	0	0
−	+	+	0	1	1
+	−	+	1	0	1
+	+	+	1	1	1

The OR gate can be synthesized by a number of different types of electronic circuits, such as the DL, RTL, TTL, and ECL schemes. One of the simplest is the diode logic (DL) circuit shown in Fig. 16-5. The two-input gate is shown for illustrative purposes only, and R_i is the impedance of the input source. A larger number of inputs than indicated can be applied. The input voltage can assume either of two voltages. Once again, for a positive logic circuit, the upper level is denoted by $V(1)$ or by a logical 1, and the lower level by $V(0)$ or by a logical 0. The output of the gate follows the most positive of the input signals—that is, v_o = maximum of (v_1, v_2).

If all the inputs of the DL circuit of Fig. 16-5 are in the 0 state, then none of the diodes is forward-biased and the output is $-V_R$. If now one or more inputs are changed to the 1 state, one or more diodes will conduct provided $V(1)$ exceeds V_R by at least the cut-in voltage V_γ of the diode. The output voltage is

$$v_o = -V_R + [V(1) - V_\gamma + V_R] \frac{R}{R_i + R_f + R}$$

$$(16\text{-}1)$$

where R_f is the diode forward resistance. Usually R is chosen to be much larger than $R_i + R_f$, and Eq. (16-1) becomes

$$v_o \approx V(1) - V_\gamma \qquad (16\text{-}2)$$

If the level $V(1)$ is not identical for all inputs, then the output level will be equal to the most positive level $V(1)$ minus V_γ.

The RTL scheme shown in Fig. 16-6 can also be used as an OR gate, and can be found in integrated circuit form. Its main advantage is simplicity and low cost, but it has the disadvantage of slow switching speed.

For the most part, OR gates are synthesized in integrated circuits using either the TTL or ECL schemes. TTL functional blocks have the advantage of relative simplicity and low power dissipation as compared to ECL blocks. However, ECL's have the fastest switching speeds attainable in gating circuitry because of their nonsaturating operation. The TTL realization of an OR gate will be dis-

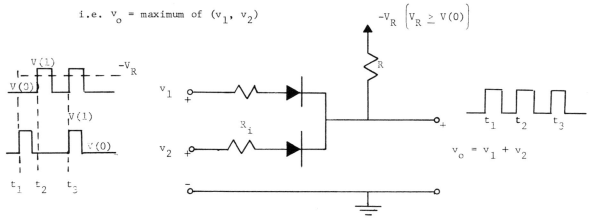

Fig. 16.5 OR gate using DL scheme.

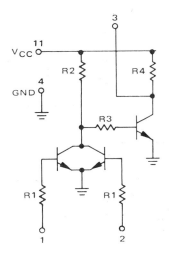

TYPICAL RESISTANCE VALUES
R1 = 450 Ω   R3 = 500 Ω
R2 = 1.8 k   R4 = 640 Ω

Fig. 16.6 IC OR gate using RTL scheme.

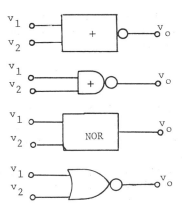

Fig. 16.7 Symbols for NOR gate.

cussed when the AND-OR-INVERT circuit is studied in the section on AND gates. The ECL scheme for an OR gate will be discussed in the section on NOR gates and ECL realizations.

NOR Gates

Although DL gates have a small number of components, they also have a serious limitation when connected in cascade to synthesize OR gates. The voltage across a number of diodes in series can be comparable to the logic levels being transmitted and, hence, deteriorate the overall performance of the digital system if level-restoring circuits are not employed. If level-restoring circuits such as the inverter circuit ($V_{CC} > V(1)$) of Fig. 16-2 are employed, then the NOT function is also provided. The OR gate followed by a NOT gate is called a NOR gate, and is a very useful logic gate. In fact, there are many more types of NOR gates than OR gates available in integrated circuits. This is due to the need for level restoration and also be-

cause NOR gates, if properly used, can be substituted for NAND gates, as will be demonstrated subsequently.

The output of a NOR gate is 1 only where all the inputs are 0. Conversely, the output is 0 when one or more inputs are 1. A few commonly used block diagrams of the NOR gate are given in Fig. 16-7. The associated voltage truth table and positive logic truth table for a NOR gate are given in Tables 16-6 and 16-7, respectively.

TABLE 16-6 VOLTAGE TRUTH TABLE.		
v_1	v_2	v_o
−	−	+
−	+	−
+	−	−
+	+	−

TABLE 16-7 POSITIVE LOGIC TRUTH TABLE.		
v_1	v_2	$v_o = \overline{v_1 + v_2}$
0	0	1
0	1	0
1	0	0
1	1	0

The NOR gate can be synthesized by a variety of electronic circuits such as the RTL, RCTL, DTL, DCTL, TTL, and ECL schemes. One of the simplest is the positive logic RTL scheme shown in Fig. 16-8.

The operation of the NOR gate can be explained if we first consider that the emitter-base junction is reverse-biased by V_{BB} in the absence of any input and the output

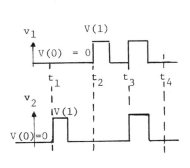
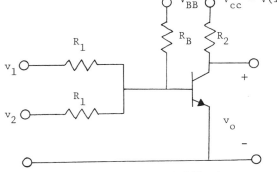
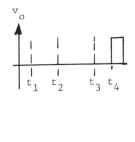

Fig. 16.8 NOR gate using positive logic RTL scheme.

$v_o \approx V_{CC} = V(1)$. If a signal $V(1)$ is now applied to at least one of the inputs, the transistor turns ON and the output drops to the saturated voltage $V_{CE(sat)}$.

$$v_o = V_{CE(sat)} = V(0) \qquad (16\text{-}3)$$

If all the inputs are excited, then the output is still $V_{CE(sat)}$, but the transistor is now driven heavily into saturation. By placing capacitors C_1 across resistor R_1, the storage time can be reduced; this scheme is called resistor capacitor transistor logic (RCTL).

A typical integrated circuit positive logic NOR gate using an RTL scheme is shown in Fig. 16-9.

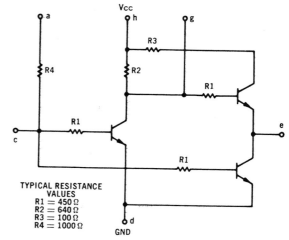

TYPICAL RESISTANCE VALUES
R1 = 450 Ω
R2 = 640 Ω
R3 = 100 Ω
R4 = 1000 Ω

Fig. 16.10 IC buffer stage.

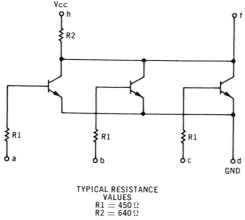

TYPICAL RESISTANCE VALUES
R1 = 450 Ω
R2 = 640 Ω

Fig. 16.9 IC NOR gate.

The inputs are applied at pins a, b, and c, with the output taken at pin f. Typical values are $V_{CC} = 3$, $V(0) = 0.0$, $V(1) = .8$, with a pulse delay of about 20 nanoseconds. Note that the different input signals are applied through resistors known as fan-in resistors. Consequently, the maximum number of input terminals connected to a gate is simply called the *fan-in*. In the case of RTL's, the fan-in is determined by the condition that when all the inputs are at $V(0)$ the transistor must remain OFF even at the highest operating temperatures. The *fan-out* is the maximum number of load gates that can be connected to the output of a gate. In order to increase fan-out, IC buffers, such as that shown in Fig. 16-10, are connected to the outputs of some RTL circuits. The input pins are a and c, and the output pins are g and e.

Another scheme for realizing a NOR gate is by the use of diode transistor logic (DTL). A transistor NOT gate following a diode logic OR gate is shown in Fig. 16-11.

If all the inputs of the NOR gate of Fig. 16-11 are in the 0 state, then all the diodes are forward-biased by $-V_{CC}$, and the input to the transistor is $V(0)$. If any input is $V(1)$, then the diode connected to this input conducts because of $-V_{CC}$, but all other diodes are now reversed-biased because node P is at $V(1)$. Thus from the input to node P we have

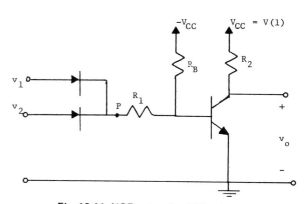

Fig. 16.11 NOR gate using DTL scheme.

an OR gate, and from node P to the output we have a NOT gate. Hence the circuit of Fig. 16-11 operates as a NOR gate.

An integrated circuit form of a negative logic NOR gate using a DTL scheme is shown in Fig. 16-12.

Another realization of a positive NOR gate can be accomplished by the use of the DCTL scheme, shown in Fig. 16-13.

This circuit implements the NOR logic in the following way. If all the inputs are at $V(0)$, which is less than the cut-in voltage V_γ of the transistors, then transistors Q_1 and Q_2 are OFF and the output is at V_{CC} or the high level $V(1)$. If now at least one of the inputs is in the high state $V(1)$, then the output drops to $V_{CE(sat)}$ or the low state $V(0)$. Generally, the output of the DCTL NOR gate drives some load circuits into saturation, and the fan-out is an important consideration in DCTL logic. In addition, the input characteristics of the loading transistors may not be identical, and it is possible that one loading gate may draw most of the available current from V_{CC} through R_L, and the other load gates may not draw enough to be driven into saturation. Thus one load gate can "hog" most of the output drive current. This defect of DCTL schemes can be

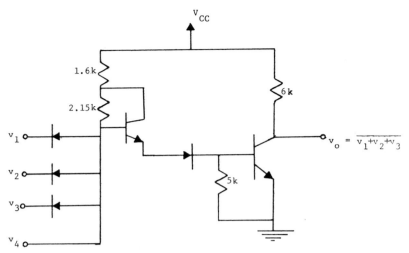

Fig. 16.12 IC negative logic NOR gate using DTL scheme.

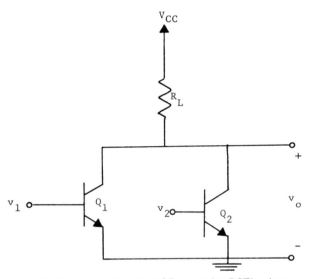

Fig. 16.13 IC positive logic NOR gate using DCTL scheme.

remedied by placing a resistor R_B in series with the base of the load gates. However, the larger the value of R_B, the smaller the fan-out capability of the NOR gate. The other important properties of DCTL schemes are their low output swing, slow speed due to saturating transistors, only one voltage supply, low power dissipation, and relatively low cost of fabrication in integrated circuit form.

Probably the most widely used NOR gate is the emitter-coupled logic scheme (ECL), which is also called the current mode logic (CML) scheme. This scheme performs both the NOR and OR logical functions. The switching speed obtainable with ECL circuits is high because the current is switched from one transistor to the other without the transistor necessarily going into saturation. The circuit of Fig. 16-14 is a typical positive NOR ECL gate. The voltage V_{EE} and emitter resistor R_E are chosen to approximate a

current source, while V_{BB} is a reference voltage which can be 0 volts.

The ECL circuit operation can be explained if we first consider that negative signals v_1 and v_2 are applied to transistors Q_1 and Q_2 to turn them OFF while transistor Q_3 is ON, so that $v_{o2} = V(0)$, and $v_{o1} = V(1)$. If a positive-going signal is now applied to one or more of the inputs, then the corresponding transistor(s) will turn ON and transistor Q_3 will turn OFF. Thus $v_{o1} = V(1)$, $v_{o2} = V(0)$ and complementary outputs are available from an ECL circuit. For this circuit, the output levels are

$$V(0) = V_{CC} - I_E R_C \approx V_{CC}\left(1 - \frac{R_C}{R_E}\right); V(1) = V_{CC}$$

One of the difficulties with this configuration is that the $V(0)$ and $V(1)$ levels in the output differ from those in the input. The input signals are positive-going from some negative level, while the output is always positive and varies between $V_{CC}[1 - (R_C/R_E)]$ and V_{CC}. Hence, emitter followers or other level-restoring circuits must be used in the output to provide the proper dc level shift. An integrated ECL three input NOR gate is shown in Fig. 16-15.

The possible higher speed obtainable with ECL is offset by the increased component count and increased power dissipation. The resistors R_{o1} and R_{o2} are called pull-down resistors and are omitted in some integrated circuits to permit the reduction of power dissipation.

AND Gates

The AND gate performs the operation of multiplication. That is, the output of an AND gate is 1 only when all the inputs are 1. Conversely, the output is 0 only when one or more of the inputs is zero. A few commonly used block diagrams of the AND gate are given in Fig. 16-16. The

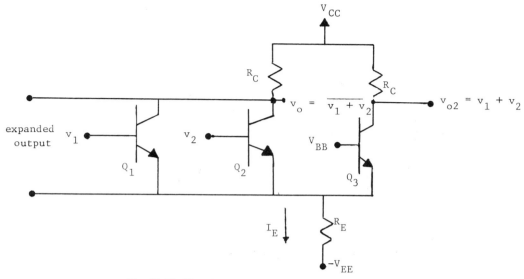

Fig. 16.14 IC positive logic NOR gate using ECL scheme.

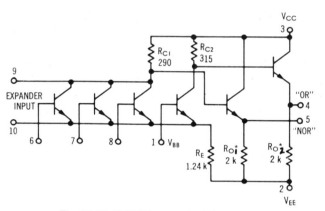

Fig. 16.15 IC NOR gate using ECL scheme.

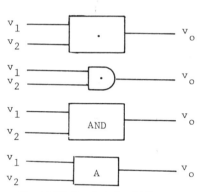

Fig. 16.16 Symbols for AND gate.

associated voltage truth table and positive logic truth table for an AND gate are given in Tables 16-8 and 16-9, respectively.

TABLE 16-8 VOLTAGE TRUTH TABLE.

v_1	v_2	v_o
−	−	−
−	+	−
+	−	−
+	+	+

TABLE 16-9 POSITIVE LOGIC TRUTH TABLE.

v_1	v_2	$v_o = v_1 \cdot v_2$
0	0	0
0	1	0
1	0	0
1	1	1

A simple DL circuit which performs the operation required by a positive logic AND gate is shown in Fig. 16-17. Observe that it is similar to the DL OR gate of Fig. 16-5 except that the diodes and supply voltage V_R are reversed.

The DL AND gate's operation can be understood if we initially assume that all source resistances R_i are zero and that the diodes are ideal. If any input is at the $V(0)$ level, the diode connected to this input conducts and the output is the voltage $V(0)$. However, if all inputs are at the $V(1)$ level (coincident), the output will be clamped to $V(1)$. The AND gate is also called a coincidence circuit. If we consider a nonideal situation, then the output impedance upon coincidence is equal to $R \| \left(\dfrac{R_i + R_f}{n} \right)$ for an n input AND gate. More precisely, let us consider that $V_R = V(1)$ and that m inputs out of a total of n inputs are at $V(1)$. The output voltage in this case is

$$v_o = V(1) - [V(1) - V(0) - V_\gamma] \frac{R}{\left[R + \dfrac{R_i + R_f}{n - m} \right]}$$

If $m \neq n$ and $\dfrac{R_i + R_f}{n - m} \ll R$, then $v_o \approx V(0) + V_\gamma$. However, if we take note that $(R_i + R_f)/(n - m)$ may not be much less R, then the output will increase in small steps as

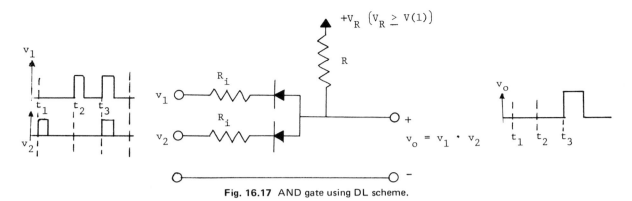

Fig. 16.17 AND gate using DL scheme.

m increases from 0 to $n - 1$. This variation in output level is called logical noise, and its effect can be reduced by connecting a diode in series with a supply voltage V', which is greater than $V(0)$ across the output of the circuit of Fig. 16-17. ECL and TTL schemes are also used for AND gates. An integrated ECL circuit which performs the positive AND is shown in Fig. 16-18.

For the most part, AND gates are synthesized in integrated circuits using the TTL scheme. TTL functional blocks have the advantage of relative simplicity and low power dissipation as compared, for example, with ECL blocks. The integrated circuit of Fig. 16-19 is a positive AND gate which can also serve as a negative OR gate.

The operation from the input of Q_1 to the output of Q_4 satisfies the positive AND logic given in Tables 16-8 and 16-9. Transistors Q_2 and Q_3 can be considered as a Darlington pair, and Q_4 is an inverter. Q_5 and Q_6 are level-shifting transistors. Transistors Q_1, Q_2, and Q_3

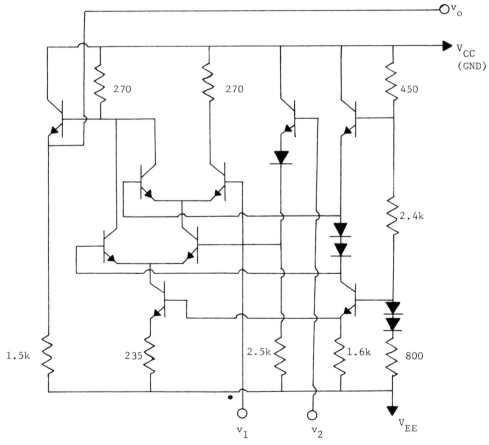

Fig. 16.18 IC positive logic AND gate using ECL scheme.

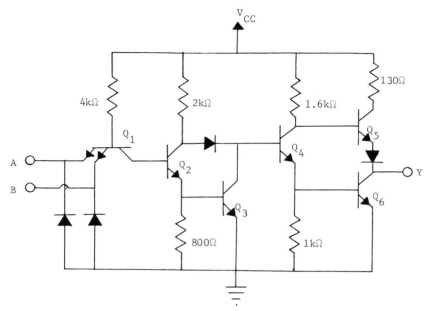

Fig. 16.19 IC positive logic AND gate using TTL scheme.

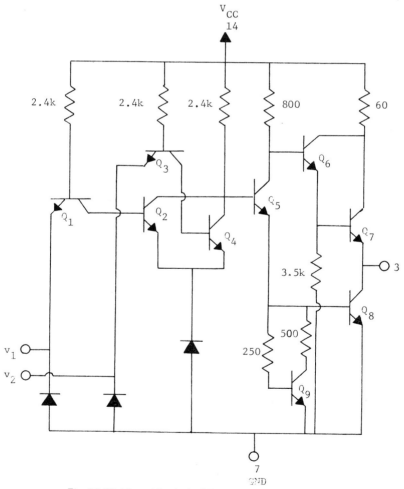

Fig. 16.20 IC positive logic OR gate using TTL scheme.

operate as a NAND gate, which will be explained in the next section. Another TTL scheme for a negative AND gate or a positive OR gate is shown in Fig. 16-20.

The input to Q_5 for positive logic is simply $\overline{v}_1 \cdot \overline{v}_2$, which can be shown to be equal to $\overline{v_1 + v_2}$ by DeMorgan's law (see NAND gate). Since Q_5 operates as an inverter, the output of Q_5 is $v_1 + v_2$. Q_6, Q_7, Q_8, and Q_9 are once again transistors of a level-shifting circuit. The circuit's total operation should become clearer after reading the next section dealing with NAND gates.

Finally, a very important TTL scheme is known as the AND-OR-INVERT circuit, and is shown in Fig. 16-21. This

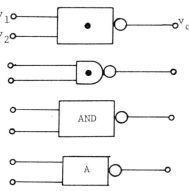

Fig. 16.22 Symbols for AND gate.

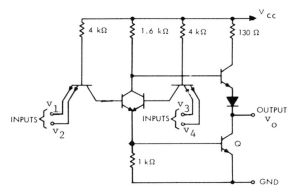

Fig. 16.21 IC AND-OR-INVERT gate using TTL scheme.

positive logic circuit can be used to perform the INVERT, AND, OR, NOR, and NAND operations. The output for positive logic is simply $v_o = \overline{v_1 \cdot v_2 + v_3 \cdot v_4}$. Typical values are $V_{CC} = 5$, $v_o = V(1) = 3.3$, $v_o = V(0) = .22$, $v_1 = V(1)_{min} = 2$, $v_1 = V(0)_{max} = .8$, and a pulse delay to a logical 1 level is typically 18 nanoseconds.

NAND Gates

The NAND gate is one of the most useful logic gates and, hence, realized by several schemes. "NAND" is a contraction of "not" "and." The output of a NAND gate equals 0

only when all of the inputs equal 1. Conversely, the output equals 1 only when one or more of the inputs equals 0. A few commonly used block diagrams of the NAND gate are given in Fig. 16-22. The associated voltage truth table and positive logic truth table for a NAND gate are given in Tables 16-10 and 16-11, respectively.

TABLE 16-10 VOLTAGE TRUTH TABLE.		
v_1	v_2	v_o
−	−	−
−	+	+
+	−	+
+	+	+

TABLE 16-11 POSITIVE LOGIC TRUTH TABLE.		
v_1	v_2	$\overline{v_1 \cdot v_2}$
0	0	0
0	1	1
1	0	1
1	1	1

There are many reasons for the popularity of the NAND gate. First of all, if an inverter is placed at the output of a NAND gate, the overall circuit is an AND gate. In fact, by using input inverters, output inverters, or both, it is possible to achieve all four basis logic functions from any single gate type. Thus the NAND and NOR gates are extremely popular and are used extensively in combination with inverter gates.

Another reason for the popularity of the NAND (and

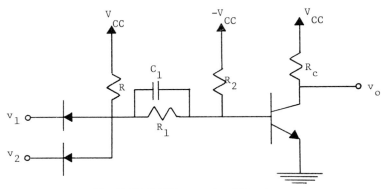

Fig. 16.23 NAND gate using DTL scheme.

NOR) gate can be explained by the use of DeMorgan's laws, which are

$$\overline{v_1 \cdot v_2 \cdot v_3 \cdots} = \overline{v}_1 + \overline{v}_2 + \overline{v}_3 + \cdots$$

$$\overline{v_1 + v_2 + \cdots} = \overline{v}_1 \cdot \overline{v}_2 \cdot \overline{v}_3 \cdots$$

These laws demonstrate that a positive logic NAND circuit can also be used as a negative logic NOR circuit, and vice versa.

A DTL scheme which can be used to perform the NAND operation is shown in Fig. 16–23.

The operation of this NAND gate can be understood by considering that the diodes and resistor R operate as an AND gate, as explained previously, while the transistor operates as an inverter. The supply $-V_{CC}$ insures that the transistor is OFF if at least one input is $V(0)$. Capacitor C_1 is used to increase the switching speed. In addition, a clamping diode in series with a supply voltage equal to $V(1)$

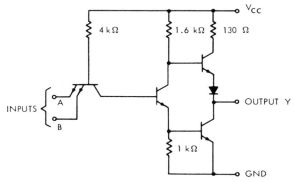

Fig. 16.26 IC NAND gate using TTL scheme.

is often connected to the output of the circuit of Fig. 16–23 to improve the switching speed.

An integrated circuit DTL which performs the NAND operation is shown in Fig. 16–24. Typical values are $V_{CC} = 5, v_o = V(1)_{min} = 2.6 \text{ V}, v_o = V(0)_{max} = .45 \text{ V}$.

This circuit is similar to the negative logic NOR gate given in Fig. 16–12.

Another popular means of realising a NAND gate is by the use of TTL circuits, such as the one shown in Fig. 16–25.

The operation of this circuit is similar to the DTL NAND gate of Fig. 16–23 except that the input transistors replace the input diodes of the DTL gate. The value of V_{BB} is chosen so that for all loading conditions the turn ON condition $V_{BB} > V(0) + V_{BE}$ and turn OFF condition $V_{BB} < V(1) + V_{BE}$ are met.

The schematic of a TTL integrated NAND gate of the type SN7420 is given in Fig. 16–26, and is similar to the integrated AND gate of Fig. 16–19. The basic difference is that Fig. 16–19 has one additional inverter gate. The two-emitter transistor is replaced by two single-emitter transis-

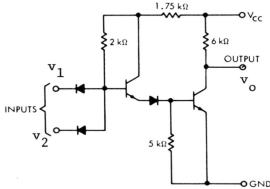

Fig. 16.24 IC NAND gate using DTL scheme.

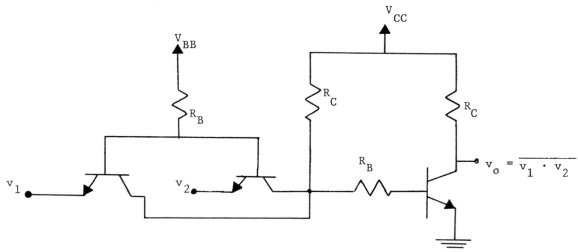

Fig. 16.25 NAND gate using TTL scheme.

```
MODEL DESCRIPTION
MODEL TTLNAND (B-E-C)
ELEMENTS
CE, B-E=EQUATION1(5.,80., TABLE1(VCE))
CC,B-C=EQUATION1(10.,200.,TABLE2(VCC))
J1,B-E=DIODE TABLE1
JA,E=B=.1*J2
J2,B-C=DIODE TABLE2
JB,C-B=.98*J1
FUNCTIONS
DIODE TABLE1
0,0,.3,0,.65,.05,.7,.6,.72,1.4,.73,2,.74,3.4,.8,10,.82,15
DIODE TABLE2
0,0,.58,0,.62,.4,.64,1,.66,2,.67,3,.69,7,.7,12
EQUATION1(A,B,C)=(A+B*C)
CIRCUIT DESCRIPTION
E1,1-5=TABLE1
DE1=TABLE3
E2,1-2=TABLE2
DE2=TABLE4
E3,1-6=5
R1,6-3=4.0
R2,6-7=1.6
R3,6-11=0.13
R4,8-1=1.0
```

```
R0,9-1=100E6
J0,10-9=DIODE EQUATION(1,E-3,38,5)
T1,3-2-4=MODEL TTLNAND
T2,3-5-4=MODEL TTLNAND
T3,4-8-7=MODEL TTLNAND
T4,7-10-11=MODEL TTLNAND
T5,8-1-9=MODEL TTLNAND
OUTPUTS
E1,E2,VR0,PLOT
FUNCTIONS
TABLE1
0,0,3000,0,3001,4,7000,4,7001,0
9000,0
TABLE2
0,4,5000,4,5001,0
9000,0
TABLE 3
0,0,3000,0,3000,4,3001,4,3001,0,7000,0,7000,-4,7001,-4,7001,0
9000,0
TABLE4
0,0,5000,0,5000,-4,5001,-4,5001,0,9000,0
RUN CONTROLS
STOP TIME=10000
MINIMUM STEP SIZE=1,OE=5
END
```

Fig. 16.27 SCEPTRE program for TTL NAND gate.

tors operating in parallel for computer analysis. Suggested nominal values for supply voltage and input voltage are 5 V and 2 V, respectively. Since the characteristics of the transistors and the diode are not supplied, typical values for

α_R and α_N for a switching transistor are assumed as 0.98 and 0.1, respectively. The SCEPTRE program is given in Fig. 16-27. The plots of the two inputs and the output are shown in Figs. 16-28 through 16-30.

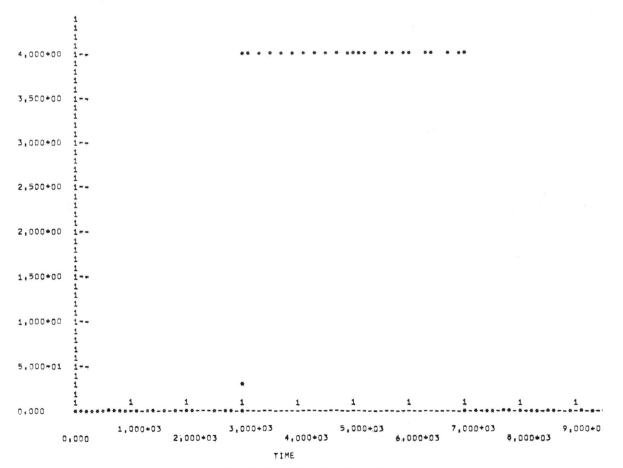

Fig. 16.28 NAND gate input vs. time.

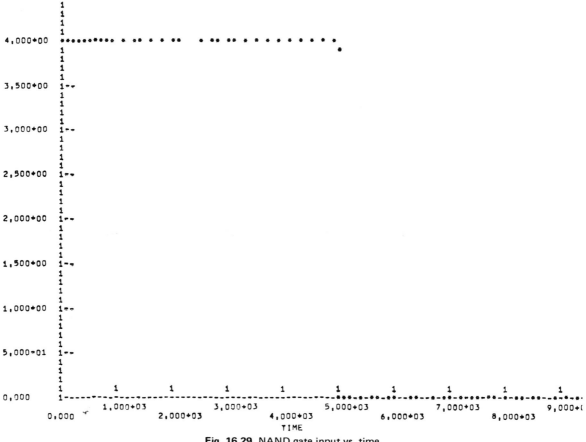

Fig. 16.29 NAND gate input vs. time.

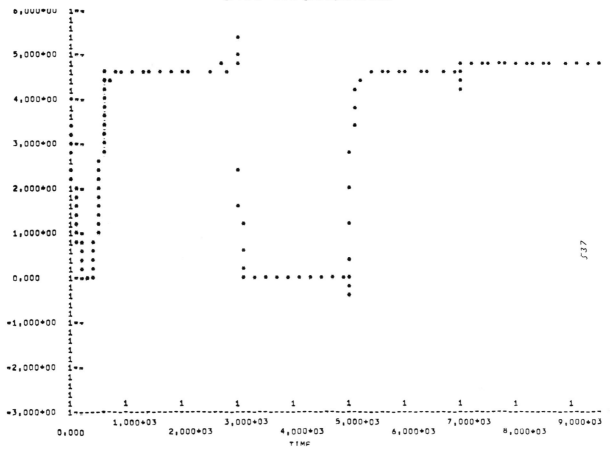

537

Fig. 16.30 NAND gate output vs. time.

Part Two

OBJECTIVE

The purpose of this experiment is to study some basic logic gates and their physical realizations in the form of discrete and integrated electronic circuits. A number of schemes, including DL, RTL, DTL, DCTL, TTL, and ECL, will be emphasized in this experiment.

REFERENCES

Chirlian, P. M., *Analysis and Design of Electronic Circuits.* New York: McGraw-Hill, 1965, Chapter 15.

Fitchen, F. C., *Transistor Circuit Analysis and Design.* New York: Van Nostrand Reinhold, 1966, Chapter 13.

Fitchen, F. C., *Electronic Integrated Circuits and Systems.* New York: Van Nostrand Reinhold, 1970, Chapter 9.

Ghausi, M. S., *Electronic Circuits: Devices, Models, Functions, Analysis, and Design.* New York: Van Nostrand Reinhold, 1971, Chapter 11.

Gray, P. E. and Searle, C. L., *Electronic Principles: Physics, Models, and Circuits.* New York: Wiley, 1967, Chapter 23.

Millman, J., and Taub, H., *Pulse, Digital, and Switching Waveforms.* New York: McGraw-Hill, 1965, Chapter 9.

Pettit, J. M., and McWhorter, M. M., *Electronic Switching, Timing, and Pulse Circuits.* New York: McGraw-Hill, 1970, Chapters 3 and 4.

Strauss, L., *Wave Generation and Shaping.* New York: McGraw-Hill, 1970, Chapter 4.

LABORATORY PREPARATION

NOT Gates

1. Design a positive logic NOT gate using a switching transistor available in your laboratory. The switching level $V(0)$ should be less than .4, and the $V(1)$ level should be greater than 2.4. Estimate the pulse delay for your circuit.

2. What value of capacitor C_1 across your resistor R (see Fig. 16-2) decreases the delay time of your output pulse?

3. Design a negative logic NOT gate using a switching transistor available in your laboratory. The switching level $V(0)$ should be greater than $-.4$, and $V(1)$ should be less than -2.4.

4. Select some IC NOT gates, such as that shown in Fig. 16-3, and study the manufacturer's specifications. What are typical input and output voltage levels and pulse delay times for your IC inverters?

OR Gates

5. Design a diode logic OR gate using some switching diodes available in your laboratory. Design both a positive logic and negative logic OR gate. Compare your designs.

6. Select an integrated RTL OR gate and study the manu-facturer's specifications. What are the fan-out and fan-in capabilities of your IC circuits?

7. Select some integrated ECL OR gates and study the manufacturer's specifications. How would you connect your integrated circuit inverters to your ECL OR gates to obtain a NOR gate?

NOR Gates

8. Design a discrete circuit NOR gate, such as that shown in Fig. 16-8, using transistors available in your laboratory. The logical level $V(0)$ should be less than .4, and $V(1)$ should be greater than 2.4. Estimate the fain-in and fan-out capabilities of your NOR gate.

9. Select an IC positive logic NOR gate using an RTL scheme as shown in Fig. 16-9. Study the manufacturer's specifications and determine typical values of V_{CC}, $V(0)$, $V(1)$, and t_{pd}.

10. Select an IC buffer compatible with your IC NOR gate. What are the possible ranges of the input and output logical levels for the IC buffer you have chosen?

11. Design a positive NOR gate using a DTL scheme. If possible, use the same components that you used to design a discrete OR gate and discrete inverter. Design this circuit so that the logic levels are compatible with the logic levels in your other logic gates.

12. Select a positive logic NAND gate which could also be used as a negative logic NOR gate and is similar to the circuit of Fig. 16-12. Study the manufacturer's specifications. Suppose that you connect a negative logic NOT gate to the output of your negative logic NOR gate. What is the resulting logic circuit?

13. Design a DCTL NOR gate using silicon transistors. Make your logic levels compatible with the levels in your other gates. What is the fan-out capability of your DCTL NOR gate?

14. Design a discrete ECL NOR gate with positive logic having two inputs. Let $V_{BB} = 0$. What are the output levels of your ECL NOR gate? Design an output level shifter for your ECL NOR gate so that the output levels of the level shifter are compatible with the input levels of your NOR gate.

15. Select an IC NOR gate that uses an ECL scheme which is available in your laboratory. What is the pulse of your IC NOR gate? Compare it with the pulse delay in your other NOR gate circuits. Select some IC expander circuits that can be connected to your ECL NOR gate.

AND Gates

16. Design a discrete DL AND gate using components available in your laboratory. If possible, use the same com-

ponents and logic levels used for your other gates. Design both a positive and a negative logic AND gate. Consider what would happen to the output levels if the number of inputs were increased. Connect a diode and voltage supply $V' < V(1)$ to the output of your AND gate to perform a clamping operation. What is the level of your output voltage?

17. Suppose that you connect your positive DL OR gate to the output of your positive DL AND gate as shown in Fig. 16-31.

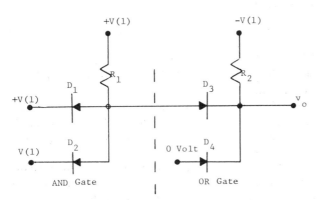

Fig. 16.31 AND gate connected to OR gate.

The output of the OR gate should be $V(1)$. Why? Since D_1 and D_2 are reversed-biased, they are nonconducting. Also D_4 is reversed-biased if v_o is not a negative voltage. If the forward resistances of D_1 and D_3 are negligible with respect to R_1 and R_2 and if $R_1 = R_2$, then $v_o \approx 0$ V. Thus v_o is not a logical 1 output, and would require that R_1 be much smaller than R_2 for v_o to be within the region of a logical 1 output. However, R_1 cannot be made too small or improper AND gate operation occurs and excessive power dissipation will result. Also if R_2 is made large, the circuit will have a slow response time because of the charging of the diode junctions. What can be concluded from the interconnnection of the DL gates?

18. Select an IC positive AND gate which utilizes an ECL scheme similar to the one of Fig. 16-18. Study the manufacturer's specifications. Compare the switching speed of the AND circuit with all your other AND circuits. What are the power requirements of the ECL AND gate?

19. Select an IC TTL AND gate similar to the one of Fig. 16-19. Compare its performance with your other AND gates. Can this circuit be followed by an OR gate without displaying the difficulties encountered in step 16?

20. Select an IC AND-OR-INVERT gate similar to the one shown in Fig. 16-21 and describe how it can be used to generate the NOR and NAND logic functions.

NAND Gates

21. Design a DTL NAND gate similar to the circuit of Fig. 16-23. Select the logic levels to be compatible with your other gates. Can a NOT gate be connected to the output of your NAND gate? What is the logical function that the total circuit performs?

22. What value of capacitor C_1 will increase the speed of response of your DTL NAND gate?

23. Select an integrated IC DTL NAND gate and compare its performance to your discrete DTL gate. Compare speed of response, logic levels, power requirements, and fan-in and fan-out capabilities.

24. Design a discrete TTL NAND gate similar to the one of Fig. 16-25. Compare its predicted performance with the DTL NAND gate you designed.

25. Select an IC TTL NAND gate and study the manufacturer's specifications. Compare with your other NAND gates. Connect two NAND's together as shown in Fig. 16-32 and verify the AND truth table.

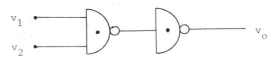

Fig. 16.32 Two NAND gate connection.

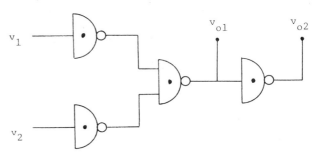

Fig. 16.33 Three NAND gate connection.

26. Connect the NAND gates as shown in Fig. 16-33 and verify the OR and NOR truth tables.

27. (optional) Select some of your gates and describe how they could be interconnected to realize the following Boolean functions

$$v_o = v_1 + \bar{v}_1 \cdot v_2 \cdot v_3$$

$$v_o = v_3 \cdot (v_1 \cdot \bar{v}_2 + \bar{v}_1 \cdot v_2) + v_1 \cdot v_2$$

You can also devise some other complicated Boolean functions that would be interesting to synthesize using either all NOR, all NAND, or combinations of logic gates.

28. (optional) Run your SCEPTRE programs to test out the logic gates of your choice.

LABORATORY PROCEDURE

NOT Gates

1. Build and completely test the NOT gates you have designed in step 1 of the preparation. Be sure to test the logic operation of your gate. Drive the circuit with a square-

wave. Decrease the period of the driving signal from a maximum allowable to a minimum period, noting if the circuit continues to function correctly.

2. Put your capacitor C_1 across R_1 and measure the pulse delay. Compare with step 1.

3. Build and test the negative logic NOT gate you designed. Compare it to the NOT gate of step 1.

4. Test your IC NOT gates. Vary V_{CC} within the maximum limits and observe the effects on the logical operation of the circuit.

OR Gates

5. Test the OR gates you have designed. Observe the effect of changing R and $-V_R$ on the logical operation of the circuit.

6. Test the IC RTL OR gate you have available in your laboratory. Be sure to test the circuit under varying input and output load conditions.

7. Test the IC ECL OR gate you have in your laboratory. Connect some IC inverters to your OR gate. Test the resulting NOR logic gate. Compare the operation of all your OR gates.

NOR Gates

8. Test your NOR gate corresponding to Fig. 16-8.

9. Test your IC positive logic NOR gate which uses an RTL scheme. Test the circuit under varying input and output load conditions.

10. Connect your IC buffer to your IC RTL NOR gate. Measure any changes in the input and output logical levels with the buffer added.

11. Build and test the positive NOR gate you have designed with a DTL scheme. Measure the effect on the logic levels if V_{CC}, R_1, R_B, and R_2 are varied. Connect some other gates to this gate and determine the logic function that results.

12. Test the IC negative logic DTL NOR gate you have selected. Connect a negative logic inverter to your negative NOR gate. Measure the overall response.

13. Test your DCTL NOR gate. Compare its performance with that of your other NOR gates.

14. Build and test your ECL NOR gate. Connect your level shifters to the output of your ECL NOR gate and test the overall circuit.

15. Test your integrated ECL NOR gate. Compare the performance of all of your NOR gates.

AND Gates

16. Build and test your DL AND gates. Increase the number of inputs to your gates and observe the effects on the output levels. Connect a clamping circuit to the output of your AND gate and test it.

17. Connect your DL OR gate to the output of your DL AND gate and see if the resulting circuit can be made to operate by adjusting R_1, R_2, and $V(1)$ as shown in Fig. 16-31.

18. Test your IC AND gate which utilizes an ECL scheme.

19. Test your IC TTL AND gate and then compare the performances of all your AND gates. Connect some NOT, OR, NOR, and AND gates together to realize some simple Boolean functions.

20. Test your IC AND-OR-invert gate and suggest some possible uses for this gate.

NAND Gates

21. Build and test your DTL NAND gate similar to the one of Fig. 16-23. Leave all but one input open. Apply an input signal to one input only and see how fast the circuit will operate. Connect a NOT gate to the output of your NAND gate and test the overall circuit.

22. Connect an appropriate capacitor C_1 to your NAND gate and measure the speed of response. Compare with step 21. See if C_1 improves the rise time. Measure the storage time for this circuit.

23. Test your IC DTL NAND gate and compare with your discrete NAND gate. Test the fan-in and fan-out capabilities of your IC NAND gate.

24. Build and test your TTL NAND gate similar to the one of Fig. 16-25. Compare with your predicted performance values.

25. Test your IC TTL NAND gate and compare with the discrete form of TTL NAND gate. Compare the performance of all your NAND gates. Construct the circuit of Fig. 16-32 and test it.

26. Build and test the circuit of Fig. 16-33. Which output (v_{o1} or v_{o2}), is the OR function, and which output is the NOR function?

27. (optional) Build and test some logic circuits which realize some complicated Boolean functions you would like to realize.

28. (optional) Run your SCEPTRE programs to test out the logic gates of your choice.

LIST OF EQUIPMENT

1. Cathode-ray oscilloscope.

2. General-purpose voltmeter or ac and dc voltmeter and ohmmeters

3. Signal sources: Function generator or sine-wave oscillator, dc power supplies.

4. Circuit board

5. Components: Resistors, capacitors, transistors, integrated digital circuits

Experiment 17/Flip-Flops and Other Multivibrators

Part One

INTRODUCTION

The flip-flop or bistable multivibrator is one of the most widely used active devices in computer circuitry. A flip-flop (FF) is simply another logic gate which possesses memory. The term flip-flop as used in this experiment represents a generic class of bistable electronic circuits that operate on a regenerative feedback principle. These bistable electronic circuits have two stable output states and the capability of changing from one output state to another with the application of an input control signal. In addition, the output remains in a state permanently after the removal of the input signal. The latter capability differentiates the flip-flop from other gates having two output states but requiring the retention of the input signals to remain in a given state. The characteristic of two stable output states also differentiates a flip-flop from a monostable multivibrator, which keeps returning to a specific state, and an astable multivibrator, which keeps changing from one output state to the other. The monostable multivibrator is frequently used as a pulse stretcher, while the astable multivibrator is commonly used as a clock pulse generator.

In this experiment we will study the RS, JK, and T flip-flops as well as a few monostable and astable multivibrators. Both the discrete and integrated circuit forms of these devices will be presented.

THEORY

Flip-Flops

A bistable multivibrator or flip-flop is obtained by interconnecting two logic gates. The interconnection or feedback from one gate to another generates a new class of logic gates which exhibit memory. They are capable of storing binary digits, and are often called binary circuits. The essential requirements of a flip-flop are the following.

(a) It must be capable of remaining indefinitely in one of two stable states.

(b) There must be at least one output available to "read" its output state.

(c) There must be an external access to change its state.

A flip-flop or binary circuit having essentially symmetrical ON/OFF transition characteristics is given in Fig. 17-1.

A vertical axis of symmetry is shown in Fig. 17-1, and each half of the circuit is a NOT (inverter) gate. Another diagram emphasizing the interconnection of the two NOT gates of Fig. 17-1 is shown in Fig. 17-2.

The important memory characteristic of the flip-flop of Fig. 17-1 is due to the feedback through resistors R_1 and R_2. The circuit may persist in a state in which one device (say, Q_2) is ON while the other (Q_1) is OFF. Thus $Y = 0$. and $\overline{Y} = 1$. This is considered as one possible stable state. A second stable state is one in which Q_2 is OFF and Q_1 is ON. In this stable state, the outputs are $Y = 1$ and $\overline{Y} = 0$.

In order to verify that the circuit of Fig. 17-1 can exist in a stable state, we assume that Q_2 is ON and Q_1 is OFF and then verify this assumption. Typical circuit parameters are $V_{CC} = -V_{BB} = 5$, $R_1 = R_2 = 5$ k, $R_{B1} = R_{B2} = 10$ k, $R_{C1} = R_{C2} = 500$, $V_{BE(\text{sat})} = .7$, $V_{CE(\text{sat})} = .2$, and $(h_{FE})_{\min} = 100$.

$$I_{C2} = \frac{5 - .2}{.5\text{ k}} - \frac{5 + .2}{15\text{ k}} = (9.6 - .35)\text{ mA} = 9.25\text{ mA} \tag{17-1}$$

$$I_{B2} = \frac{5 - .7}{5.5\text{ k}} - \frac{5 + .7}{10\text{ k}} = (.78 - .57)\text{ mA} = .21\text{ mA} \tag{17-2}$$

Thus $I_{C2} = 9.2$ mA $< (h_{FE})_{\min} I_{B2} = (100)(.21\text{ mA}) = 21$ mA, and Q_2 is saturated. The base voltage of Q_1 is

$$v_{B1} = \frac{5\text{ k}}{(10 + 5)\text{ k}}(-5) + \frac{10\text{ k}}{15\text{ k}}(.2) = -1.53\text{ V} \tag{17-3}$$

This back bias has Q_1 cut off. The collector of Q_1 is

$$v_{C1} = 5 - (500)(.78\text{ mA}) = 4.6\text{ V} \tag{17-4}$$

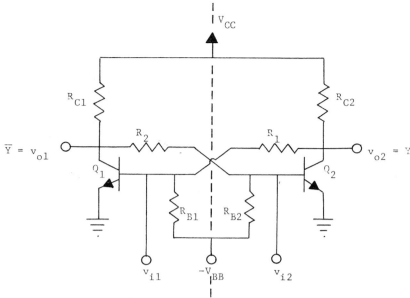

Fig. 17.1 Flip-flop (binary) circuit.

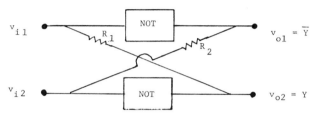

Fig. 17.2 Interconnection of two NOT gates (binary).

Thus the stable state currents and voltages when $Y = 0$ and $\overline{Y} = 1$ are

$$Q_1 : I_{B1} = I_{C1} = 0, \quad v_{C1} = 4.6 \text{ V}, \quad v_{B1} = -1.53 \text{ V}$$

$$Q_2 : I_{B2} = .21 \text{ mA}, \quad I_{C2} = 9.25 \text{ mA}, \quad v_{C2} = .2 \text{ V}, \quad v_{B2} = .7 \text{ V}$$

The output swing of the flip-flop is $4.6 - .2 = 4.4$ V.

Again assume that the circuit of Fig. 17-1 is in a stable state with Q_1 cutoff and Q_2 saturated. The circuit can now be made to regenerate by applying an external input signal to the base of Q_2. The input signal is assumed to be applied in the form of a short pulse, referred to as the "trigger pulse." In this case, a negative trigger pulse is applied to the base of Q_2 to bring Q_2 out of saturation and cause the transistor operating point to move into the active region. As the loop gain becomes greater than unity (see Experiment 13), the circuit will regenerate through R_1 and R_2 until Q_2 is driven OFF and Q_1 is ON. Following a certain amount of storage time delay t_s, which is usually very small, Q_2 will come into the active region and the collector of Q_2 will begin to rise. At some point, the collector of Q_2 will have risen sufficiently to allow Q_1 to come out of cutoff. After a brief delay, which is the normal turn-on delay associated with a cutoff transistor and which is usually larger than the storage time delay, the collector of

Q_1 will begin to drop, causing regeneration to occur. If speed-up capacitors C_1 and C_2 are placed across resistors R_1 and R_2, the collector voltage waveforms for the circuit of Fig. 17-1 are shown in Fig. 17-3. The speed-up or commutating capacitors cause the base of one transistor to respond more rapidly to an abrupt change at the collector

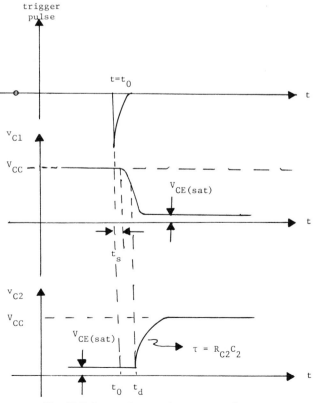

Fig. 17.3 Input trigger and output waveforms.

of the other transistor. In essence, the speed-up capacitors hasten the removal of base charge of a transistor when it switches from saturation to cutoff.

The time required for the collector of Q_2, the transistor being switched OFF, to rise to its equilibrium voltage level is known as the collector recovery time. In applications where it is necessary to switch the flip-flop between states very rapidly, the collector recovery time is obviously undesirable. However, the decrease in the settling or regeneration time afforded by the use of proper-sized speed-up capacitors will more than offset the detrimental recovery or transition effects. The regeneration time constant can be approximated by

$$\tau \approx \frac{R_1 R_2 C_1}{R_1 + R_2} \qquad (17\text{-}5)$$

If we assume that a time of 2τ is allowed between triggers, then the recovery transients will have died down sufficiently so that the flip-flop can be triggered reliably. That is,

$$f_{max} = \frac{1}{2\tau} = \frac{R_1 + R_2}{2C_1 R_1 R_2} \qquad (17\text{-}6)$$

A slower switching speed would be achieved if the two inverter circuits were directly connected together without the use of resistors R_1 and R_2. This is called a dc flip-flop, and has the advantage of extreme simplicity. It can be constructed as an integrated circuit, and will be discussed in the section on RS flip-flops.

Other types of binaries include the self-biased and Schmitt trigger or emitter-coupled binary. Examples of these devices are shown in Figs. 17–4 and 17–5, respectively.

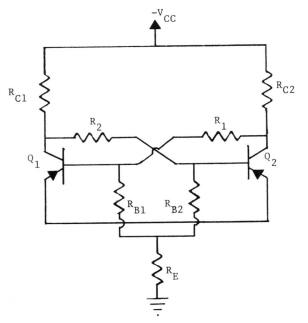

Fig. 17.4 Self-biased binary.

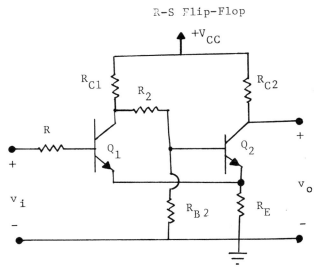

Fig. 17.5 Schmitt trigger circuit.

The advantage of the self-biased binary of Fig. 17–4 is in the elimination of one power supply. Its operation is similar to that of the collector-coupled binary of Fig. 17–1. The Schmitt trigger of Fig. 17–5 has the advantage of fast switching times, and can be triggered on nonpulse inputs. It can be used as a waveform restorer, signal-level shifter, and dc-level detector. It differs from the conventional bistable multivibrator in that one of the coupling networks is replaced by a common-emitter transistor, which augments feedback in order to obtain faster switching time. The feedback between Q_1 and Q_2 is preceded by connection of two emitters. If both transistors are temporarily assumed to be in their active region, then a positive signal at the base of Q_1 will cause the voltage at the collector of Q_1 to drop, which is then coupled as a negative signal for the base of Q_2. The emitter voltage of Q_2 will then drop, causing the emitter voltage of Q_1 to drop. Thus, the initial positive base-emitter signal is reinforced, and regeneration takes place. After the input trigger pulse, regeneration will take place until one or both transistors are driven out of the active region and the circuit becomes stable. This action causes the output state to depend upon the amplitude of the input voltage. A speed-up capacitor C can be added across R_2, and it may also be desirable to limit the ON base current to each transistor in order to minimize the storage time delays.

A Schmitt trigger in an integrated circuit form in shown in Fig. 17–6. A basic ECL NOR gate (MC306 type) is used in which two external resistors (R_F and R_i) are added. The NOR output (pin 5) is connected to the bias reference (pin 1) through a feedback resistor R_F. The operation of the circuit is basically the same as that of Fig. 17–5.

The application of a sinusoidal input to the Schmitt trigger of Fig. 17–6 will yield the pulsed output of Fig. 17–7.

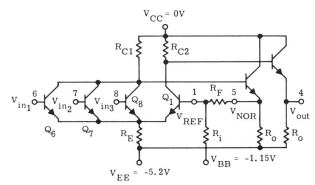

Fig. 17.6 IC Schmitt trigger.

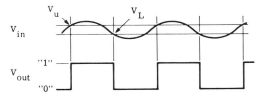

Fig. 17.7 Input and output waveforms.

The voltages V_u and V_L are given by $V_{BB} + (R_i/(R_i + R_F)) \cdot (V_{NOR} - V_{BB})$ depending on whether $V_{NOR} - V_{BB}$ is positive or negative. Typically V_{NOR} has a low value of -1.55 V and a high value of $-.75$ V. If $R_i = 500$, $R_F = 100$ and $V_{out} = V_{NOR} = -.75$, then $V_{in} = V_u = -1.0$. If $V_{out} = V_{NOR} = -1.55$, then $V_{in} = V_L = -1.25$.

One of the essential requirements of a flip-flop is that

there be an external access to change its state by means of a pulse and/or level signal. Triggering circuits (steering networks) are added to a basic flip-flop in order for an external pulse and/or level signal to be accessed to the flip-flop. The circuit of Fig. 17–8 contains the flip-flop of Fig. 17–1 and a symmetrical steering network.

The trigger capacitors C_T charge and discharge in such a manner that nodes A and B follow the collectors of Q_1 and Q_2, respectively. The flip-flop is triggered with each negative excursion of the input signal. In particular, if the triggering circuit is in the steady state and Q_1 is ON and Q_2 is OFF, the voltage at node A will be $V_{CE(sat)} = V(0)$ and the voltage at node B will be $(R_1/(R_1 + R_{C2}))$ V_{CC}. The diode D_2 has a large reverse bias, while D_1 has a small reverse bias. An incoming pulse will now forward-bias D_1 and turn Q_1 OFF and Q_2 ON. This process is repeated for opposite conditions when the next input triggering pulse occurs. As a first approximation, the value of C_T is given by

$$C_T = K \frac{Q_B}{V_{CC}} \qquad (17\text{–}7)$$

where Q_B is the total stored base charge and K is an empirical safety factor ranging between 1.5 and 2.0. If the rise time of the triggering pulse is long, then it can be shown that

$$C_T \geqslant \frac{K(Q_B + t_r I_{B1})}{.8 V_p}$$

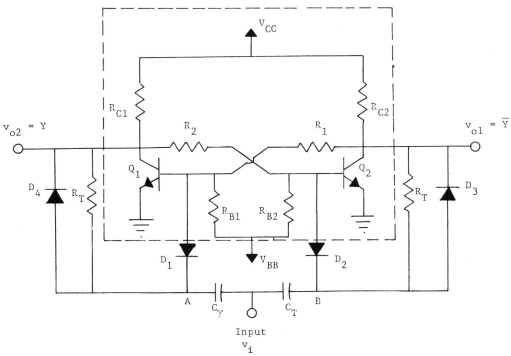

Fig. 17.8 Flip-flop with symmetrical steering network.

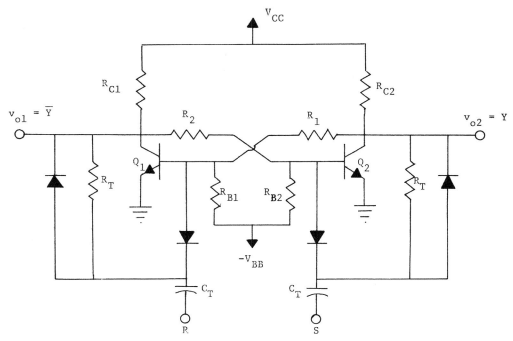

Fig. 17.9 Flip-flop with unsymmetrical trigger.

where V_p is the trigger pulse amplitude, I_{B1} is the base current supplied to the ON transistor, and t_r is the voltage rise time of the trigger pulse. In addition, R_T should be large to minimize loading, but $R_T C_T$ should be small to permit recovery of the steering network within a regeneration cycle. When speed-up diodes D_3 and D_4 are not used, the condition $3R_T C_T < \tau_p/2$ must be met. The quantity τ_p is the period of the trigger pulse. If D_3 and D_4 are used, then $.7R_T C_T < \tau_p/2$. Finally, the diodes should have a recovery time in the order of the flip-flop regenera-

tion time, and the capacitance of the diodes should be much lower than the circuit capacitances.

A flip-flop can also be triggered unsymmetrically, as shown in Fig. 17-9.

For a positive logic system, the output Y is taken from the collector of the *npn* transistor, say, Q_2. The output $\overline{Y}$ is taken from the collector of Q_1. The triggering signal is a negative pulse, and is applied at the terminal labeled S, which stands for "set." After the pulse excitation, Q_2 will be OFF and Q_2 ON, so that $Y = 1$ and $\overline{Y} = 0$. This is

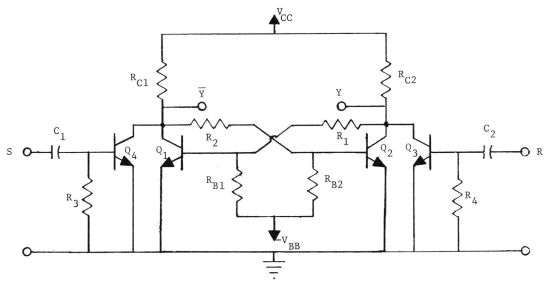

Fig. 17.10 Flip-flop with input amplifiers.

called the set state. Similarly, after a triggering signal is applied at the reset terminal R, Q_2 will be ON and Q_1 OFF, so that $Y = 0$ and $\overline{Y} = 1$. This is the reset state. The total circuit of Fig. 17-9 is often called a set-reset binary (RS flip-flop), and will be described in more detail in the next section.

If the trigger amplitude available is small, it may be necessary to amplify this signal before applying it to a flip-flop. The circuit of Fig. 17-10 is a flip-flop, with transistors Q_3 and Q_4 providing the required amplification.

This circuit can be simply realized in integrated circuit form when transistors Q_2 and Q_3 are provided by one NOR gate and Q_1 and Q_4 by another NOR gate. The proper interconnection of these two NOR gates realizes an RS flip-flop similar to the one of Fig. 17-10.

RS Flip-Flops

It was shown that the circuit of Fig. 17-2 has two stable states with v_{o1} and v_{o2} having complementary values. In the case where v_{o1} and v_{o2} are forced to both be 1 (or 0), the circuit is unstable because it cannot remain in that condition when the forcing inputs are removed. In fact, if the inputs are removed one at a time, the flip-flop will remember the last one present. During the time while v_{o1} and v_{o2} are forced to the same level, each NOT circuit is attempting without success to change its output to the complementary level. Consequently, when both forcing inputs are removed simultaneously, a race exists between the two NOT gates to change states. The faster NOT gate wins because its change holds the other NOT gate in the original state forced on it by the input. Thus it is clearly desirable to have the inputs separated from the outputs. This separation can be achieved, for example, by having an OR gate precede each NOT gate. The circuit of Fig. 17-11 implements such a modification, while Fig. 17-12 is the equivalent using two NOR gates.

It should be apparent that the bistable quality is still inherent in the circuit of Fig. 17-12. However, the effect of the possible input combinations on the output needs to be determined. Suppose that the initial state $v_{o1} = 0$ and the inputs $v_{i1} = v_{i2} = 0$. NOR gate N_2 has an output

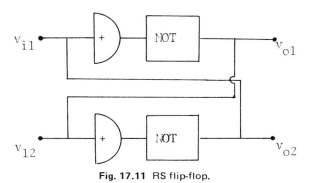

Fig. 17.11 RS flip-flop.

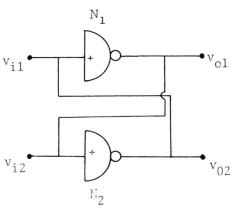

Fig. 17.12 RS flip-flop.

$v_{o2} = 1$ since both of its inputs v_{i2} and v_{o1} are zero. Thus NOR gate N_1 has an output of 0 regardless of the value of v_{i1}, and the circuit is stable. If v_{o1} is 0 and the inputs are now changed to $v_{i2} = 1$ and $v_{i1} = 0$, it can be shown that a new stable state $v_{o1} = 1$ results, while $v_{o2} = 0$. If the initial state v_{o1} is 0 and the inputs are $v_{i1} = v_{i2} = 1$, then $v_{o1} = v_{o2} = 0$. Now the outputs are not complementary, and a third stable state occurs as long as both inputs are present at the 1 level.

Now, if v_{i1} is changed to 0 while $v_{i2} = 1$, the output v_{o1} changes to 1 and $v_{o2} = 0$. At this point, let v_{o2} change to 0—that is, both inputs are zero; the circuit now remains stable, with $v_{o1} = 1$ and $v_{o2} = 0$. Taking the opposite situation, with $v_{i1} = 1$ and v_{i2} changed to zero, produces an output change of $v_{o2} = 1$ and $v_{o1} = 0$. Now, letting v_{i1} change to 0 (both inputs 0), the circuit remains stable, with $v_{o1} = 0$ and $v_{o2} = 1$. We can now conclude that the flip-flop remembers the last input, which was 1, and cannot have both inputs 1 because it cannot be easily predicted which of the inputs was removed last after both have been 1. The circuit of Fig. 17-12 is a simple RS flip-flop with v_{i2} the S terminal, v_{i1} the R terminal, v_{o1} the Q terminal, and v_{o2} the $\overline{Q}$ terminal. A truth table describing the operation of the RS flip-flop is given by Table 17-1.

TABLE 17-1
RS Flip-Flop.

R	S	Q^{n+1}
0	0	Q^n
0	1	1
1	0	0
1	1	X

The Q^{n+1} column shows the resulting next state of the flip-flop read from the Q output. When both R and S are 0, the table indicates that the next state is Q^n, meaning that the output of the flip-flop remains in the same state. If $R = 0$ and $S = 1$, the flip-flop's next state is 1, meaning that the circuit is set to a 1. The previous state Q^n could have been a 1, in which case there would be no change in state; or Q^n could have been 0, whereupon its state would change to 1. Similarly, when $R = 1$ and $S = 0$, the next state $Q^{n+1} = 0$ and the circuit is reset to 0, which may or may not constitute a change of state. The X in the last row means that, for inputs $R = S = 1$, the next state is indeterminate and this pair of inputs is forbidden. This is sometimes labeled *DC* meaning "don't care."

A realization of the RS flip-flop using discrete components is shown in Fig. 17–9, while an integrated form can be constructed by interconnecting DTL NOR gates with typical response times of 30 to 50 nanoseconds and a fan-out of 10. By using TTL NOR gates, the switching time can be reduced to 10 to 20 nanoseconds; with ECL NOR gates, switching times of under 5 nanoseconds can be achieved.

An IC flip-flop type MC352A using ECL gates is shown in Fig. 17–13.

IC flip-flops designed exclusively for RS operation are not always available in every type of realization because of limited usage. Other types of flip-flops, such as the JK flip-flop described in the next section, can be converted to the simple RS type of flip-flop.

Another form of the RS flip-flop can be designed with NAND gates, as shown in Fig. 17–14.

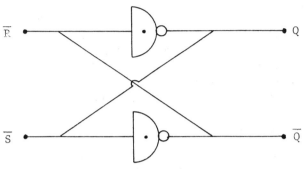

Fig. 17.14 RS flip-flop.

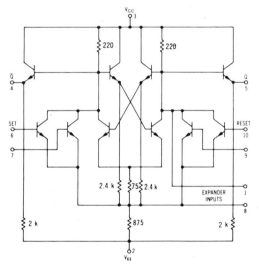

Fig. 17.13 IC flip-flop with ECL scheme.

The advantage of designing flip-flops with NAND gates is that they can be easily designed for clocking of the inputs. Clocked or gated operation, known also as synchronous operation, is essential for the proper functioning of many complex digital systems. Thus far, only asynchronous flip-flops have been discussed with terminals through which data can be entered but only upon command of the clock. A clocked or gated RS flip-flop using four NAND gates is shown in Fig. 17–15.

When the clock pulse is low or OFF, $(\bar{R})$ and $(\bar{S})$ are 1's and the flip-flop rests. During the time of a clock pulse, NAND gates N_1 and N_2 are enabled, and the state of the flip-flop is set or reset as a function of the R and S inputs at that time. Thus the flip-flop responds to input levels only during the time interval specified by the clock pulse.

Another feature desired for the flip-flop of Fig. 17–15 is a direct, asynchronous or unclocked, set and reset

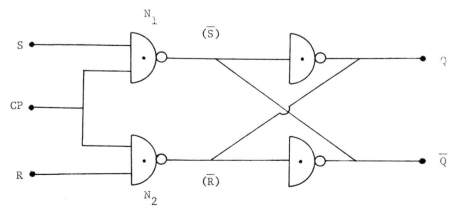

Fig. 17.15 Gated RS flip-flop.

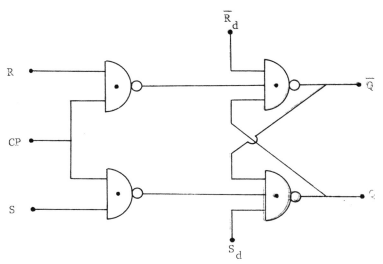

Fig. 17.16 Clocked flip-flop with set and reset.

capability. The circuit of Fig. 17-15 may be easily modified to handle this requirement by using a third input to
each of the cross-coupled NAND gates. However, the direct
set and reset inputs, indicated by S_d and R_d, must be in-
verted. That is, they both should be normally at the one
level and the selected direct input brought to the zero level
for direct setting or resetting. As before, they should not
both be brought to the zero level simultaneously. This
modification has been incorporated in the circuit shown in
Fig. 17-16, which represents a fairly versatile memory
element.

The RS flip-flop can also be converted into a type D gated
flip-flop, used primarily in shift registers and counters.
The truth table (Table 17-2) and realization (Fig. 17-17)
for a type D (delayed) flip-flop follow from the basic
memory element of Fig. 17-16. The type D flip-flop behaves as a delay line, having a delay time of one clock

TABLE 17-2
D Flip-Flop.

D	Q^{n+1}
0	0
1	1

interval. The next state Q^{n+1} is clearly not a function of
the present state Q^n, and the realization requires merely
an inverter to provide the S input, which replaces the
R input.

The RS flip-flop can also be converted to a RST flip-flop.
The implementation (Fig. 17-18) follows from the truth
table (Table 17-3). The T, or toggle input, causes the
flip-flop to change states.

The asynchronous version of the RST flip-flop has been
employed often in counter circuits in which the R and S

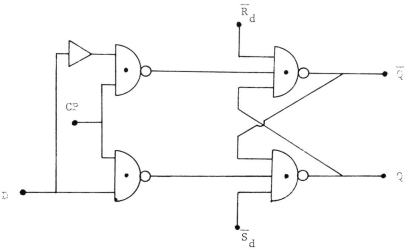

Fig. 17.17 Interconnection of gates for D flip-flop.

TABLE 17–3
RST Flip-Flop.

R	S	T	Q^{n+1}
0	0	0	Q^n
0	1	0	1
1	0	0	0
1	0	0	X
0	0	1	$\overline{Q}^n$
0	1	1	X
1	0	1	X
1	1	1	X

inputs are used for clearing and presetting the flip-flop. However, it is difficult to find an advantage of the synchronous version of the RST (Fig. 17–18) compared with the synchronous JK flip-flop that is discussed in the next section. In fact, the RST was the forerunner of the JK flip-flop; the latter possesses the same desirable trigger

capability without the four indeterminate inputs of the RST.

JK Flip-Flops

A truth table for the JK flip-flop is given in Table 17–4. Its advantage over the RS flip-flop is that all input combinations of J and K are valid and a fewer number of components are required in its realization.

TABLE 17–4
JK Flip-Flop.

J	K	Q^{n+1}
0	0	Q^n
0	1	0
1	0	1
1	1	$\overline{Q}^n$

An RS flip-flop could be operated satisfactorily as a JK type if suitable steering networks are provided at the inputs to accommodate simultaneous 1 inputs at S and R. Steering is provided, as shown in Fig. 17–19, by connecting one side of the input differentiating network resistors to Q and $\overline{Q}$.

The operation of this JK flip-flop can be verified if we first assume that it is set and $J = K = 0$. Then C_1 and C_2 will be charged to approximately 0 and V_0 volts respectively. If now a logical 1 (positive pulse) is applied to both J and K, the voltage on C_2 will block the input at J, but the input at K will be differentiated by C_1 and R_1. The trailing edge of the input pulse will then pass through D_1 and cut Q_1 OFF. The flip-flop is now reset, and causes C_2 to discharge to $\approx 0V$ and C_1 to charge to some voltage ($\approx V_0$). A second input (1) to J and K will now be steered to Q_2 as required.

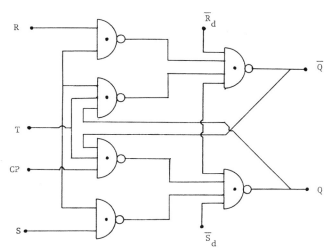

Fig. 17.18 Clocked RST flip-flop.

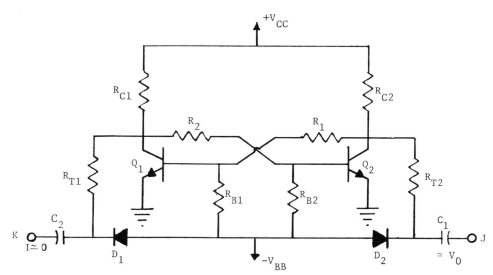

Fig. 17.19 JK flip-flop.

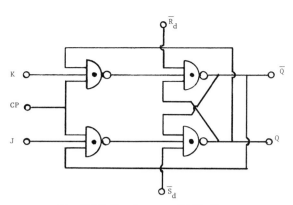

Fig. 17.20 Synchronous JK flip-flop.

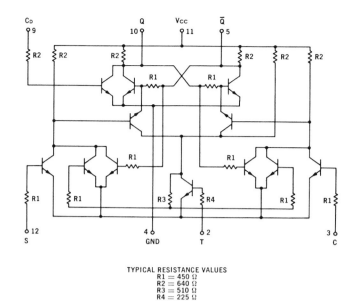

TYPICAL RESISTANCE VALUES
R1 = 450 Ω
R2 = 640 Ω
R3 = 510 Ω
R4 = 225 Ω

Fig. 17.21 IC JK flip-flop using RTL scheme.

A logic diagram representation of a synchronous JK flip-flop is given in Fig. 17–20.

An inexpensive integrated circuit RTL scheme which realizes a JK flip-flop and has a direct clear input in addition to the clocked input is shown in Fig. 17–21. This is a MC723P device.

For reliable synchronous operation of a group of flip-flops in a system, it is necessary to provide a means of temporary storage at the input (or, equivalently, the output) of each flip-flop. At a clock time when a particular flip-flop is sampling its input (S), its output is being sampled to drive gates and other flip-flops. Thus, there is a need for some method of holding, say, the input levels to each flip-flop after the inputs themselves are removed, so that variations in each flip-flop's response time is tolerable within a specified range. A method for accomplishing this is to use two flip-flops, a master and a slave, interconnected so that the output of the master is used as the input to the slave with the transfer controlled as follows. At clock time CP, the external inputs to the master flip-flop are gated in to set or reset it, while the master's output is inhibited from setting or resetting the slave flip-flop. At nonclock time $\overline{CP}$,

the inputs to the master are inhibited, while the state of the master is gated in to set or reset the slave. The slave remains stable throughout the rest of $\overline{CP}$ and the next CP period.

An inexpensive integrated circuit TTL JK master-slave flip-flop employing four NAND gates, four AND gates, and two NOR gates is given in Figs. 17–22 and 17–23. This circuit is a Texas Instruments type SN 7472. Typical values are $V_{CC} = 5$, $V(1) = 3.5$, $V(0) = .22$, and a maximum clock frequency of approximately 20 MHz. Observe that the clocking of master and slave flip-flops is accomplished by a single clock pulse. The leading edge of the clock pulse permits the master flip-flop to be set or reset. The trailing edge of the clock pulse can then be used to enable the slave flip-flop.

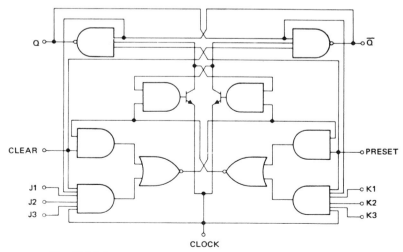

Fig. 17.22 Interconnection of gates for JK master slave flip-flop.

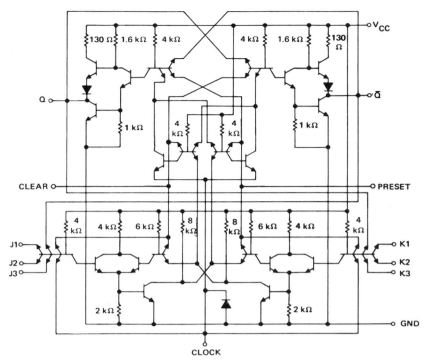

Fig. 17.23 JK master slave flip-flop using TTL scheme.

Monostable Multivibrator

The monostable multivibrator (also called a one-shot multi) is similar to the flip-flop insofar as both are closed-loop devices with positive feedback. In the monostable circuit, an energy storage element, usually a capacitor, is introduced in series with the feedback loop. This creates a device with one stable state and one quasistable state. The circuit rests in the stable state until triggered by an input excitation signal, and then positive feedback causes the device to switch into the quasistable state. The circuit remains in the quasistable state for a fixed time, determined by the circuit component values, and then switches back to the stable state. The monostable multi is used to generate rectangular output pulses of a predetermined width, and is often called a pulse stretcher. The circuit of Fig. 17–24 is a monostable multi.

When the monostable multi is in the stable state, Q_2 is biased into saturation by R_{B2} and V_{CC}. The output is then equal to $V_{CE(sat)}$, and Q_1 is cut off by the reverse bias

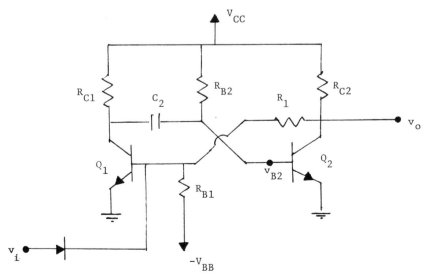

Fig. 17.24 Monostable multivibrator.

supplied by V_{BB}, R_1, and R_{B1}. In the stable state, capacitor C_2 charges to $V_{CC} - V_{BE(sat)}$. Saturation of Q_2 yields

$$I_{C2(sat)} = \frac{V_{CC} - V_{CE(sat)}}{R_{C2}} - \frac{V_{CE(sat)} - V_{BB}}{R_1 + R_{B1}} \approx \frac{V_{CC}}{R_{C2}} \tag{17-8}$$

the minimum value of I_{B2} required is

$$(I_{B2})_{min} = \frac{I_{C2(sat)}}{(h_{FE})_{min}} \tag{17-9}$$

and the maximum value of R_{B2} is

$$R_{B2} = \frac{V_{CC} - V_{BE(sat)}}{(I_{B2})_{min}} \tag{17-10}$$

Excluding the leakage current of transistor Q_1 when in cutoff, the base voltage of Q_1 is

$$v_{B1} = \frac{-R_1}{R_1 + R_{B1}} V_{BB} + \frac{R_{B1}}{R_1 + R_{B1}} V_{CE(sat)} \tag{17-11}$$

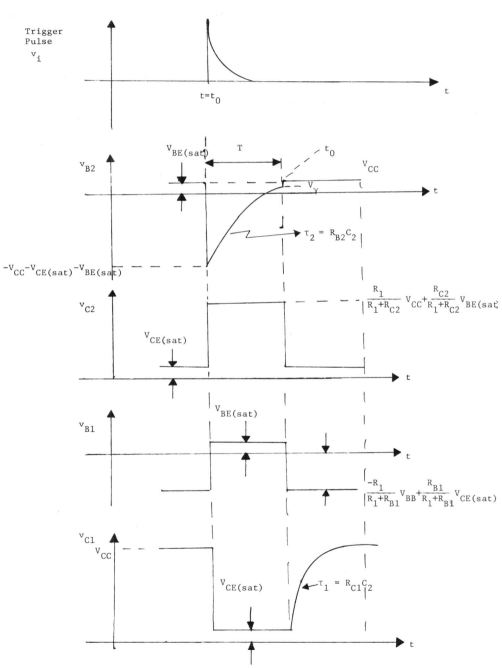

Fig. 17.25 Input and output waveforms.

A positive input excitation pulse of sufficient amplitude and duration will cause the monostable multi to change to the quasistable state. Now transistor Q_1 will turn ON, and regeneration will cause a transition in the state of Q_2 and will turn Q_2 OFF. The collector and base waveforms are given in Fig. 17-25. The effects of $r_{bb'}$ and leakage currents are neglected in these waveforms.

The monostable period T, which is defined as the time during which Q_2 is in the OFF state, can be calculated as follows

$$v_{B2} = V_{CC} - [2V_{CC} - V_{BE(sat)} - V_{CE(sat)}] e^{-(t/R_{B2}C_2)}$$
(17-12)

and when v_{B2} equals the cut-in voltage V_γ of Q_2, the circuit switches back to the stable state.

$$V_\gamma = V_{CC} - [2V_{CC} - V_{BE(sat)} - V_{CE(sat)}] e^{-(T/R_{B2}C_2)}$$
(17-13)

or

$$T = R_{B2} C_2 \ln \frac{2V_{CC} - V_{BE(sat)} - V_{CE(sat)}}{V_{CC} - V_\gamma}$$
(17-14)

If we neglect $V_{BE(sat)}$, $V_{CE(sat)}$, and V_γ, the gate width T is

$$T \approx R_{B2} C_2 \ln 2 = .69 R_{B2} C_2$$
(17-15)

Integrated circuit monostable multi's are available on a single chip. A DTL scheme (MC 951), having both an internal timing network and provisions for connecting external timing capacitors and resistors, is shown in Fig. 17-26. When using an external capacitor C_{ext} in picofarads

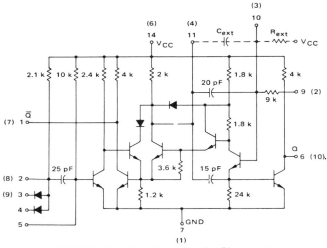

NOTE: When the internal timing resistor (9 kΩ) is to be used, connect Pin 9 to Pin 14 (flat and dual in-line packages) or pins 2 and 6 (can). DO NOT MAKE THIS CONNECTION IF USING THE EXTERNAL CAPACITOR AND RESISTOR.

Number at end of terminal represents pin number for flat and dual in-line packages. Number in parenthesis indicates pin number for metal can.

Fig. 17.26 IC monostable multivibrator.

and resistor R_{ext} between 9 kΩ and 15 kΩ, the manufacturer specifies that the pulse width in nanoseconds can be approximated by

$$T \approx .5 R_{ext} (C_{ext} + 20)$$
(17-16)

Astable Multivibrator

The astable multivibrator is a closed-loop regenerative feedback device similar to the monostable multivibrator except that it is free-running and does not require external triggering. The free-running operation is achieved because there is no dc coupling between transistors, and thus the loop transmission at dc is always less than 1. The output switches between quasistable states. A discrete circuit design of an astable multivibrator is given in Fig. 17-27.

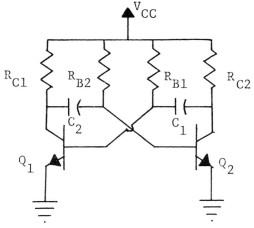

Fig. 17.27 Astable multivibrator.

The output from the collectors of the astable multivibrator of Fig. 17-27 approximates a continuous squarewave. The circuit operates by alternately switching one transistor ON and the other transistor OFF. If we neglect junction voltages and assume that capacitors C_1 and C_2 alternately charge to V_{CC} through R_{B1} and R_{B2}, respectively, then the time t_1 during which Q_2 is OFF can be determined from the charging equation of the base voltage v_{B2}

$$v_{B2} = V_{CC} - 2V_{CC}e^{-(t/R_{B2}C_2)}$$
(17-17)

At $t = t_1$, $v_{B2}(t = t_1) = 0$, and

$$t_1 = R_{B2} C_2 \ln 2$$
(17-18)

Similarly the time t_2, during which Q_1 is OFF, is

$$t_2 = R_{B1} C_1 \ln 2$$
(17-19)

The total period is

$$T = t_1 + t_2 = (R_{B1} C_1 + R_{B2} C_2) \ln 2$$
(17-20)

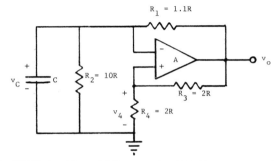

Fig. 17.28 Astable multivibrator using IC differential amplifier.

One limitation of the astable multi shown in Fig. 17-27 is that is may not always turn ON when the power supply is turned ON. This is due to the fact that both transistors Q_1 and Q_2 can simultaneously be ON. In addition, it may not be possible to adjust the period precisely when used for timing in clocked digital circuits. Thus, a more recent design approach is to use linear integrated circuit amplifiers

(see Experiments 13 and 14). The circuit of Fig. 17-28 cannot "lock up" in either output state, and is self-starting.

Assuming that the output saturates at V_S, then $v_4 = \dfrac{2R}{2R + 2R} V_S = \frac{1}{2} V_S$. The capacitor now charges to $\frac{1}{2} V_S$, and the output switches to $-V_S$. This action is identical to that of the Schmitt trigger discussed previously. The time t_1 for C to charge from $\frac{1}{2} V_S$ to $-\frac{1}{2} V_S$ is

$$- \frac{1}{2} V_S = \frac{-10}{11.1} V_S + \left[- \frac{1}{2} V_S - \frac{10}{11.1} V_S \right] e^{-(t_1/RC)}$$

$$(17\text{-}21)$$

$$t_1 = RC \ln \frac{\dfrac{1}{2} - \dfrac{10}{11.1}}{\dfrac{1}{2} + \dfrac{10}{11.1}} = 1.25 RC \qquad (17\text{-}22)$$

The total period of this astable multi is

$$T = 2 t_1 = 2.5 RC$$

Part Two

OBJECTIVE

The purpose of this experiment is to study the operation of several flip-flops and other multivibrators. Several discrete multivibrators will be designed and tested. In addition, integrated circuit versions of some of these circuits will also be studied.

REFERENCES

Chirlian, P. M., *Analysis and Design of Electronic Circuits*. New York: McGraw-Hill, 1965, Chapter 15.

Fitchen, F. C., *Transistor Circuit Analysis and Design*. New York: Van Nostrand Reinhold 1966, Chapter 13.

Fitchen, F. C., *Electronic Integrated Circuits and Systems*. New York: Van Nostrand Reinhold, 1970, Chapter 10.

Ghausi, M. S., *Electronic Circuits: Devices, Models, Functions, Analysis, and Design*. New York: Van Nostrand Reinhold, 1971, Chapters 10 and 11.

Gray, P. E., and Searle, C. L., *Electronic Principles: Physics, Models, and Circuits*. New York: Wiley, 1967, Chapter 24.

Millman, J., and Taub, H., *Pulse, Digital, and Switching Waveforms*. New York: McGraw-Hill, 1965, Chapters 10 and 11.

Pettit, J. M., and McWhorter, M. M., *Electronic Switching, Timing, and Pulse Circuits*. New York: McGraw-Hill, 1970, Chapter 5.

Strauss, L., *Wave Generation and Shaping*. New York: McGraw-Hill, 1970, Chapters 8, 9, and 10.

LABORATORY PREPARATION

1. The flip-flop of Fig. 17-1 is to be designed using readily available supply voltages and transistors. Power dis-

sipation is relatively unimportant in this design, and room-temperature operation can be assumed.

2. Select a *pnp* transistor with characteristics similar to the *npn* transistor of step 1. Equal but opposite power supplies from step 1 will now be used. Give a detailed analysis of this circuit.

3. Assume a maximum frequency of operation of 1 MHz and allow two time constants between triggers. Solve for the value of speed-up capacitors C_1 and C_2 placed across R_1 and R_2, respectively. Standard values of capacitors near these calculated values will be used.

4. Design a symmetrical triggering circuit similar to the one of Fig. 17-8. What are reasonable values for R_T and C_T? What are the minimum amplitude and pulse width of the triggering pulse for your circuit?

5. Design another symmetrical triggering circuit as shown in Fig. 17-29. What should the minimum amplitude and pulse width of the triggering pulse v_i be?

6. Design a self-biased transistor flip-flop similar to the one of Fig. 17-4. Assume f_{max} = 200 kHz and R_E = 270 Ω. Describe the operation of the circuit and compare with the binary of Fig. 17-1.

7. Design the Schmitt trigger circuit of Fig. 17-5. Give a detailed analysis of your circuit, including the important waveforms at various points in the circuit. If a sinusoidal waveform is applied to your Schmitt trigger, estimate the amplitude of the output square-wave. At what input levels will your circuit trigger (V_u and V_L)?

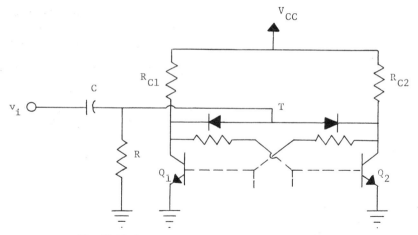

Fig. 17.29 Symmetrical triggering circuit for a flip-flop.

8. What is the phase relationship between v_i and v_o for the Schmitt trigger?

9. Approximately what would the input impedance of the Schmitt trigger be if Q_1 were saturated?

10. What value of capacitance across R_2 would speed up the response of your Schmitt trigger?

11. Select an IC Schmitt trigger such as the MC 306 and study the manufacturer's specifications.

RS Flip-Flops

12. Show that the circuits of Figs. 17–8 and 17–9 are RS flip-flops.

13. Design an RS flip-flop using two IC NOR gates. Prepare a truth table for the RS flip-flop, entering calculated voltages instead of 1's and 0's. Estimate typical response times and fan-out for your RS flip-flop.

14. Select an IC RS flip-flop such as type MC 352A (Fig. 17–13). Study the operation of this circuit and predict from the data given by the manufacturer, what the output waveforms will look like.

15. Design an asynchronous RS flip-flop using two IC NAND gates. Predict the output waveforms for some given inputs.

16. Design a synchronous RS flip-flop using four IC NAND gates. Estimate the response times, the maximum clock frequency, and fan-out of your flip-flop.

17. Design a synchronous RS flip-flop using four IC NAND gates (Fig. 17–16) with direct set and reset capabili-

ties. Estimate the response times and sketch the transient response.

18. Design the type D flip-flop of Fig. 17–17 using an inverter and four NAND gates. Verify truth table 17–2 and study the complete operation of this type of flip-flop. How could this type of flip-flop be used in a digital circuits application?

19. Select an IC type D flip-flop and study the manufacturer's specifications.

20. Design the RST flip-flop using six IC NAND gates as shown in Fig. 17–18. Verify truth table 17–3 and sketch the output and input waveforms.

JK Flip-Flops

21. Design the asynchronous JK flip-flop of Fig. 17–19 and prepare a truth table, entering calculated voltages instead of 1's and 0's.

22. Design the synchronous JK flip-flop of Fig. 17–20 using four NAND gates. Sketch the input and output waveforms, including the clock pulse waveform.

23. Select an IC synchronous JK flip-flop such as MC 723P shown in Fig. 17–21. If the J and K AND inputs are connected in parallel, what happens to the output as the clock goes from high to low?

24. Suppose that the JK flip-flops are connected as shown in Fig. 17–30. Sketch the input and output waveforms and explain the purpose of this circuit.

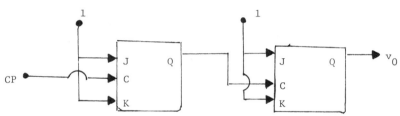

Fig. 17.30 Interconnection of two JK flip-flops.

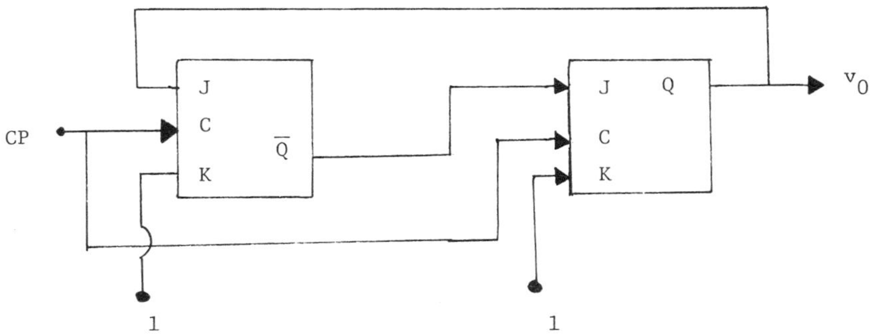

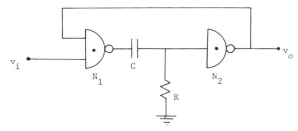

Fig. 17.31 A modulo 3 counter.

25. A modulo 3 counter can be implemented by connecting the JK flip-flops together as shown in Fig. 17-31. Draw the input and output waveforms for this circuit.

26. A JK flip-flop can be converted into a type D flip-flop using a NAND gate, as shown in Fig. 17-32. Verify the truth table for this circuit and sketch the input and output waveforms.

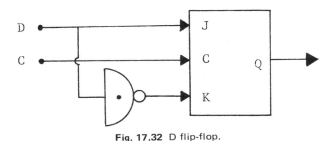

Fig. 17.32 D flip-flop.

27. Select a JK master-slave flip-flop similar to the SN 7472 type shown in Fig. 17-23. Study the manufacturer's specifications in order to understand its operation.

Monostable Multivibrator

28. Design the monostable multivibrator of Fig. 17-24 to have a pulse width of 5 microseconds. The type of transistor required for this circuit is a high-speed switch. The selection of transistor is obtained by comparing the specifications of those available and making a final choice based on price and availability. Good rise time and fall times can be expected from transistors having large f_T's. Also desirable for this kind of circuit are small $V_{CE(\text{sat})}$ and small storage time. Why?

29. Sketch the important waveforms for your monostable multi. What is the polarity of the input waveform?

30. Select an IC monostable multi such as the MC 951 of Fig. 17-26. Study the manufacturer's specifications and design an external timing circuit.

31. Another inexpensive design of a monostable multivibrator can be achieved by using IC NAND gates as shown in Fig. 17-33. Switching to the quasistable state is

Fig. 17.33 Interconnection of IC gates as a monostable multi.

initiated by a negative-going input pulse that is equivalent to a 0 level input. The output of gate N_1 goes high and causes C to charge through R. This couples a 1 level to gate N_2, which drives the output to the 0 level and keeps the output of gate N_1 high. When the voltage across R drops below the 1 threshold level, the output of gate N_2 goes back to the high or stable level. This circuit is used between two logic gates to delay the transmission of the logic level from one gate to another. R is usually in the order of 10 to 1000 ohms and C between .1μ to 1 μ farad.

Astable Multivibrators

32. Design a symmetrical astable multivibrator to operate at 10 kHz. Sketch the waveforms at one base and one collector for the circuit of Fig. 17-27.

33. What is the maximum recovery time that you expect with this circuit? If you double the value of C_1 and C_2, would any redesign be required for correct operation at the new frequency?

34. A free-running emitter-coupled multivibrator is shown in Fig. 17-34. Assume both Q_1 and Q_2 switch between cutoff and saturation. Assume that Q_1 turns ON at V_{BE} = .2 volts, and design the circuit for free-running operation. What is the time constant associated with the turn ON of Q_1? What is the time constant associated with the turn ON of Q_2?

35. Design an astable multivibrator similar to the one of Fig. 17-28 using an IC linear differential amplifier. Estimate the period of your astable multi. Note that the

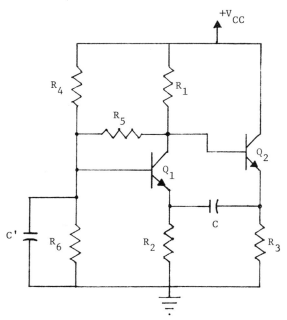

Fig. 17.34 Free running emitter coupled multi.

range of R is limited at the lower end by drift resulting from input offset current. A reasonable range for R is from a few hundred to 25k ohms.

LABORATORY PROCEDURE

Flip-Flops

1. Test the bistable multivibrator corresponding to Fig. 17–1 that you have designed. Test to see if one transistor is ON and the other is OFF. Do the saturation values agree with the manufacturer's specifications? Do the cut-off voltages agree with the designed value? To check that the circuit functions correctly, momentarily connect the OFF collector to ground to force a change of state.

2. Test the bistable circuit with your *pnp* transistors. Compare the measured values with step 1.

3. Drive the flip-flop with a square-wave of sufficient amplitude and frequency. (Usually about 5 to 10 volts and a frequency of 10 kHz will work.) Test the polarity of the drive pulse to see if it matters. Connect speed-up capacitors to your flip-flop and see if they truly do speed up the output response.

4. Connect the symmetrical trigger of Fig. 17–8 to your binary. Vary the amplitude and pulse width of your trigger to measure how it affects the binary's operation. Vary R_T and C_T and observe the Y output and $\overline{Y}$ output simultaneously on your scope. Can you now understand why one output is called Y and the other $\overline{Y}$.

5. Connect the symmetrical triggering circuit of Fig. 17–29 to your binary. Study the waveform at node T. Will the circuit function if R is removed? Test this by re-

moving R. Measure the rise time, fall time, and delay time of the output voltage of the circuit of Fig. 17–29. Test how large v_i must be to reliably drive the flip-flop. Verify that the minimum necessary v_i decreases as C increases. How fast will the circuit flip and flop? Can the maximum frequency be increased by reducing R? (Observe the waveform at node T with maximum triggering frequency and then note the effect of reducing R.)

6. Completely test the self-biased transistor flip-flop you have designed and compare it with your binary of Fig. 17–1.

7. Test the Schmitt trigger you have designed. Observe the waveforms at the bases and collectors Q_1 and Q_2 as well as the emitter of Q_1. Measure V_u and V_L by using a dc supply as v_i. Place a small resistor in series with the emitter of Q_1 (try < 100 ohms) and verify that V_u changes. Drive the circuit of Fig. 17–5 with a direct-coupled ac source having a fixed peak output (set $R = 3.3$k). Sketch v_i and v_o on the same time axis. Measure the relationship between the magnitude of v_i and the width of the output pulse.

8. Measure the relationship between the phase of v_i and v_o.

9. Apply a square-wave input v_i with an amplitude slightly larger than V_u and measure the effect of changing the frequency of v_i.

10. Connect a capacitor C across R_1 (for C in the range of 0 – 500 pf) and repeat step 9.

11. Test the IC Schmitt trigger you have available and compare its operation with the discrete form you have tested.

RS Flip-Flops

12. Test the RS flip-flops of Figs. 17–8 and 17–9 and verify the truth table for them. Start with $Y = 0$ and try $S = 0, R = 1; S = 1, R = 1; S = 1, R = 0; S = 1, R = 1$ in that sequence. Using a pulse generator, investigate the speed of these gates. Measure rise time, propagation delay, and so on. Repeat with Fig. 17–8 connected to Fig. 17–9— that is, connect Y to S and $\overline{Y}$ to R.

13. Test your IC RS flip-flop using two NOR gates. Verify the truth table.

14. Test your IC RS flip-flop such as type MC 352A of Fig. 17–13. Measure the response times and verify the truth table.

15. Test your asynchronous RS flip-flop designed with two NAND gates. Compare its response with the RS flip-flop designed with two NOR gates.

16. Test the synchronous RS flip-flop you designed using four IC NAND gates. Measure the response times and maximum clock frequency if possible.

17. Test your synchronous RS flip-flop using four IC NAND gates (Fig. 17–16). Apply signals to the direct set and reset inputs to verify a complete truth table for this circuit.

18. Test your type D flip-flop of Fig. 17–17. Compare its operation and response times with your other flip-flops.

19. Test an IC type D flip-flop and compare its response with the discrete form of step 18.

20. Test the RST flip-flop of Fig. 17–18 that you designed. Verify truth table 17–3.

JK Flip-Flops

21. Test your asynchronous JK flip-flop of Fig. 17–19.

22. Test your synchronous JK flip-flop of Fig. 17–20.

23. Test your IC synchronous JK flip-flop. Connect the J and K AND gates inputs in parallel and observe the output changes as the clock pulse goes from high to low. Now set J and K to logical 1 and connect a pulse generator to the clock input. Sketch the transient response, and note the dividing action by observing the input and output waveforms.

24. Connect the circuit of Fig. 17–30 and observe how this circuit behaves as a "divider circuit."

25. Connect and test the circuit of Fig. 17–31. Show how this circuit can be used as a counter.

26. Test the circuit of Fig. 17–32. Compare this type D flip-flop with the previous ones studied.

27. Test your integrated circuit JK master-slave flip-flop. Show that the flip-flop alternates output states when clocked if J and K are both 1. Show the effect of a 0 level at the J and K inputs.

Monostable Multivibrators

28. Test your monostable multivibrators of Fig. 17–24. Vary C_2 and R_{B2}, and note the effect on the output waveform. Measure all overshoots and undershoots.

29. Change the polarity of your input waveform, and note the effect on the output.

30. Test your IC monostable multi and compare the maximum pulse width and response times with your discrete circuit form of monostable multi.

31. Test the circuit of Fig. 17–33 for various pulse widths. Measure the maximum input frequency by increasing the frequency of the triggering input until the triggering of successive pulses becomes erratic. The maximum duty cycle is defined as the pulse width divided by the minimum time between input trigger pulses.

Astable Multivibrator

32. Build and test your circuit of Fig. 17–27. Verify the correctness of your predicted waveforms.

33. Test the circuit when both C_1 and C_2 are increased by a factor of 100.

34. Test the free-running emitter-coupled multivibrator you designed. Observe the waveform at the collector of Q_1 and the emitters of Q_1 and Q_2. Measure the period and response time of the circuit.

35. Test your IC astable multivibrator of Fig. 17–28. Vary C and observe the effect on the period.

LIST OF EQUIPMENT

1. Cathode-ray oscilloscope

2. General-purpose voltmeter or ac and dc voltmeters and ohmmeters

3. Signal sources: Function generator or sine-wave oscillator and square-wave oscillator, dc power supplies

4. Circuit board

5. Components: resistors, capacitors, transistors, and integrated circuits

APPENDIX A
MANUFACTURERS' SPECIFICATION SHEETS
for
SOME DEVICES SUGGESTED IN THIS MANUAL

The manufacturers' specifications and circuit diagrams in this manual were supplied courtesy of the following companies:
General Electric
Motorola
RCA
Texas Instruments

SILICON JUNCTION RECTIFIER

These alloy junction silicon rectifiers are intended for low reverse current applications such as magnetic amplifiers. They feature the same hermetically sealed construction and highly efficient junction design which is found in General Electric's 1N536-1N540 Series. The 1N440B Series is recommended wherever low leakage current and high forward conductance are required in rectifier applications.

TYPES 1N440, 1N441, 1N442, 1N443, 1N444, 1N445, 1N440B, 1N441B, 1N442B, 1N443B, 1N444B, 1N445B

RATINGS AND SPECIFICATIONS
(60 CPS, Resistive or Inductive)

	1N440	1N441	1N442	1N443	1N444	1N445	1N440B	1N441B	1N442B	1N443B	1N444B	1N445B	
Transient Peak Reverse Voltage (non-recurrent 5 ms. max. Tj = 0°C to 175°C)	200	350	450	600	700	800	200	350	450	600	700	800	volts
Max. Allowable Peak Reverse Voltage	100	200	300	400	500	600	100	200	300	400	500	600	volts
Max. Allowable RMS Voltage	70	140	210	280	350	420	70	140	210	280	350	420	volts
Max. Allowable Continuous Reverse D.C. Voltage	100	200	300	400	500	600	100	200	300	400	500	600	volts
Max. Allowable D.C. Output Current (at 50°C Ambient)*	300	300	300	300	300	300	750	750	750	750	650	650	ma
Max. Allowable D.C. Output Current (at 100°C Ambient)*	300	300	300	300	300	300	500	500	500	500	425	400	ma
Max. Allowable D.C. Output Current (at 150°C Ambient)*	0	0	0	0	0	0	250	250	250	250	0	0	ma
Max. Allowable Peak Recurrent Forward Current	1.5	1.5	1.5	1.5	1.5	1.5	3.5	3.5	3.5	3.5	3.5	3.5	amps
Max. Allowable One Cycle Surge Current (Peak)	15	15	15	15	15	15	15	15	15	15	15	15	amps
Max. Full Load Voltage Drop (D.C. at 25°C)	1.5	1.5	1.5	1.5	1.5	1.5	1.5	1.5	1.5	1.5	1.5	1.5	volts
Max. Reverse Current (D.C.): at Rated PIV at 25°C	0.30	0.75	1.00	1.50	1.75	2.0	0.30	0.75	1.00	1.50	1.75	2.0	μa
Max. Operating Temperature	150	150	150	150	150	150	165	165	165	165	150	150	°C
Max. Storage Temperature	175	175	175	175	175	175	175	175	175	175	175	175	°C

General Electric Silicon Rectifiers can be furnished to meet rigid military mechanical specifications. Details will be supplied upon request.

*For current ratings at other ambient temperatures, see curve on reverse side.

FEATURES

- **No Heat Sink Required**
- **Axial Leads for Easy Assembly**
- **Ratings up to 165°C. Ambient**
- **Low Forward Drop**
- **Forward Currents Up to ¾ Ampere**
- **Low Leakage at High Temperatures**
- **Operating Reliability Assured Under All Conditions**

OUTLINE DRAWING

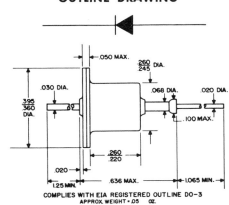

COMPLIES WITH EIA REGISTERED OUTLINE DO-3
APPROX. WEIGHT · .05   OZ.

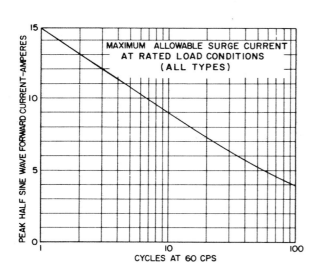

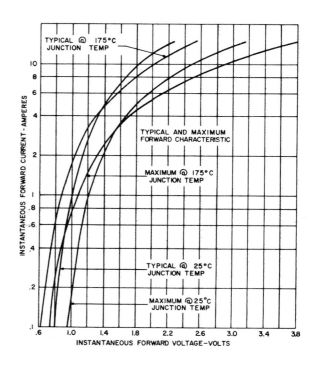

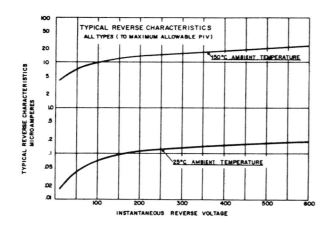

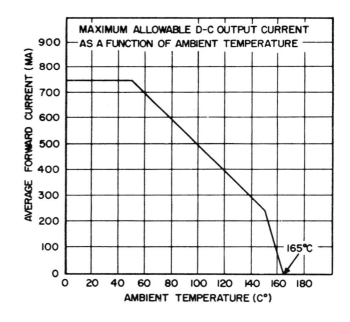

Germanium
Computer — Industrial
Tunnel Diodes

1N3712-20
1N3713-21

The General Electric 1N3712 through 1N3720 and 1N3713 through 1N3721 are Germanium Tunnel Diodes offering peak currents of 1.0, 2.2, 4.7, 10, and 22 ma. These devices, which make use of the quantum mechanical tunneling phenomenon to obtain a negative conductance characteristic, are designed for low level switching and small signal applications at very high frequencies. All 1N3713-1N3721 version parameters are closely controlled for use in critical applications such as level detection, frequency converters, etc. These devices are housed in General Electric's new hermetically sealed subminiature axial package.

FEATURES:

▶ V_FS Specified for more accurate designing of load lines

▶ Low capacitance

▶ Fast speed

absolute maximum ratings

	1N3712 1N3713	1N3714 1N3715	1N3716 1N3717	1N3718 1N3719	1N3720 1N3721	
Forward Current*	5	10	25	50	100	ma
Reverse Current*	10	20	50	50	100	ma
Storage Temperature	←		−55 to +100		→	°C
Lead Temperature ⅟₁₆″ ± ⅟₃₂″ from case for 10 seconds	←		260		→	°C

*Derate maximum currents 1% per °C ambient temperature above 25°C.

AXIAL DIODE OUTLINE

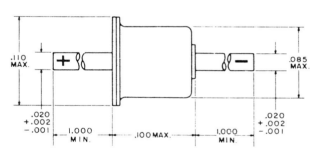

.110 MAX.

.085 MAX.

.020 +.002 −.001   1.000 MIN.   .100 MAX.   1.000 MIN.   .020 +.002 −.001

ALL DIMENSIONS IN INCHES.
DIMENSIONS ARE REFERENCE UNLESS TOLERANCED.

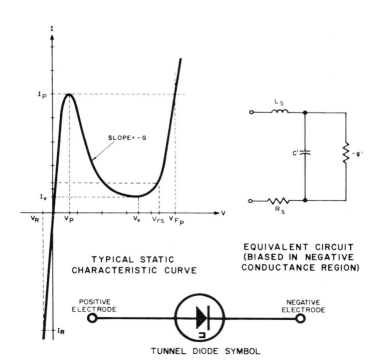

TYPICAL STATIC
CHARACTERISTIC CURVE

EQUIVALENT CIRCUIT
(BIASED IN NEGATIVE
CONDUCTANCE REGION)

POSITIVE ELECTRODE   NEGATIVE ELECTRODE

TUNNEL DIODE SYMBOL

electrical characteristics:

STATIC CHARACTERISTICS		1N3712			1N3713			1N3714			1N3715		
		Min.	Typ.	Max.	Min.	Typ.	Max.	Min.	Typ.	Max.	Min.	Typ.	Max.
Peak Point Current	I_P	0.9	1.0	1.1	0.975	1.000	1.025	2.0	2.2	2.4	2.15	2.20	2.25
Valley Point Current	I_V		0.12	0.18	.075	.095	.140		0.29	0.48	.165	.210	.310
Peak Point Voltage	V_P		65		58	65	72		65		58	65	72
Valley Point Voltage	V_V		350		315	355	395		350		315	355	395
Reverse Voltage ($I_R = I_P$ typ.)	V_R			40	20		40			40	20		40
Forward Voltage ($I_F = I_P$ typ.)	V_{FP}		500		475	510	535		500		475	510	535
► ($I_F = .25\ I_P$ typ.)	V_{FS}*				410	450					410	450	
DYNAMIC CHARACTERISTICS													
Total Series Inductance	L_S		0.5			0.5			0.5			0.5	
Total Series Resistance	R_S		1.5	4.0		1.7	4.0		1.0	3.0		1.1	3.0
► Valley Point Terminal Capacitance	C		5	10		3.5	5.0		10	25		7.0	10.0
Max. Negative Terminal Conductance	-G		8		7.5	8.5	9.5		18		16	19	22
Resistive Cutoff Frequency	f_{ro}		2.3			3.2			2.2			3.0	
Self-Resonant Frequency	f_{xo}		3.2			3.8			2.2			2.7	
Frequency of Oscillation	F_{osc}**		3.2			3.8			2.2			2.7	
► Rise Time	t_r***					1.7						1.6	

*V_{FS} is defined as the value of forward voltage at a forward current of one quarter the typical peak current.
**The frequency of oscillation (under short circuit conditions) for steady state large signal sinusoidal oscillation is given by equation (3) which is the maximum frequency attainable without capacitance compensation.

***Switching speed with constant current drive. $t_r \approx \dfrac{V_{FP} - V_P}{I_P - I_V} C$

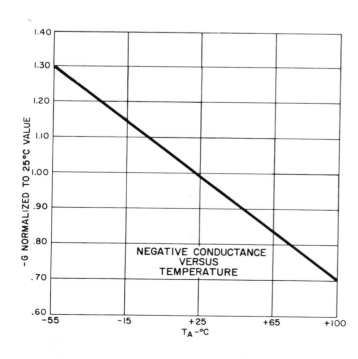

NEGATIVE CONDUCTANCE VERSUS TEMPERATURE

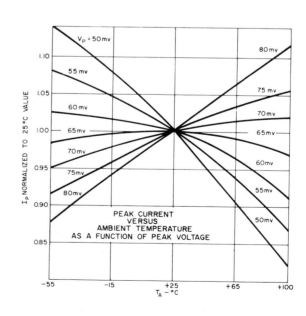

PEAK CURRENT VERSUS AMBIENT TEMPERATURE AS A FUNCTION OF PEAK VOLTAGE

MOTOROLA Semiconductors
BOX 955 • PHOENIX, ARIZONA 85001

THE RF LINE

MV1620
thru
MV1650

SILICON EPICAP* DIODES

. . . epitaxial passivated tuning diodes designed for AFC applications in radio, TV, and general electronic-tuning.

- Maximum Working Voltage of 20 V
- Excellent Q Factor at High Frequencies
- 100% Hermetic Seal Check
- Solid-State Reliability to Replace Mechanical Tuning Methods

VOLTAGE-VARIABLE CAPACITANCE DIODES

6.8 — 100 pF
20 VOLTS

DECEMBER 1966 — DS 8517

DO-7 GLASS

MAXIMUM RATINGS (T_c = 25°C unless otherwise noted)

Characteristic	Symbol	Rating	Unit
Reverse Voltage	V_R	20	Volts
Forward Current	I_F	250	mA
Device Dissipation @ T_A = 25°C	P_D	400	mW
Derate above 25°C		2.67	mW/°C
Device Dissipation @ T_C = 25°C	P_D	2	Watts
Derate above 25°C		13.3	mW/°C
Junction Temperature	T_J	+175	°C
Storage Temperature Range	T_{stg}	-65 to +200	°C

*Trademark of Motorola Inc.

0.092 / 0.104 DIA

0.018 / 0.022 DIA

1.00 MIN

0.300 MAX

CATHODE

1.00 MIN

DO-7

MOTOROLA *Semiconductor Products Inc.* A SUBSIDIARY OF MOTOROLA INC.

ELECTRICAL CHARACTERISTICS ($T_A = 25°C$ unless otherwise noted)

Characteristic – All Types	Test Conditions	Symbol	Min	Typ	Max	Unit
Reverse Breakdown Voltage	$I_R = 10 \ \mu Adc$	BV_R	20	--	--	Vdc
Reverse Voltage Leakage Current	$V_R = 15 \ Vdc$	I_R	--	--	0.1	μAdc
Series Inductance	f = 250 MHz, lead length ≈ 1/16"	L_S	--	5.0	10	nH
Case Capacitance	f = 1 MHz, lead length ≈ 1/16"	C_C	--	0.25	0.3	pF

Device	C_T, Diode Capacitance $V_R = 4 \ Vdc, f = 1 \ MHz$ pF			Q, Figure of Merit $V_R = 4 \ Vdc,$ $f = 50 \ MHz$	TR, Tuning Ratio C_2 / C_{20} $f = 1 \ MHz$	
	Min	Nom	Max	Min	Min	Max
MV1620	6.1	6.8	7.5	300	2.0	3.2
MV1622	7.4	8.2	9.0	300	2.0	3.2
MV1624	9.0	10.0	11.0	300	2.0	3.2
MV1626	10.8	12.0	13.2	300	2.0	3.2
MV1628	13.5	15.0	16.5	250	2.0	3.2
MV1630	16.2	18.0	19.8	250	2.0	3.2
MV1632	18.0	20.0	22.0	250	2.0	3.2
MV1634	19.8	22.0	24.2	250	2.0	3.2
MV1636	24.3	27.0	29.7	200	2.0	3.2
MV1638	29.7	33.0	36.3	200	2.0	3.2
MV1640	35.1	39.0	42.9	200	2.0	3.2
MV1642	42.3	47.0	51.7	200	2.0	3.2
MV1644	50.4	56.0	61.6	150	2.0	3.2
MV1646	61.2	68.0	74.8	150	2.0	3.2
MV1648	73.8	82.0	90.2	150	2.0	3.2
MV1650	90.0	100.0	110.0	150	2.0	3.2

TR, Tuning Ratio, is the ratio of C_T measured at 2 Vdc divided by C_T measured at 20 Vdc.

 MOTOROLA Semiconductor Products Inc.

BOX 955 • PHOENIX, ARIZONA 85001 • A SUBSIDIARY OF MOTOROLA INC.

TYPES 1N746 THROUGH 1N759
SILICON VOLTAGE REGULATOR DIODES

3.3 TO 12 VOLTS • 400 mw

GUARANTEED DYNAMIC ZENER IMPEDANCE

Designed to your most stringent military requirements

Available in 5% and 10% tolerances

-65 to 175°C operation & storage

ACTUAL SIZE

TYPES 1N746 THROUGH 1N759
BULLETIN NO. DL-S 1008, MARCH, 1959
REPLACES BULLETIN NO. DL-S 972, NOVEMBER, 1958

mechanical data

Hard glass hermetically-sealed case. Unit weight is 0.195 gram.

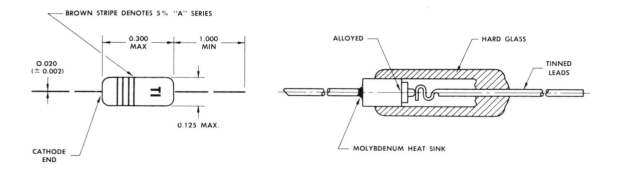

maximum ratings

Power Dissipation at 25°C	P	400 mw
Power Dissipation at 150°C	P	100 mw
Average Rectified Forward Current at 25°C	I_o	230 ma
Average Rectified Forward Current at 150°C	I_o	85 ma
Operating and Storage Temperature	T_A	−65 to + 175°C

electrical specifications

Type	V_Z* I_z = 20 ma dc v	LI_b E_b = −1 v μa 25°C	LI_b 150°C	Z_Z I_z = 20 ma dc I_{AC} = 1 ma ohms (max)	Typical Temperature Coefficient %/°C	VOLTAGE RANGE ±10% Series Min	±10% Series Max	±5% "A" Series Min	±5% "A" Series Max
1N746	3.3	10	30	28	−0.062	2.97	3.63	3.135	3.465
1N747	3.6	10	30	24	−0.055	3.24	3.96	3.420	3.780
1N748	3.9	10	30	23	−0.049	3.51	4.29	3.705	4.095
1N749	4.3	2	30	22	−0.036	3.87	4.73	4.085	4.515
1N750	4.7	2	30	19	−0.018	4.23	5.17	4.465	4.935
1N751	5.1	1	20	17	−0.008	4.59	5.61	4.845	5.355
1N752	5.6	1	20	11	+0.006	5.04	6.16	5.320	5.880
1N753	6.2	0.1	20	7	+0.022	5.58	6.82	5.890	6.510
1N754	6.8	0.1	20	5	+0.035	6.12	7.48	6.460	7.140
1N755	7.5	0.1	20	6	+0.045	6.75	8.25	7.125	7.875
1N756	8.2	0.1	20	8	+0.052	7.38	9.02	7.790	8.610
1N757	9.1	0.1	20	10	+0.056	8.19	10.01	8.645	9.555
1N758	10.0	0.1	20	17	+0.060	9.00	11.00	9.500	10.500
1N759	12.0	0.1	20	30	+0.060	10.80	13.20	11.400	12.000

*±10% zener voltage tolerance   For ± 5% devices specify 1N746A through 1N759A.

SEMICONDUCTOR—COMPONENTS DIVISION

TEXAS INSTRUMENTS
INCORPORATED
SEMICONDUCTOR-COMPONENTS DIVISION
POST OFFICE BOX 312 · 13500 N. CENTRAL EXPRESSWAY
DALLAS, TEXAS

TYPES 2N524, 2N525, 2N526, AND 2N527
P-N-P ALLOY-JUNCTION GERMANIUM TRANSISTORS

BULLETIN NO. DL-S 622411, MARCH 1962
REVISED OCTOBER 1966

- **General Purpose Medium-Power Amplifier and Switch**
- **Designed for High Reliability and Extreme Stability of Operation**

environmental tests

To ensure maximum integrity, stability, and long life, finished devices are subjected to the following tests and conditions prior to thorough testing for rigid adherence to specified characteristics.

- All devices receive a 100°C stabilization bake for 100 hours minimum.
- The hermetic seal is verified for all devices by helium leak testing.
- Production samples are life tested to ensure maximum reliability under extreme operating conditions.
- Continuous Quality Control checks on in-process assembly are maintained.

mechanical data

Metal case with glass-to-metal hermetic seal between case and leads. Unit weight is approximately 1 gram.

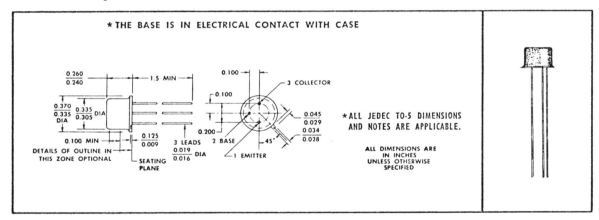

*absolute maximum ratings at 25°C free-air temperature (unless otherwise noted)

Collector-Base Voltage . . . . −45 v
Collector-Emitter Voltage (See Note 1) . . . . −30 v
Emitter-Base Voltage . . . . −15 v
Continuous Collector Current . . . . −500 ma
Continuous Emitter Current . . . . 500 ma
Total Device Dissipation (See Note 2) . . . . 225 mw
Operating Collector Junction Temperature . . . . 100°C
Storage Temperature Range . . . . −65°C to + 100°C
Lead Temperature 1/16 Inch from Case for 10 Seconds . . . . 230°C

NOTES: 1. This value applies when base-emitter resistance, $R_{BE} \leqq 10 \ K\Omega$.

2. Derate linearly to 100°C free-air temperature at the rate of 3 mw/°C.

*Indicates JEDEC registered data.

TEXAS INSTRUMENTS
INCORPORATED
SEMICONDUCTOR-COMPONENTS DIVISION
POST OFFICE BOX 5012 • DALLAS, TEXAS 75222

TYPES 2N524, 2N525, 2N526, AND 2N527
P-N-P ALLOY-JUNCTION GERMANIUM TRANSISTORS

electrical characteristics at 25°C free-air temperature

PARAMETER		TEST CONDITIONS	2N524			2N525			2N526			2N527			UNIT
			MIN*	TYP	MAX*	MIN*	TYP	MAX*	MIN*	TYP	MAX*	MIN*	TYP	MAX*	
BV_{CER}	Collector-Emitter Breakdown Voltage	$I_C = -600\ \mu a$, $R_{BE} = 10\ K\Omega$	-30	—	—	-30	—	—	-30	—	—	-30	—	—	v
V_{PT}	Punch-Through Voltage†	$V_{EBfl} = -1\ v$	-30	—	—	-30	—	—	-30	—	—	-30	—	—	v
I_{CBO}	Collector Cutoff Current	$V_{CB} = -30\ v$, $I_E = 0$	—	-4.5	-10	—	-4.5	-10	—	-4.5	-10	—	-4.5	-10	μa
I_{EBO}	Emitter Cutoff Current	$V_{EB} = -15\ v$, $I_C = 0$	—	-1.8	-10	—	-1.8	-10	—	-1.8	-10	—	-1.8	-10	μa
h_{FE}	Static Forward Current Transfer Ratio	$V_{CE} = -1\ v$, $I_C = -20\ ma$	25	35	42	34	53	65	53	72	90	72	90	121	—
		$V_{CE} = -1\ v$, $I_C = -100\ ma$	23	32	—	30	45	—	47	60	—	65	78	—	—
V_{BE}	Base-Emitter Voltage	$V_{CE} = -1\ v$, $I_C = -20\ ma$	-0.22	-0.25	-0.32	-0.20	-0.24	0.30	-0.19	-0.24	-0.28	-0.18	-0.23	-0.26	v
$V_{CE(sat)}$	Collector-Emitter Saturation Voltage	$I_B = -2.0\ ma$, $I_C = -20\ ma$	—	-83	-130	—	—	—	—	—	—	—	—	—	mv
		$I_B = -1.33\ ma$, $I_C = -20\ ma$	—	—	—	—	-86	-130	—	—	—	—	—	—	mv
		$I_B = -1.0\ ma$, $I_C = -20\ ma$	—	—	—	—	—	—	—	-90	-130	—	—	—	mv
		$I_B = -0.67\ ma$, $I_C = -20\ ma$	—	—	—	—	—	—	—	—	—	—	-93	-30	mv
h_{ib}	Small-Signal Common-Base Input Impedance	$V_{CB} = -5\ v$, $I_E = 1\ ma$, $f = 270\ c/s$	26	29	36	26	28	35	26	28	33	26	28	31	ohm
h_{rb}	Small-Signal Common-Base Reverse Voltage Transfer Ratio	$V_{CB} = -5\ v$, $I_E = 1\ ma$, $f = 270\ c/s$	1×10^{-4}	3.6×10^{-4}	10×10^{-4}	1×10^{-4}	4.4×10^{-4}	11×10^{-4}	1×10^{-4}	4.8×10^{-4}	12×10^{-4}	1×10^{-4}	6.0×10^{-4}	14×10^{-4}	—
h_{ob}	Small-Signal Common-Base Output Admittance	$V_{CB} = -5\ v$, $I_E = 1\ ma$, $f = 270\ c/s$	0.10	0.70	1.30	0.10	0.58	1.20	0.10	0.52	1.00	0.10	0.48	0.90	μmho
h_{fe}	Small-Signal Common-Emitter Forward Current Transfer Ratio	$V_{CE} = -5\ v$, $I_C = -1\ ma$, $f = 270\ c/s$	18	30	41	30	48	64	44	65	88	60	90	120	—
f_{hfb}	Common-Base Alpha-Cutoff Frequency	$V_{CB} = -5\ v$, $I_E = 1\ ma$	0.8	1.8	5.0	1.0	2.3	5.5	1.3	2.9	6.5	1.5	3.9	7.0	mc
C_{ob}	Common-Base Open-Circuit Output Capacitance	$V_{CB} = -5\ v$, $I_E = 1\ ma$, $f = 1\ mc$	5	20	40	5	20	40	5	20	40	5	20	40	pf

†V_{PT} is determined by measuring the emitter-base floating potential, V_{EBfl}. Collector-base voltage, V_{CB}, is increased until $V_{EBfl} = 1\ v$; this value of $V_{CB} = (V_{PT} + 1\ v)$.

switching characteristics at 25°C free-air temperature

PARAMETER		TEST CONDITIONS	2N524			2N525			2N526			2N527			UNIT
			MIN	TYP	MAX	MIN	TYP	MAX	MIN	TYP	MAX	MIN	TYP	MAX	
t_d	Delay Time	$I_C = -100\ ma$,	—	0.22	—	—	0.18	—	—	0.15	—	—	0.12	—	μsec
t_r	Rise Time	$I_{B(1)} = -I_{B(2)} = -8.7\ ma$,	—	1.4	—	—	1.0	—	—	0.80	—	—	0.60	—	μsec
t_s	Storage Time	$V_{BE(off)} = 2.3\ v$, $R_L = 97.6\ \Omega$	—	0.45	—	—	0.65	—	—	0.70	—	—	0.75	—	μsec
t_f	Fall Time	(See Circuit Page 3.)	—	0.80	—	—	0.70	—	—	0.60	—	—	0.50	—	μsec

operating characteristics at 25°C free-air temperature

PARAMETER		TEST CONDITIONS	2N524			2N525			2N526			2N527			UNIT
			MIN*	TYP	MAX*	MIN*	TYP	MAX*	MIN*	TYP	MAX*	MIN*	TYP	MAX*	
NF	Spot Noise Figure	$V_{CB} = -5\ v$, $I_E = 1\ ma$, $f = 1\ kc$, $R_G = 1\ K\Omega$, $BW = 1\ c/s$	—	7.0	15	—	6.0	15	—	5.5	15	—	5.0	15	db

*Indicates JEDEC registered data.

TYPICAL CHARACTERISTICS
COMMON-EMITTER COLLECTOR CHARACTERISTICS

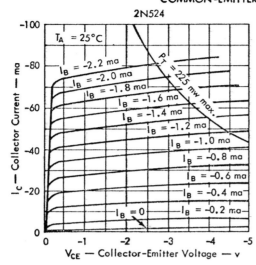

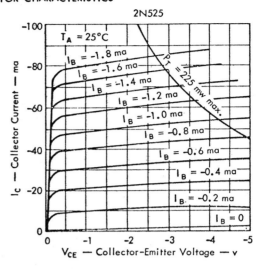

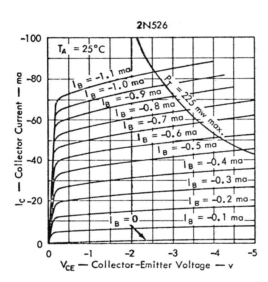

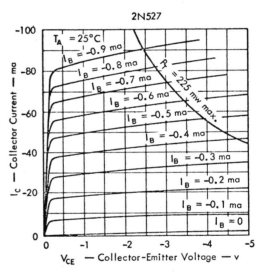

NOTE: These characteristics are measured by the sweep method using Tektronix 575 curve tracer or equivalent.

PARAMETER MEASUREMENT INFORMATION

SWITCHING TEST CIRCUIT

VOLTAGE WAVEFORMS

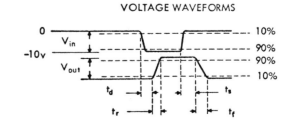

NOTES: 1. Input pulse supplied by generator with following characteristics:
   a. Output impedance: 50 ohms
   b. Repetition rate: 1 kc
   c. Rise and fall time: 20 nanoseconds maximum
   d. Pulse width: 10 microseconds

2. Waveforms monitored on scope with following characteristics:
   a. Input resistance: 10 megohms minimum
   b. Input capacitance: 15 picofarad maximum
   c. Risetime: 15 nanoseconds maximum
3. All resistors ± 1% tolerance per MIL-STD-90169

TYPES 2N524, 2N525, 2N526, AND 2N527
P-N-P ALLOY-JUNCTION GERMANIUM TRANSISTORS

TYPICAL CHARACTERISTICS

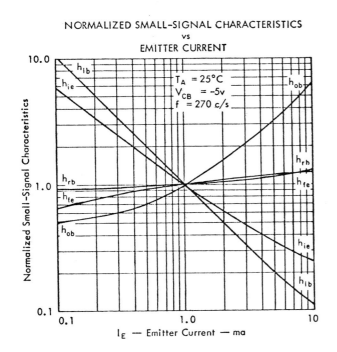

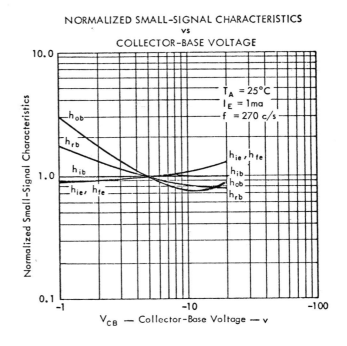

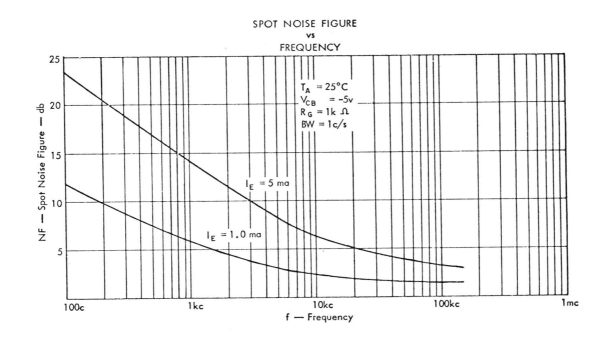

N-P-N DOUBLE-DIFFUSED SILICON MESA TRANSISTOR

High-Speed Medium Power Transistor

- 2 Watts at 25°C case temperature
- Beta 40 to 120
- 10-ohm saturation resistance (max)

environmental tests

Each unit is heat cycled from −65°C to +175°C for ten cycles. A rigorous tumbling test subjects each unit to 12 mechanical shocks of up to 500 G's to ensure mechanical reliability. Each unit is thoroughly tested to determine the electrical characteristics. Production samples are life tested at regularly scheduled periods to ensure maximum reliability under extreme operating conditions.

mechanical data

The transistor is in a JEDEC TO-5 hermetically sealed, welded package with glass-to-metal hermetic seal between case and leads. Approximate weight is 1.0 gram. The case is black enameled.

THE COLLECTOR IS IN ELECTRICAL CONTACT WITH THE CASE

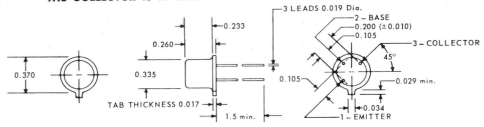

DIMENSIONS ARE MAXIMUM IN INCHES UNLESS OTHERWISE SPECIFIED

maximum ratings at 25°C ambient (unless otherwise noted)

Collector – Base Voltage . . . . 60 v
Collector – Emitter Voltage (R_{BE} = 10 ohms. See note 1) . . . . 40 v
Emitter – Base Voltage . . . . 5 v
Total Device Dissipation (See note 2) . . . . 0.6 w
Total Device Dissipation at case temperature 25°C (See note 3) . . . . 2 w
Storage Temperature Range . . . . −65°C to +175°C

electrical characteristics at 25°C ambient (unless otherwise noted)

	PARAMETERS	TEST CONDITIONS		min.	max.	unit
I_{CBO}	Collector Reverse Current	V_{CB} = 30 v	I_E = 0	—	1.0	μa
I_{CBO}	Collector Reverse Current at 150°C	V_{CB} = 30 v	I_E = 0	—	100	μa
BV_{CBO}	Collector-Base Breakdown Voltage	I_{CBO} = 100 μa	I_E = 0	60	—	v
BV_{CER}*	Collector-Emitter Breakdown Voltage	I_{CER} = 100 ma	R_{BE} = 10 ohms	40	—	v
BV_{EBO}	Emitter-Base Breakdown Voltage	I_{EBO} = 100 μa	I_C = 0	5	—	v
h_{FE}*	D-C Forward Current Transfer Ratio	I_C = 150 ma	V_{CE} = 10 v	40	120	—
V_{BE}*	Base-Emitter Voltage	I_C = 150 ma	I_B = 15 ma	—	1.3	v
$V_{CE(sat)}$*	Collector-Emitter Saturation Voltage	I_C = 150 ma	I_B = 15 ma	—	1.5	v
$|h_{fe}|$	A-C Common-Emitter Forward Current Transfer Ratio	I_C = 50 ma	V_{CE} = 10 v f = 20 mc	2.5	—	—
C_{ob}	Collector Capacitance	I_E = 0	V_{CB} = 10 v f = 1 mc	—	35	$\mu\mu f$

* Pulse conditions: length = 300 μs; duty cycle < 2%.

Note 1 — This is the voltage at which h_{FB} approaches one when R_{BE} = 10 ohms. When the emitter-base diode has a reverse voltage applied, peak collector-emitter voltage equal to BV_{CBO} minus V_{EB} may be allowed. Such conditions may be encountered in class B or C amplifiers and oscillators.
Note 2 — Derate linearly to +175°C ambient at the rate of 4 mw/C°
Note 3 — Derate linearly to +175°C case at the rate of 13⅓ mw/C°

TEXAS INSTRUMENTS
INCORPORATED
SEMICONDUCTOR-COMPONENTS DIVISION
P. O. BOX 312 • 13500 N. CENTRAL EXPRESSWAY
DALLAS, TEXAS

SEMICONDUCTOR COMPONENTS DIVISION

TYPICAL CHARACTERISTICS

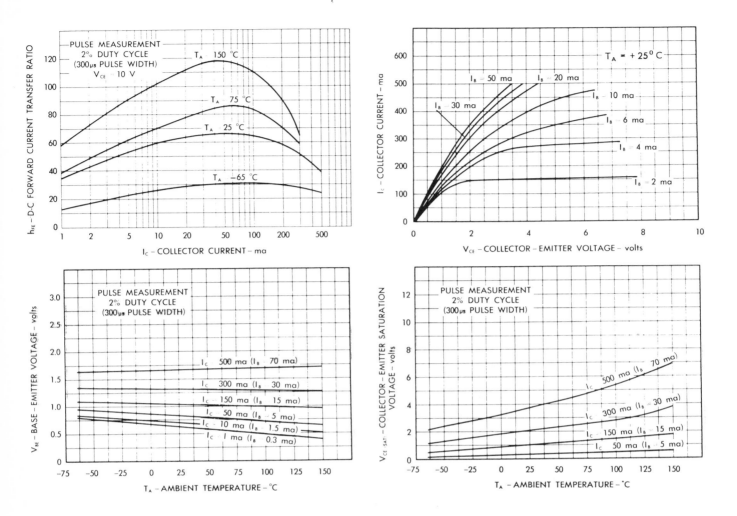

SWITCHING CIRCUIT FOR 2N697

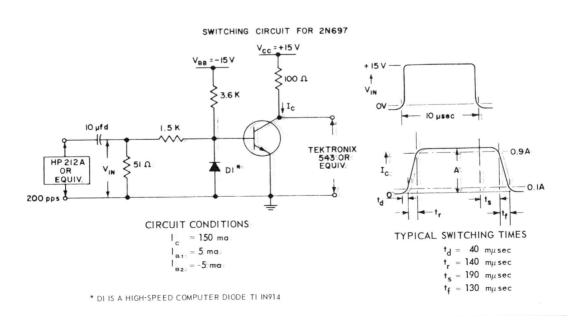

CIRCUIT CONDITIONS

$I_C \approx 150$ ma
$I_{B1} = 5$ ma
$I_{B2} = -5$ ma

* DI IS A HIGH-SPEED COMPUTER DIODE TI 1N914

TYPICAL SWITCHING TIMES

$t_d = 40$ mμsec
$t_r = 140$ mμsec
$t_s = 190$ mμsec
$t_f = 130$ mμsec

TYPE 2N3819
BULLETIN NO. DL-S 688047, AUGUST 1965
REVISED MAY 1968

SILECT† FIELD-EFFECT TRANSISTOR

For Industrial and Consumer Small-Signal Applications

- **Low C_{rss}:** $\leq$ **4 pf**   • **High y_{fs}/C_{iss} Ratio (High-Frequency Figure of Merit)**
- **Cross Modulation Minimized by Square-Law Transfer Characteristics**

mechanical data

This transistor is encapsulated in a plastic compound specifically designed for this purpose, using a highly mechanized process‡ developed by Texas Instruments. The case will withstand soldering temperatures without deformation. This device exhibits stable characteristics under high-humidity conditions and is capable of meeting MIL-STD-202C method 106B. The transistor is insensitive to light.

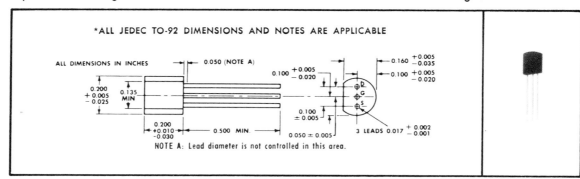

*ALL JEDEC TO-92 DIMENSIONS AND NOTES ARE APPLICABLE

NOTE A: Lead diameter is not controlled in this area.

*absolute maximum ratings at 25°C free-air temperature (unless otherwise noted)

Drain-Gate Voltage	25 v
Drain-Source Voltage	25 v
Reverse Gate-Source Voltage	— 25 v
Gate Current	10 ma
Continuous Device Dissipation at (or below) 25°C Free-Air Temperature (See Note 1)	360 mw
Storage Temperature Range	—65°C to 150°C
Lead Temperature 1/16 Inch from Case for 10 Seconds	260°C

*electrical characteristics at 25°C free-air temperature (unless otherwise noted)

PARAMETER		TEST CONDITIONS	MIN	MAX	UNIT
$V_{(BR)GSS}$	Gate-Source Breakdown Voltage	$I_G = -1 \mu a$, $V_{DS} = 0$	— 25		v
I_{GSS}	Gate Cutoff Current	$V_{GS} = -15$ v, $V_{DS} = 0$		— 2	na
		$V_{GS} = -15$ v, $V_{DS} = 0$, $T_A = 100°C$		— 2	μa
I_{DSS}	Zero-Gate-Voltage Drain Current	$V_{DS} = 15$ v, $V_{GS} = 0$, See Note 2	2	20	ma
V_{GS}	Gate-Source Voltage	$V_{DS} = 15$ v, $I_D = 200 \mu a$	— 0.5	— 7.5	v
$V_{GS(off)}$	Gate-Source Cutoff Voltage	$V_{DS} = 15$ v, $I_D = 2$ na		— 8	v
$\|y_{fs}\|$	Small-Signal Common-Source Forward Transfer Admittance	$V_{DS} = 15$ v, $V_{GS} = 0$, $f = 1$ kc, See Note 2	2000	6500	μmho
$\|y_{os}\|$	Small-Signal Common-Source Output Admittance	$V_{DS} = 15$ v, $V_{GS} = 0$, $f = 1$ kc, See Note 2		50	μmho
C_{iss}	Common-Source Short-Circuit Input Capacitance	$V_{DS} = 15$ v, $V_{GS} = 0$, $f = 1$ Mc		8	pf
C_{rss}	Common-Source Short-Circuit Reverse Transfer Capacitance			4	pf
$\|y_{fs}\|$	Small-Signal Common-Source Forward Transfer Admittance	$V_{DS} = 15$ v, $V_{GS} = 0$, $f = 100$ Mc	1600		μmho

NOTES: 1. Derate linearly to 150°C free-air temperature at the rate of 2.88 mw/C°.
      2. These parameters must be measured using pulse techniques. PW $\approx$ 100 msec, Duty Cycle $\leq$ 10%.
*Indicates JEDEC registered data.
†Trademark of Texas Instruments
‡Patent Pending

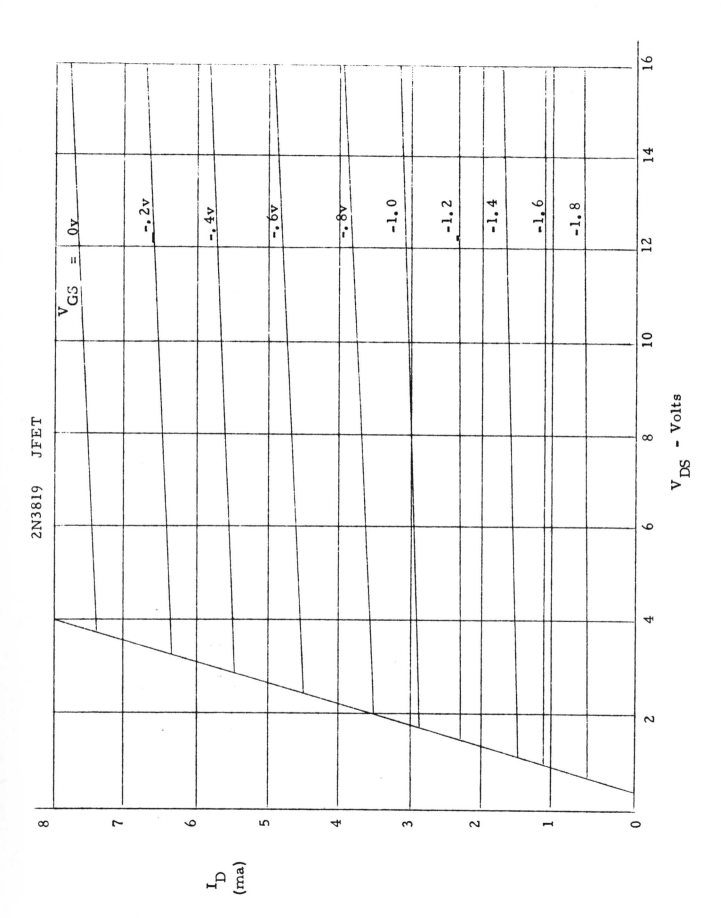

TYPE 2N3820
P-CHANNEL PLANAR SILICON FIELD-EFFECT TRANSISTOR

BULLETIN NO. DL-S 657947, AUGUST 1965

SILECT† FIELD-EFFECT TRANSISTOR
For Industrial and Consumer
Small-Signal Applications

mechanical data

This transistor is encapsulated in a plastic compound specifically designed for this purpose, using a highly mechanized process‡ developed by Texas Instruments. The case will withstand soldering temperatures without deformation. This device exhibits stable characteristics under high–humidity conditions and is capable of meeting MIL-STD-202C method 106B. The transistor is insensitive to light.

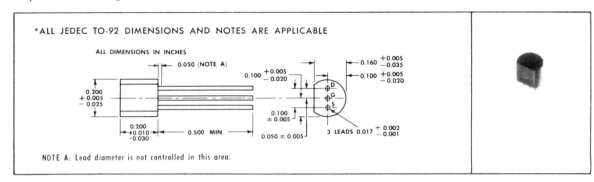

*ALL JEDEC TO-92 DIMENSIONS AND NOTES ARE APPLICABLE

ALL DIMENSIONS IN INCHES

NOTE A: Lead diameter is not controlled in this area.

*absolute maximum ratings at 25°C free-air temperature (unless otherwise noted)

Drain-Gate Voltage . . . . −20 v
Drain-Source Voltage . . . . −20 v
Reverse Gate-Source Voltage . . . . 20 v
Gate Current . . . . −10 ma
Continuous Device Dissipation at (or below) 25°C Free-Air Temperature (See Note 1) . . . . 200 mw
Storage Temperature Range . . . . −55°C to +150°C
Lead Temperature 1/16 Inch from Case for 10 Seconds . . . . 260°C

*electrical characteristics at 25°C free-air temperature (unless otherwise noted)

	PARAMETER	TEST CONDITIONS	MIN	MAX	UNIT
$V_{(BR)GSS}$	Gate-Source Breakdown Voltage	$I_G = 10\ \mu a,\ V_{DS} = 0$	20		v
I_{GSS}	Gate Cutoff Current	$V_{GS} = 10\ v,\ V_{DS} = 0$		20	na
		$V_{GS} = 10\ v,\ V_{DS} = 0,\quad T_A = 100°C$		2	μa
I_{DSS}	Zero-Gate-Voltage Drain Current	$V_{DS} = -10\ v,\ V_{GS} = 0,\quad$ See Note 2	−0.3	−15	ma
V_{GS}	Gate-Source Voltage	$V_{DS} = -10\ v,\ I_D = -30\ \mu a$	0.3	7.9	v
$V_{GS(off)}$	Gate-Source Cutoff Voltage	$V_{DS} = -10\ v,\ I_D = -10\ \mu a$		8	v
y_{fs}	Small-Signal Common-Source Forward Transfer Admittance	$V_{DS} = -10\ v,\ V_{GS} = 0,\quad f = 1\ kc,$ See Note 2	800	5000	μmho
y_{os}	Small-Signal Common-Source Output Admittance	$V_{DS} = -10\ v,\ V_{GS} = 0,\quad f = 1\ kc,$ See Note 2		200	μmho
C_{iss}	Common-Source Short-Circuit Input Capacitance	$V_{DS} = -10\ v,$ $V_{GS} = 0,$		32	pf
C_{rss}	Common-Source Short-Circuit Reverse Transfer Capacitance	$f = 1\ Mc$		16	pf
y_{fs}	Small-Signal Common-Source Forward Transfer Admittance	$V_{DS} = -10\ v,\ V_{GS} = 0,\quad f = 10\ Mc$	700		μmho

NOTES: 1. Derate linearly to 125°C free-air temperature at the rate of 2 mw/C°.
    2. These parameters must be measured using pulse techniques. PW ≈ 100 msec, Duty Cycle ≤ 10%.
*Indicates JEDEC registered data.
†Trademark of Texas Instruments Incorporated
‡Patent Pending

PRINTED IN U.

TEXAS INSTRUMENTS
INCORPORATED
SEMICONDUCTOR-COMPONENTS DIVISION
POST OFFICE BOX 5012 • DALLAS 22, TEXAS

TEXAS INSTRUMENTS RESERVES THE RIGHT TO MAKE CHANGES AT ANY TIME IN ORDER TO IMPROVE DESIGN AND TO SUPPLY THE BEST PRODUCT POSSIBLE.

TYPE SN724N
BULLETIN NO. DL-S 6710013, MAY 1967

A SERIES 72 SEMICONDUCTOR-NETWORK GENERAL-PURPOSE AMPLIFIER

for application as

- Buffer Amplifier
- Differentiator
- Integrator
- Multivibrator
- Level Detector
- Summing Amplifier

description

The SN724N is a general-purpose operational amplifier consisting of two differential-gain stages and a single-ended emitter-follower output. The input stage utilizes Darlington-connected n-p-n transistors for high input impedance.

The SN724N, one of Texas Instruments Series 72 catalog line of linear integrated circuits, offers higher reliability, lower cost, smaller size, and lower weight than equivalent discrete component circuits. Each Series 72 device is a monolithic semiconductor structure comprising diffused resistors and both n-p-n and p-n-p transistors.

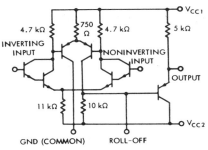

NOTE: Component values shown are nominal.

SCHEMATIC DIAGRAM

mechanical data

The SN724N is mounted on a 14-lead frame and encapsulated within a plastic compound.

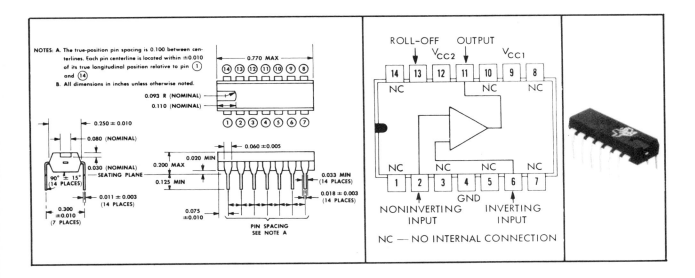

†Patented by Texas Instruments

TEXAS INSTRUMENTS
INCORPORATED
SEMICONDUCTOR-COMPONENTS DIVISION
POST OFFICE BOX 5012 • DALLAS, TEXAS 75222

TYPE SN724N
GENERAL-PURPOSE OPERATIONAL AMPLIFIER

absolute maximum ratings over operating free-air temperature range (unless otherwise noted)

Supply Voltages (See Note 1): V_{CC1} . . . . +15 V

V_{CC2} . . . . −15 V

Differential Input Voltage . . . . 12 V

Common-Mode Input Voltage . . . . ±10 V

Operating Free-Air Temperature Range . . . . 0°C to 70°C

Storage Temperature Range . . . . −55°C to 150°C

NOTE 1: Voltage values are with respect to network ground.

electrical characteristics at 25°C free-air temperature (unless otherwise noted)

	PARAMETER	TEST CONDITIONS§	MIN	TYP	MAX	UNIT
V_{DI}	Differential-input offset voltage			15		mV
		$T_A = 0°C$ to $70°C$			40	mV
α_{VDI}	Differential-input offset voltage temperature coefficient	$T_A = 0°C$ to $70°C$		30		μV/deg
I_{in}	Input current			110	500	nA
I_{DI}	Differential-input offset current			44		nA
		$T_A = 0°C$		18		nA
		$T_A = 70°C$		70		nA
V_{OM}	Maximum peak-to-peak output voltage	$f = 1$ kHz, $T_A = 0°C$ to $70°C$	8			V
		$f = 1$ kHz		12		V
		10 kΩ load, $f = 1$ kHz, $T_A = 0°C$ to $70°C$	6			V
		10 kΩ load, $f = 1$ kHz		11		V
V_{CMIM}	Maximum common-mode input voltage			±5		V
A_V	Voltage gain	$f = 1$ kHz, $T_A = 0°C$ to $70°C$	400			
		$f = 1$ kHz		1200		
CMRR	Common-mode rejection ratio	$f = 1$ kHz, $T_A = 0°C$ to $70°C$		55		dB
BW	Bandwidth (−3 dB)		60	140		kHz
z_{in}	Input impedance	$f = 1$ kHz	250	800		kΩ
z_{out}	Output impedance	$f = 1$ kHz		300		Ω
P_T	Total power dissipation	No input signal, no external load		120		mW

§Unless otherwise noted test conditions are: $V_{CC1} = +12$ V, $V_{CC2} = −12$ V, ground and V_{DI} applied; roll-off terminal open, no external loading. The unused input is grounded for all tests except when common-mode characteristics are under test.

letter symbol and parameter definitions

V_{DI} That d-c voltage which must be applied between the input terminals to obtain zero-output voltage referenced to ground. The application of this voltage balances the amplifier.

I_{in} The current into either input of the amplifier.

I_{DI} The difference in the currents into the two input terminals when the output is balanced.

V_{OM} The maximum peak-to-peak output voltage swing that can be obtained without clipping when the output is balanced.

V_{CMIM} The maximum common-mode voltage that can be impressed on the input terminals while maintaining differential operation.

CMRR   The ratio of the differential-mode voltage gain to the common-mode voltage gain.

BW   The range of frequencies within which the voltage gain is within 3 dB of the mid-frequency value.

z_{in} The impedance between either input terminal and ground with the other input terminal a-c grounded and the output balanced.

z_{out} The impedance between the output terminal and ground when the output is balanced.

TEXAS INSTRUMENTS
INCORPORATED
SEMICONDUCTOR-COMPONENTS DIVISION
POST OFFICE BOX 5012 • DALLAS, TEXAS 75222

8014

Index